ALLIANCE TABERNACLE
108 EAST STONE AVENUE
GREENVILLE, SOUTH CAROLINA
"ALWAYS WELCOME"

TABERNACLE HYMNS

NUMBER FOUR

A choice collection of hymns and songs for every religious use

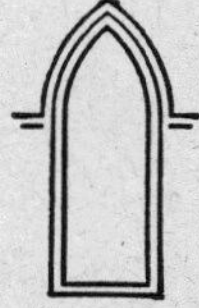

Available in Either
Round or Shaped Note Editions

Complete Orchestrations Available
For Twenty-nine Instruments

1948

Printed in U. S. A.

TABERNACLE PUBLISHING COMPANY

Corner Lake St. and Waller Ave.
CHICAGO, ILLINOIS

Copyright, 1941, by Tabernacle Publishing Company

LET the Word of Christ dwell in you richly in all wisdom; teaching and admonishing one another in psalms and hymns and spiritual songs, singing with grace in your hearts to the Lord.

AND whatsoever ye do in word or deed, do all in the name of the Lord Jesus, giving thanks to God and the Father by Him.

Colossians 3:16, 17

Doxology

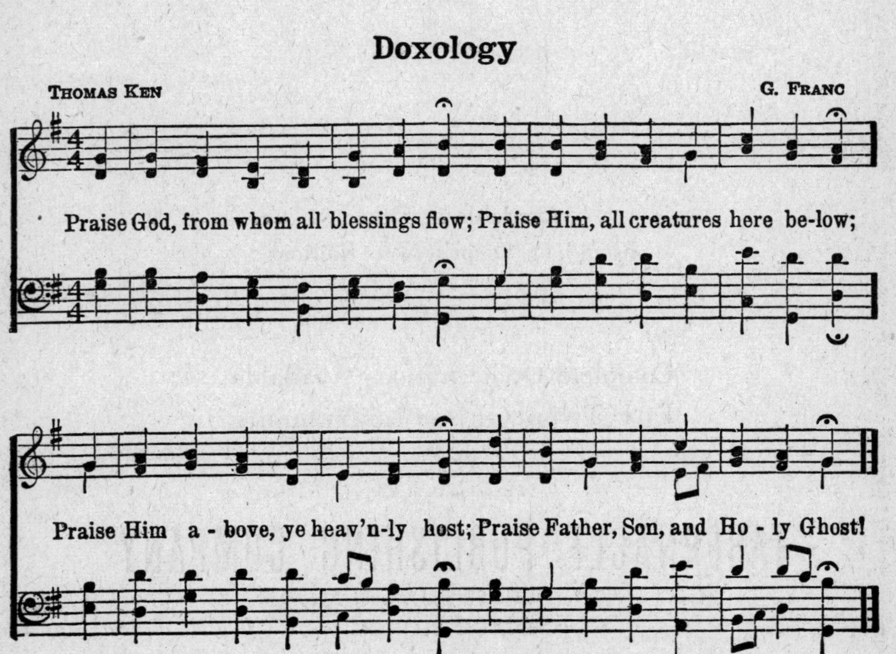
THOMAS KEN
G. FRANC
Praise God, from whom all blessings flow; Praise Him, all creatures here be-low;
Praise Him a - bove, ye heav'n-ly host; Praise Father, Son, and Ho - ly Ghost!

TABERNACLE HYMNS

NUMBER FOUR

Beneath the Cross of Jesus 1

ELIZABETH C. CLEPHANE FREDERICK C. MAKER

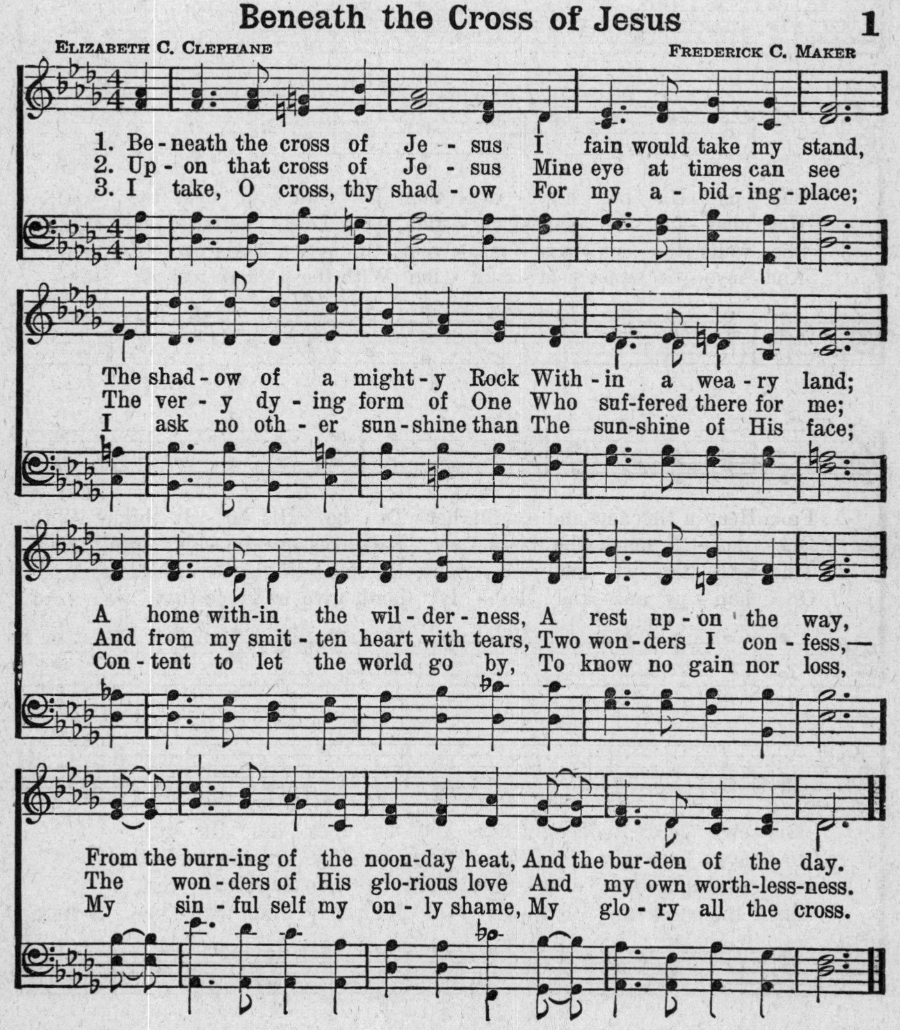
1. Be-neath the cross of Je-sus I fain would take my stand,
2. Up-on that cross of Je-sus Mine eye at times can see
3. I take, O cross, thy shad-ow For my a-bid-ing-place;
The shad-ow of a might-y Rock With-in a wea-ry land;
The ver-y dy-ing form of One Who suf-fered there for me;
I ask no oth-er sun-shine than The sun-shine of His face;
A home with-in the wil-der-ness, A rest up-on the way,
And from my smit-ten heart with tears, Two won-ders I con-fess,—
Con-tent to let the world go by, To know no gain nor loss,
From the burn-ing of the noon-day heat, And the bur-den of the day.
The won-ders of His glo-rious love And my own worth-less-ness.
My sin-ful self my on-ly shame, My glo-ry all the cross.

2 The Church's One Foundation

Samuel J. Stone
Samuel S. Wesley
1. The Church-'s one foun - da - tion Is Je - sus Christ her Lord;
2. E - lect from ev - 'ry na - tion, Yet one o'er all the earth,
3. 'Mid toil and trib - u - la - tion, And tu - mult of her war,
4. Yet she on earth hath un - ion With God the Three in One,
She is His new cre - a - tion By wa - ter and the word:
Her char - ter of sal - va - tion, One Lord, one faith, one birth;
She waits the con - sum - ma - tion Of peace for - ev - er - more;
And mys - tic sweet com - mun - ion With those whose rest is won:
From Heav'n He came and sought her To be His ho - ly bride; With
One ho - ly name she bless - es, Par-takes one ho - ly food, And
Till, with the vi - sion glo - rious, Her long - ing eyes are blest, And
O hap - py ones and ho - ly! Lord, give us grace that we, Like
His own blood He bought her, And for her life He died.
to one hope she press - es, With ev - 'ry grace en - dued.
the great church vic - to - rious Shall be the church at rest.
them, the meek and low - ly, On high may dwell with Thee. A-MEN.

The Church of God Is One 3

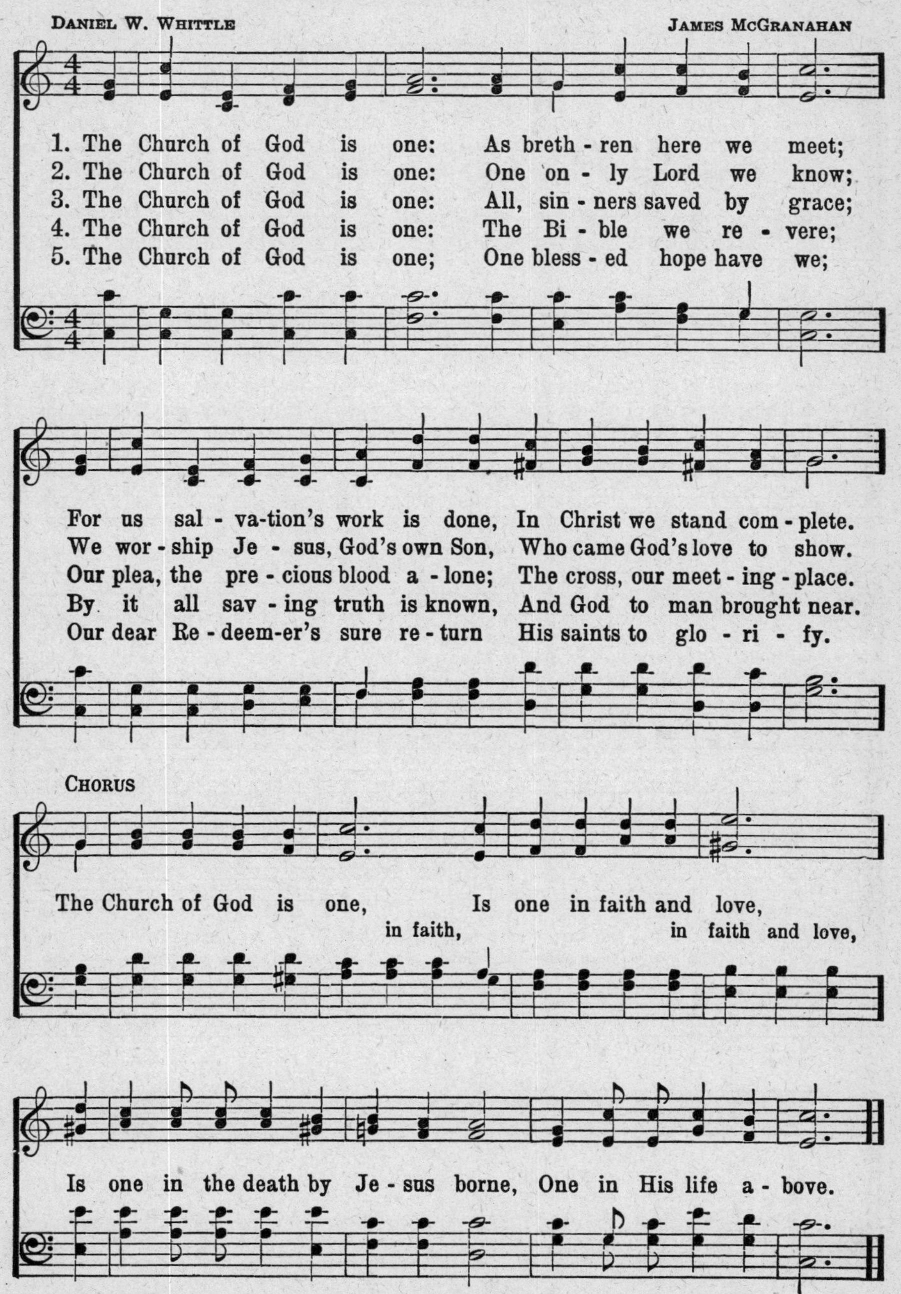
Daniel W. Whittle
James McGranahan
1. The Church of God is one: As breth - ren here we meet;
2. The Church of God is one: One on - ly Lord we know;
3. The Church of God is one: All, sin - ners saved by grace;
4. The Church of God is one: The Bi - ble we re - vere;
5. The Church of God is one; One bless - ed hope have we;
For us sal - va-tion's work is done, In Christ we stand com - plete.
We wor - ship Je - sus, God's own Son, Who came God's love to show.
Our plea, the pre - cious blood a - lone; The cross, our meet - ing - place.
By it all sav - ing truth is known, And God to man brought near.
Our dear Re - deem-er's sure re - turn His saints to glo - ri - fy.
Chorus
The Church of God is one, Is one in faith and love,
in faith, in faith and love,
Is one in the death by Je - sus borne, One in His life a - bove.

Copyright, 1932, Renewal. Hope Publishing Company, owner

His Love Can Never Fail

E. S. Hall
E. O. Excell
1. I do not ask to see the way My feet will have to tread; But on - ly that my
2. And if my feet would go a-stray, They can-not, for I know That Je-sus guides my
3. I will not fear, tho' darkness come A-broad o'er all the land, If I may on - ly
soul may feed Up - on the liv - ing bread. 'Tis bet - ter far that I should walk By
falt'ring steps, As joy - ful-ly I go. And tho' I may not see His face, My
feel the touch Of His own lov - ing hand. And tho' I trem-ble when I think How
faith close to His side,— I may not know the way I go, But oh, I know my Guide.
faith is strong and clear, That in each hour of sore dis-tress My Sav - ior will be near.
weak I am, how frail, My soul is sat - is - fied to know His love can nev - er fail.
Chorus
His love . . . . can nev - er fail, His love . . . . can nev - er fail;
His love can nev - er fail, His love can nev - er fail;
My soul is sat - is - fied to know His love can nev - er fail.

Copyright, 1925. Renewal. Hope Publishing Co., owner

Wonderful

A. H. ACKLEY A. H. ACKLEY

1. Won-der-ful birth, to a man-ger He came, Made in the like-ness of
2. Won-der-ful life, full of serv-ice so free, Friend to the poor and the
3. Won-der-ful death, for it meant not de-feat, Cal-va-ry made His great
4. Won-der-ful hope, He is com-ing a-gain, Com-ing as King o'er the
man, to pro-claim God's bound-less love for a world sick with sin, Pleading with
need-y was He; Un-fail-ing good-ness on all He be-stowed, Un-dy-ing
mis-sion com-plete, Wrought our re-demp-tion, and when He a-rose, Ban-ished for-
na-tions to reign; Glo-ri-ous prom-ise, His Word can-not fail, His right-eous
CHORUS.
sin-ners to let Him come in.
faith in the vil-est He showed. Won-der-ful name He bears, Won-der-ful
ev-er the last of our foes.
king-dom at last must pre-vail!
accel.
a tempo
crown He wears, Won-der-ful bless-ings His tri-umphs af-ford; Won-der-ful
Cal-va-ry, Won-der-ful grace for me, Wonderful love of my Won-der-ful Lord!

Copyright, 1938, by The Rodeheaver Company. Used by permission

6 Love Found a Way

Constance B. Ried
Harry Dixon Loes

1. Won-der-ful love that res-cued me, Sunk deep in sin, Guilt-y and
2. Love bro't my Sav-ior here to die On Cal-va-ry, For such a
3. Love o-pened wide the gates of light To heav'n's do-main, Where in e-
vile as I could be—No hope with-in; When ev-'ry ray of light had fled,
sin-ful wretch as I, How can it be? Love bridged the gulf 'twixt me and heav'n,
ter-nal pow'r and might Je-sus shall reign; Love lift-ed me from depths of woe
O glo-rious day! Rais-ing my soul from out the dead, Love found a way.
Taught me to pray; I am redeemed, set free, for-giv'n, Love found a way.
To end-less day, There was no help in earth be-low, Love found a way.
Chorus
Love found a way . . to re-deem my soul, . . Love found a
a way, to re-deem my soul,
way . . . that could make me whole; . . Love sent my Lord . . to the
a way could make me whole; my Lord

Copyright, 1921. Hope Publishing Co., owner

Love Found a Way
ad lib
cross of shame, Love found a way, O praise His ho-ly name!
to the cross of shame,
Victory in My Soul
7
James M. Gray
D. B. Towner
Cho. arr. by Fred Jacky
1. The bur-den of my fear and sin On Christ by faith I roll;
2. I know there is a test for me, A bat-tle to be won;
3. On bat-tle-fields of long a-go, When saints have drawn the sword,
4. While lean-ing on His arm a-lone I can-not know de-feat;
5. E'en death it-self I do not fear Since Christ hath borne its sting;
And now I have His peace with-in And vic-t'ry in my soul.
But God en-sures the vic-to-ry Be-fore it is be-gun.
Their strength did not o'er-come the foe, But—trust-ing in the Lord.
The glo-ry shall be all His own When vic-t'ry is com-plete.
His pres-ence thro' the val-ley drear Will help us then to sing.
Chorus
There's vic-to-ry in my soul,.......... Vic-to-ry in my soul;..........
Ah!............ Vic-t'ry in my soul, Ah!............... Vic-t'ry in my soul;
I grasp the prom-is-es by faith,—There's vic-to-ry,.......... Vic-t'ry in my soul.
Vic-to-ry
f
ff

Copyright, 1938. Renewal. Arr. Copyright 1941. Hope Publishing Co., owner

8 That Blessed Canaan Land

LOUISE L. NANKIVELL LOUISE L. NANKIVELL

1. There's a bless - ed land that we call Ca - naan, Land of
2. In the land of Ca - naan there is bless - ing, All His
3. Have you crossed the Jor - dan in - to Ca - naan, Have you
prom - ise, land of vic - to - ry, Where the Spir - it's giv - en
full - ness as He takes con - trol, Bless - ed full - ness of the
left the wil - der - ness be - hind And re - ceived the Spir - it
with - out meas - ure, Where the soul from self has been set free.
Ho - ly Spir - it; O what glo - ry He brings to the soul!
in His full - ness? If you have - n't then make up your mind.
CHORUS
{It is won-der-ful to live in Ca-naan, Where the milk and honey flow,
{It is won-der-ful to live in Ca-naan, Just a love - ly place to dwell;
1
Where the land is bear-ing in a-bun-dance And the grapes of Es-chol grow.

Copyright, 1940, in "Heavenly Glory Songs." Hope Publishing Co., owner

That Blessed Canaan Land

Won't you join that band, Where the life is grand, In that bless-ed Canaan land?

Impatient Heart, Be Still 9

Geo. A. Warburton — Geo. C. Stebbins

1. Im - pa - tient heart, be still! What tho' He tar - ries long? What tho' the tri-umph song Is still (is still) de-layed? Thou hast His promise sure, And that is all se - cure; Be not a - fraid! Be not a - fraid!
2. My ea - ger heart, be still! Thy Lord will sure - ly come, And take thee to His home, With Him (with Him) to dwell; It may not be to-day; And yet, my soul, it may; I can - not tell, I can - not tell.
3. My anx - ious heart, be still! Watch, work, and pray, and then It will not mat-ter when Thy Lord (Thy Lord) shall come; At midnight, or at noon; He can-not come too soon To take thee home, To take thee home.

Refrain *rit.*

Be still!........ be still! Be still! be still! {Im - pa-tient / My ea - ger / My anx-ious} heart.... be still! be still,

Copyright, 1924, Renewal. Hope Publishing Co., owner.

10 Everlasting Life

W. A. OGDEN — W. A. OGDEN

1."Ev-er-last-ing life!" 'tis the promise giv'n Un-to him . . . who loves the
2."Ev-er-last-ing life!" shout it far and wide, Bless-ed ti - - dings of sal-
3."Ev-er-last-ing life!" there is naught to do But to take . . . the words He
(1) Un-to him
Sav - ior dear; "Ev - er-last-ing life!" and a home in heav'n, If you
va - tion free; "Ev - er-last-ing life!" thro' His blood ap - plied, To the
gives you now; "Ev - er-last-ing life!" prec-ious gift for you, Thro' the
CHORUS
will . . . . be-lieve His name.(His name.) Then be - lieve Him; oh, re-
sin - - - ner in his woe.(his woe.)
Sav - - - ior cru - ci - fied. (for thee.) Then be-lieve,
If you will
ceive Him, Bless-ed Sav - - ior! King-ly fa - vor, Give Him
Him re-ceive, Bless-ed Sav - ior, King of grace,
ev - - - er best en-deav - or, For with Him is ev - er-last-ing life!
Ev-er giv'n, trust and live,

Cross of My Heart

Ed McConnell
Ed McConnell
1. Cross of my heart on yon - der hill, Em - blem of Cal - v'ry's suf - f'ring; still Hope of my soul e - ter - nal - ly; Bless - ed, O Cross, art thou to me.
2. There on thine arms, O Cross, He bled; There on thine arms my sins were shed; Lift thou me up that I may see Je - sus my Lord who died for me.
3. Cross of my heart, may I but prove Wor - thy of Him whose cross I love; Keep thou me hum - ble day by day; Be thou His light to guide my way.
Chorus
Cross of my heart, Cross of my heart, Em - blem of glo - ry and life thou art; Lift thou mine eyes my Lord to see; Cross of my heart, He died for me.
won-drous

Copyright, 1940, by Ed McConnell. Used by permission

12 I Could Not Get Along without My Bible

LOUISE L. NANKIVELL
LOUISE L. NANKIVELL
1. I could not get a-long with-out my Bi-ble, It tells me of a Christ who died to save, Re-lates to me the plan of His sal-va-tion, Makes plain just how a Chris-tian should be-have.
2. I could not get a-long with-out my Bi-ble, Its words are life and spir-it to my soul, Re-veal-ing all there is for me in Je-sus, Re-new-ing, cleans-ing, burn-ing, mak-ing whole.
3. I could not get a-long with-out my Bi-ble, A lamp un-to my feet, a bea-con light; It gives the an-swer to my ev-'ry prob-lem, Di-rect-ing, point-ing, show-ing what is right.
CHORUS
I could not get a-long with-out my Bi-ble, I read its sa-cred pag-es ev-'ry day; Its words are there to com-fort, strength-en,

With credit to "Heartaches," copyright 1933. The Rodeheaver Co., owner
Copyright 1940, in "Heavenly Glory Songs." Hope Publishing Co., owner

I Could Not Get Along without My Bible

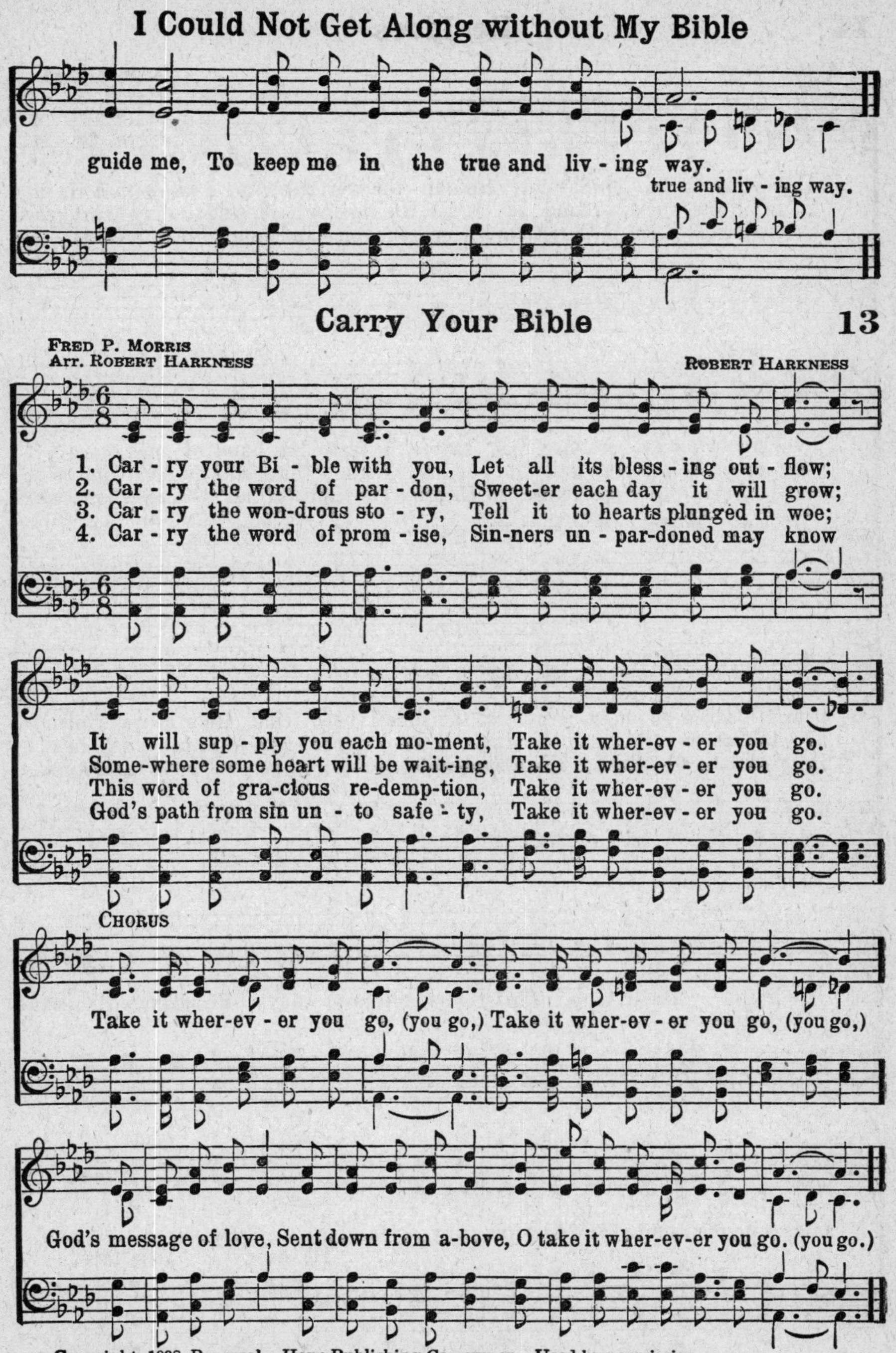
guide me, To keep me in the true and liv - ing way.
true and liv - ing way.
Carry Your Bible
13
Fred P. Morris
Arr. Robert Harkness
Robert Harkness
1. Car - ry your Bi - ble with you, Let all its bless - ing out - flow;
2. Car - ry the word of par - don, Sweet-er each day it will grow;
3. Car - ry the won-drous sto - ry, Tell it to hearts plunged in woe;
4. Car - ry the word of prom - ise, Sin-ners un - par-doned may know
It will sup - ply you each mo-ment, Take it wher-ev - er you go.
Some-where some heart will be wait-ing, Take it wher-ev - er you go.
This word of gra-cious re-demp-tion, Take it wher-ev - er you go.
God's path from sin un - to safe - ty, Take it wher-ev - er you go.
Chorus
Take it wher-ev - er you go, (you go,) Take it wher-ev - er you go, (you go,)
God's message of love, Sent down from a-bove, O take it wher-ev-er you go. (you go.)

Copyright, 1938, Renewal. Hope Publishing Co., owner. Used by permission

14 He Lives

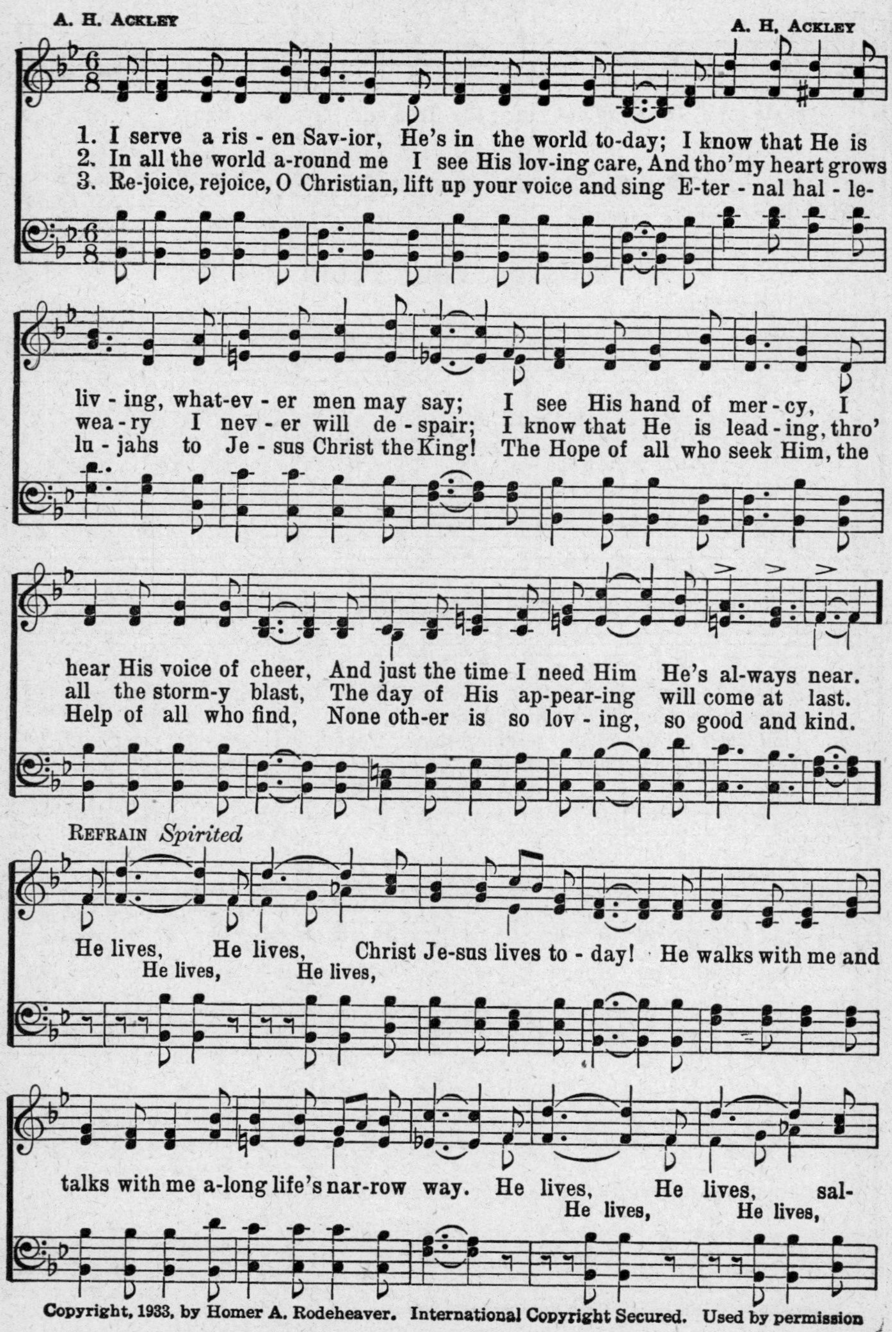
A. H. Ackley
A. H. Ackley
1. I serve a ris - en Sav-ior, He's in the world to-day; I know that He is
2. In all the world a-round me I see His lov-ing care, And tho' my heart grows
3. Re-joice, rejoice, O Christian, lift up your voice and sing E-ter - nal hal - le-
liv - ing, what-ev - er men may say; I see His hand of mer - cy, I
wea - ry I nev - er will de - spair; I know that He is lead - ing, thro'
lu - jahs to Je - sus Christ the King! The Hope of all who seek Him, the
hear His voice of cheer, And just the time I need Him He's al-ways near.
all the storm-y blast, The day of His ap-pear-ing will come at last.
Help of all who find, None oth-er is so lov - ing, so good and kind.
Refrain Spirited
He lives, He lives, Christ Je-sus lives to - day! He walks with me and
He lives, He lives,
talks with me a-long life's nar-row way. He lives, He lives, sal-
He lives, He lives,

Copyright, 1933, by Homer A. Rodeheaver. International Copyright Secured. Used by permission

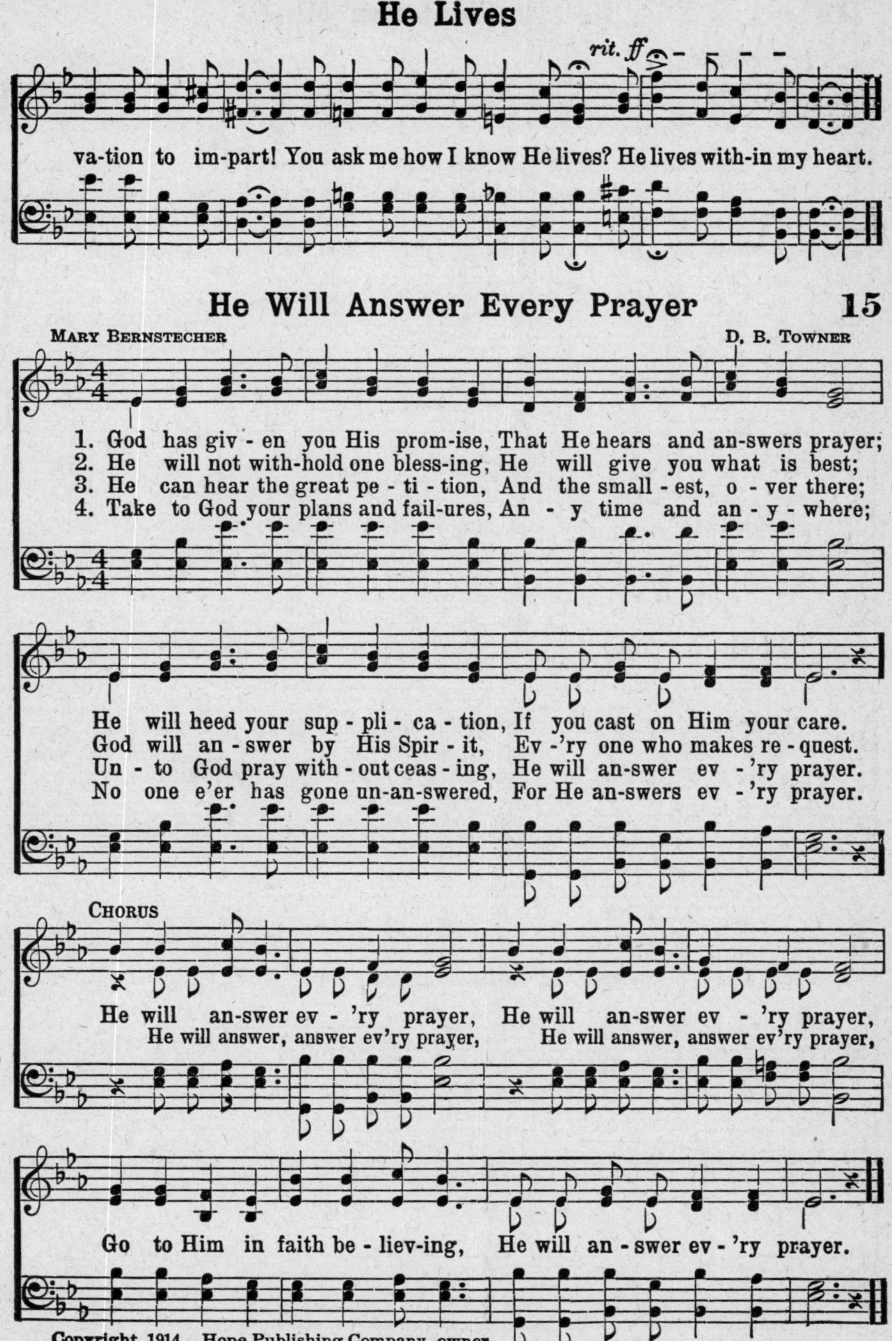
He Lives
rit. ff
va-tion to im-part! You ask me how I know He lives? He lives with-in my heart.
He Will Answer Every Prayer
15
Mary Bernstecher
D. B. Towner
1. God has giv - en you His prom-ise, That He hears and an-swers prayer;
2. He will not with-hold one bless-ing, He will give you what is best;
3. He can hear the great pe - ti - tion, And the small - est, o - ver there;
4. Take to God your plans and fail-ures, An - y time and an - y - where;
He will heed your sup - pli - ca - tion, If you cast on Him your care.
God will an - swer by His Spir - it, Ev - 'ry one who makes re - quest.
Un - to God pray with - out ceas - ing, He will an-swer ev - 'ry prayer.
No one e'er has gone un-an-swered, For He an-swers ev - 'ry prayer.
Chorus
He will an-swer ev - 'ry prayer, He will an-swer ev - 'ry prayer,
He will answer, answer ev'ry prayer, He will answer, answer ev'ry prayer,
Go to Him in faith be - liev-ing, He will an - swer ev - 'ry prayer.

Copyright, 1914. Hope Publishing Company, owner

16 He's a Friend of Mine

J. H. SAMMIS — D. B. TOWNER

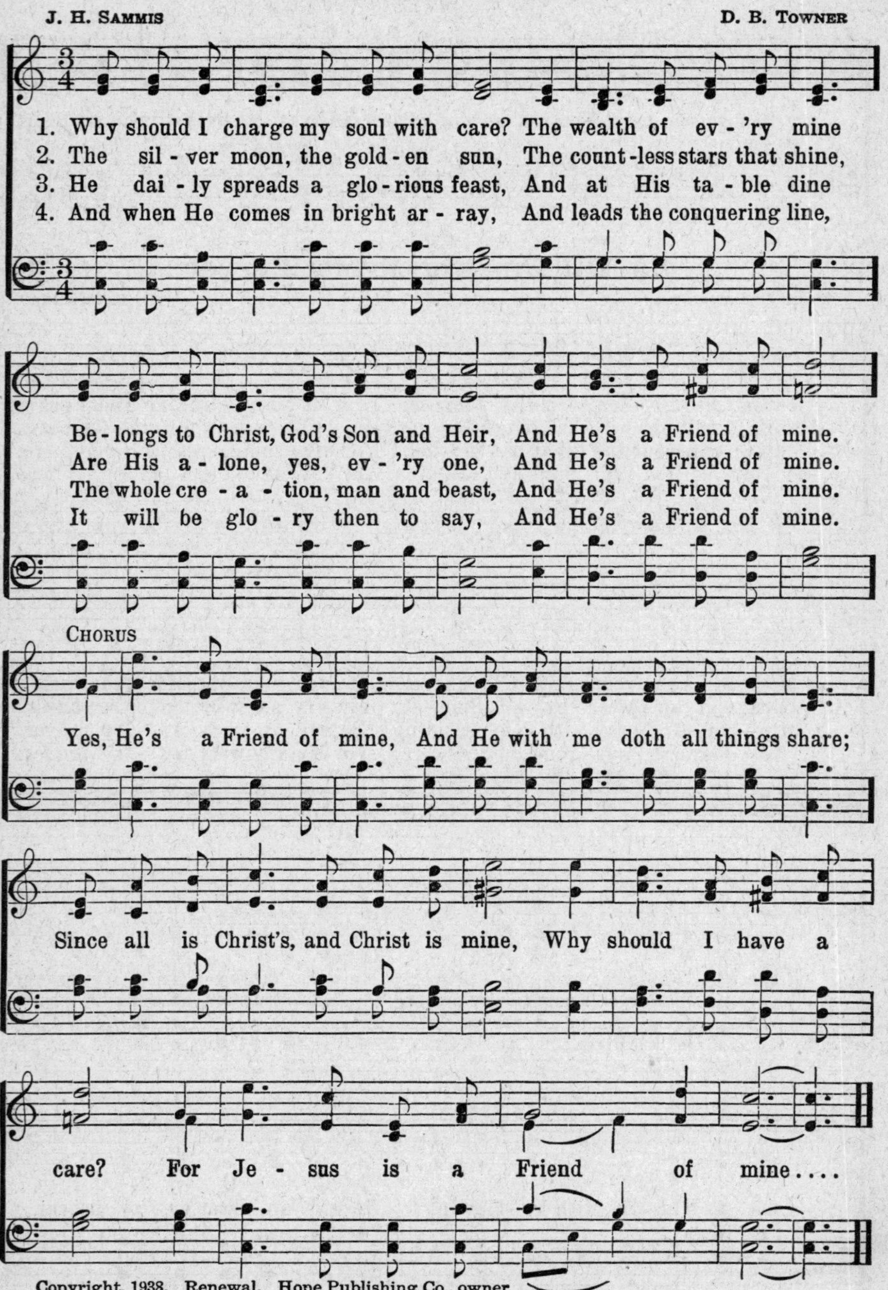

1. Why should I charge my soul with care? The wealth of ev-'ry mine
2. The sil-ver moon, the gold-en sun, The count-less stars that shine,
3. He dai-ly spreads a glo-rious feast, And at His ta-ble dine
4. And when He comes in bright ar-ray, And leads the conquering line,
Be-longs to Christ, God's Son and Heir, And He's a Friend of mine.
Are His a-lone, yes, ev-'ry one, And He's a Friend of mine.
The whole cre-a-tion, man and beast, And He's a Friend of mine.
It will be glo-ry then to say, And He's a Friend of mine.
CHORUS
Yes, He's a Friend of mine, And He with me doth all things share;
Since all is Christ's, and Christ is mine, Why should I have a
care? For Je-sus is a Friend of mine....

Copyright, 1938. Renewal. Hope Publishing Co., owner

All Things in Jesus

H. D. L. — Harry Dixon Loes

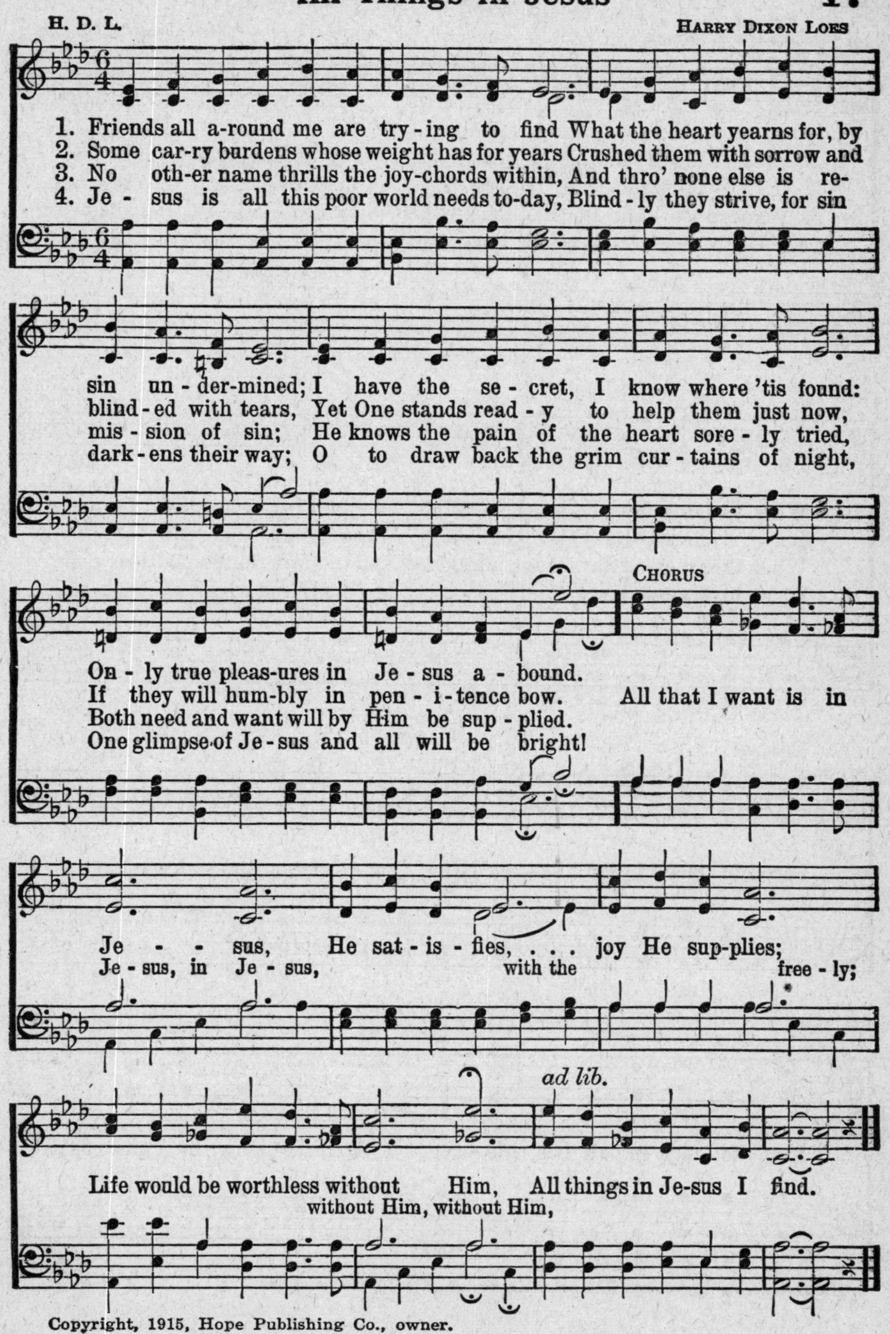
1. Friends all a-round me are try - ing to find What the heart yearns for, by
2. Some car-ry burdens whose weight has for years Crushed them with sorrow and
3. No oth-er name thrills the joy-chords within, And thro' none else is re-
4. Je - sus is all this poor world needs to-day, Blind - ly they strive, for sin
sin un - der-mined; I have the se - cret, I know where 'tis found:
blind - ed with tears, Yet One stands read - y to help them just now,
mis - sion of sin; He knows the pain of the heart sore - ly tried,
dark - ens their way; O to draw back the grim cur - tains of night,
On - ly true pleas-ures in Je - sus a - bound.
If they will hum-bly in pen - i - tence bow.
Both need and want will by Him be sup - plied.
One glimpse of Je - sus and all will be bright!
CHORUS
All that I want is in
Je - - sus, He sat - is - fies, . . . joy He sup-plies;
Je - sus, in Je - sus, with the free - ly;
ad lib.
Life would be worthless without Him, All things in Je-sus I find.
without Him, without Him,

Copyright, 1915, Hope Publishing Co., owner.

18 Face to Face

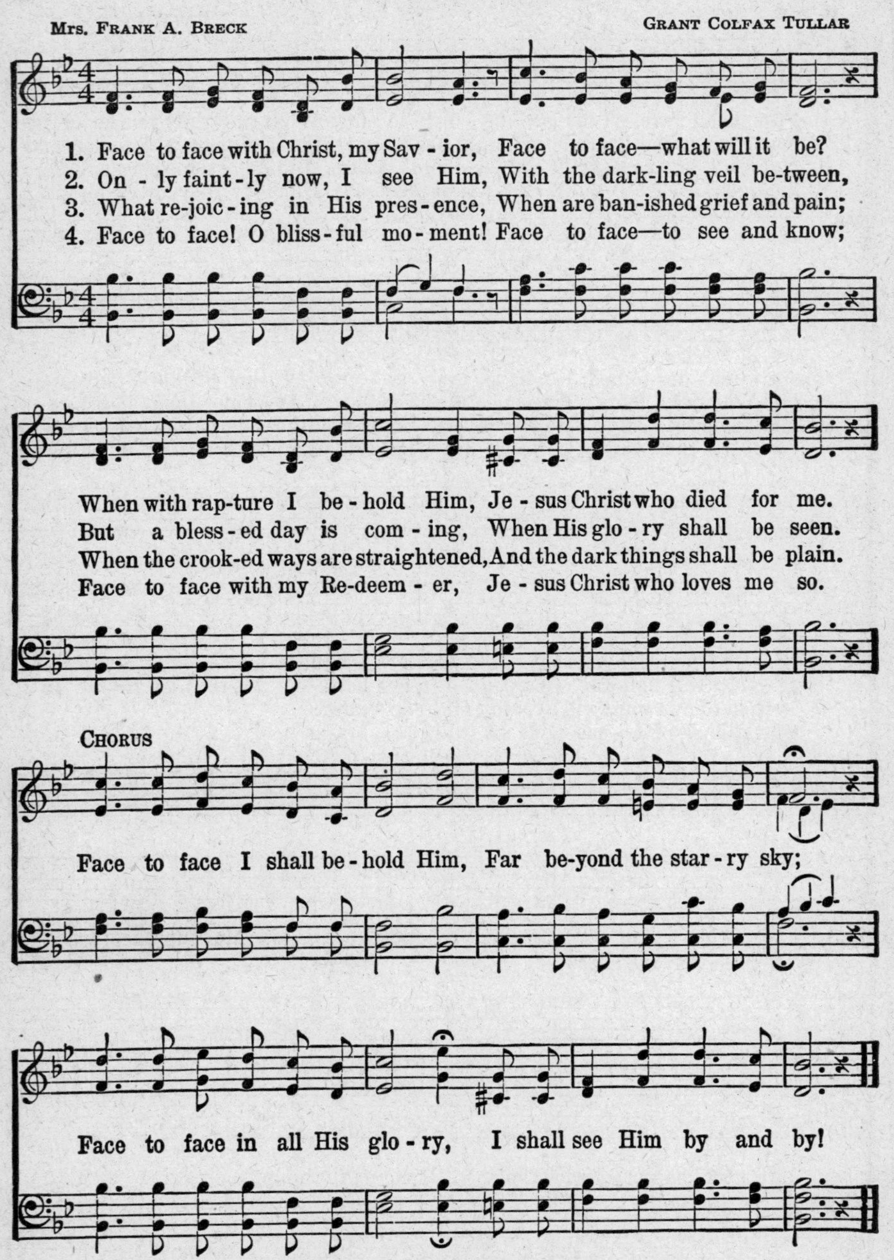
Mrs. Frank A. Breck
Grant Colfax Tullar
1. Face to face with Christ, my Sav - ior, Face to face—what will it be?
2. On - ly faint - ly now, I see Him, With the dark-ling veil be-tween,
3. What re-joic - ing in His pres - ence, When are ban-ished grief and pain;
4. Face to face! O bliss - ful mo - ment! Face to face—to see and know;
When with rap-ture I be - hold Him, Je - sus Christ who died for me.
But a bless - ed day is com - ing, When His glo - ry shall be seen.
When the crook-ed ways are straightened, And the dark things shall be plain.
Face to face with my Re-deem - er, Je - sus Christ who loves me so.
Chorus
Face to face I shall be - hold Him, Far be-yond the star - ry sky;
Face to face in all His glo - ry, I shall see Him by and by!

Copyright, 1927, by Grant C. Tullar. Renewal. Used by permission

Name of Names

ALBERT TROY HARDY — ALBERT TROY HARDY

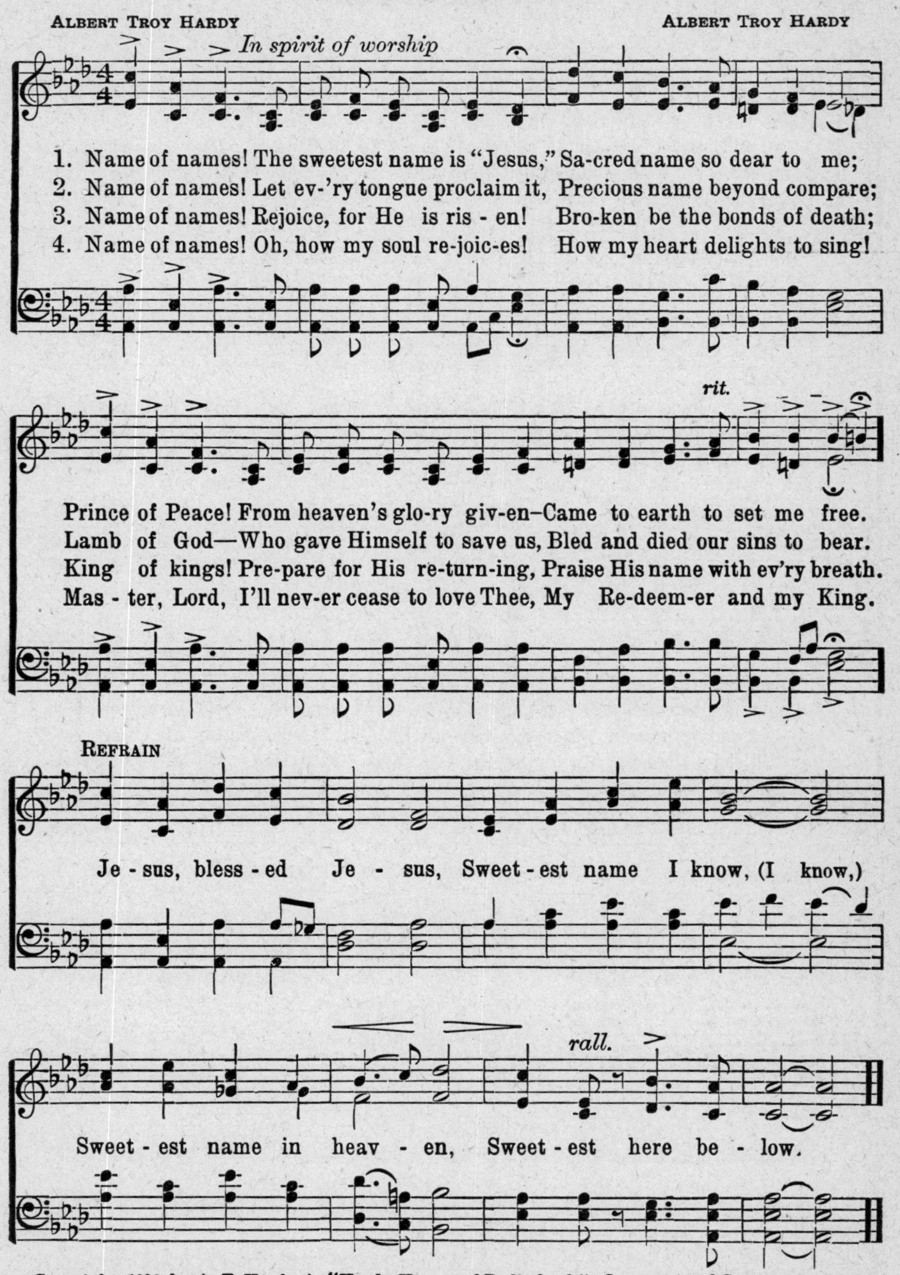
In spirit of worship
1. Name of names! The sweetest name is "Jesus," Sa-cred name so dear to me;
2. Name of names! Let ev-'ry tongue proclaim it, Precious name beyond compare;
3. Name of names! Rejoice, for He is ris - en! Bro-ken be the bonds of death;
4. Name of names! Oh, how my soul re-joic-es! How my heart delights to sing!
rit.
Prince of Peace! From heaven's glo-ry giv-en—Came to earth to set me free.
Lamb of God—Who gave Himself to save us, Bled and died our sins to bear.
King of kings! Pre-pare for His re-turn-ing, Praise His name with ev'ry breath.
Mas - ter, Lord, I'll nev-er cease to love Thee, My Re-deem-er and my King.
REFRAIN
Je - sus, bless - ed Je - sus, Sweet - est name I know, (I know,)
rall.
Sweet - est name in heav - en, Sweet - est here be - low.

Copyright, 1936, by A. T. Hardy, in "Hardy Hymns of Radio-land." International Copyright secured
Used by permission

Come Unto Me

CHARLES P. JONES — CHARLES P. JONES

1. Hear the bless-ed Sav-ior call-ing the op-pressed, "O ye heav-y-la-den, come to Me and rest; Come, no lon-ger tar-ry, I your load will bear, Bring Me ev-'ry bur-den, bring Me ev-'ry care."
2. Are you dis-ap-point-ed, wan-d'ring here and there, Drag-ging chains of doubt and load-ed down with care? Do un-ho-ly feel-ings struggle in your breast? Bring your case to Je-sus, He will give you rest.
3. Stum-bling on the moun-tains dark with sin and shame, Stumbling tow'rd the pit of hell's con-sum-ing flame, By the pow'rs of sin de-lud-ed and op-pressed, Hear the ten-der Shep-herd,—"Come to Me and rest."
4. Have you by temp-ta-tion of-ten con-quered been, Has a sense of weak-ness brought dis-tress with-in? Christ will sanc-ti-fy you, if you'll claim His best, In the Ho-ly Spir-it, He will give you rest.
CHORUS
Come un-to Me; I . . . . will give you rest;
Come un-to Me, Come un-to Me, I will give you rest, I will give you rest;
Take. . . . . . My yoke up-on you, Hear. . . . Me and be blest; . . . .
Take My yoke up-on you, Take My yoke up-on you, Hear Me and be blest, Hear Me and be blest;

Come Unto Me

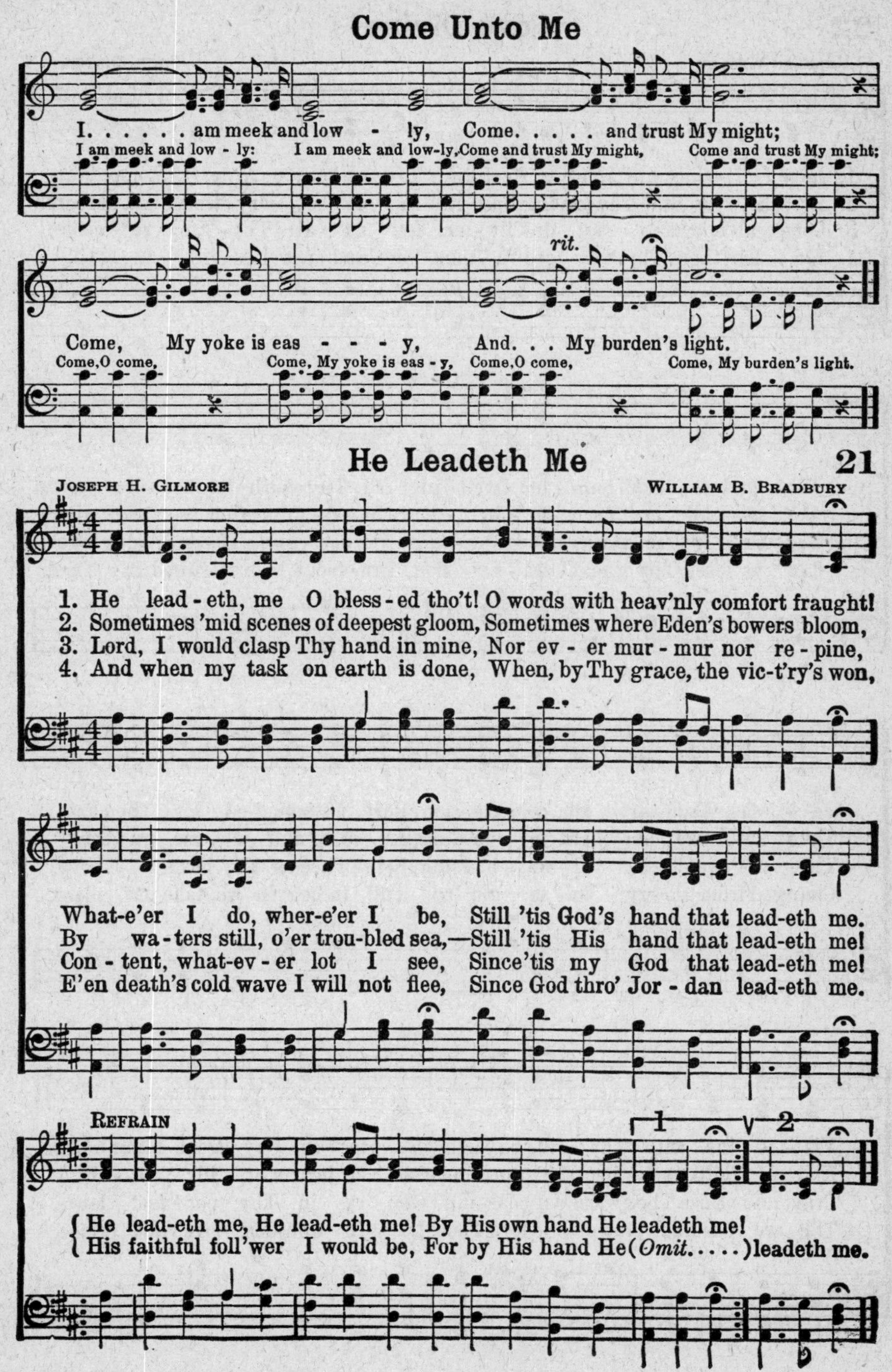

I. . . . . . am meek and low - ly, Come. . . . . and trust My might;
I am meek and low - ly: I am meek and low-ly, Come and trust My might, Come and trust My might;
rit.
Come, My yoke is eas - - - y, And. . . My burden's light.
Come, O come, Come, My yoke is eas - y, Come, O come, Come, My burden's light.
He Leadeth Me
21
Joseph H. Gilmore
William B. Bradbury
1. He lead - eth, me O bless - ed tho't! O words with heav'nly comfort fraught!
2. Sometimes 'mid scenes of deepest gloom, Sometimes where Eden's bowers bloom,
3. Lord, I would clasp Thy hand in mine, Nor ev - er mur - mur nor re - pine,
4. And when my task on earth is done, When, by Thy grace, the vic-t'ry's won,
What-e'er I do, wher-e'er I be, Still 'tis God's hand that lead-eth me.
By wa - ters still, o'er trou-bled sea,—Still 'tis His hand that lead-eth me!
Con - tent, what-ev - er lot I see, Since 'tis my God that lead-eth me!
E'en death's cold wave I will not flee, Since God thro' Jor - dan lead-eth me.
Refrain
1
2
He lead-eth me, He lead-eth me! By His own hand He leadeth me!
His faithful foll'wer I would be, For by His hand He (Omit. . . . .) leadeth me.

22 Love Divine

Charles Wesley | John Zundel

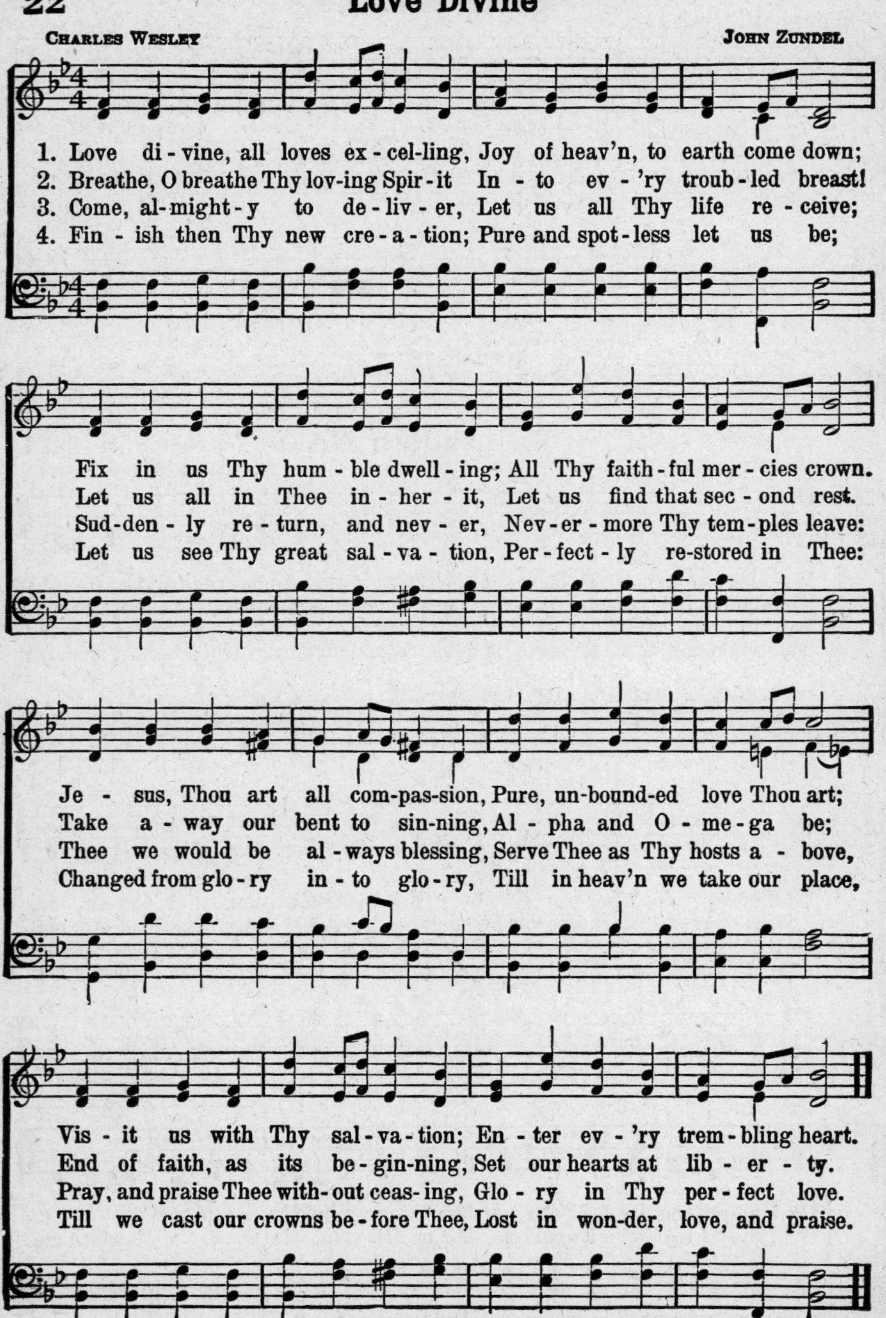
1. Love di - vine, all loves ex - cel-ling, Joy of heav'n, to earth come down;
2. Breathe, O breathe Thy lov-ing Spir - it In - to ev - 'ry troub - led breast!
3. Come, al-might - y to de - liv - er, Let us all Thy life re - ceive;
4. Fin - ish then Thy new cre - a - tion; Pure and spot - less let us be;
Fix in us Thy hum - ble dwell - ing; All Thy faith - ful mer - cies crown.
Let us all in Thee in - her - it, Let us find that sec - ond rest.
Sud-den - ly re - turn, and nev - er, Nev - er - more Thy tem - ples leave:
Let us see Thy great sal - va - tion, Per - fect - ly re-stored in Thee:
Je - sus, Thou art all com-pas-sion, Pure, un-bound-ed love Thou art;
Take a - way our bent to sin-ning, Al - pha and O - me - ga be;
Thee we would be al - ways blessing, Serve Thee as Thy hosts a - bove,
Changed from glo - ry in - to glo - ry, Till in heav'n we take our place,
Vis - it us with Thy sal - va - tion; En - ter ev - 'ry trem - bling heart.
End of faith, as its be - gin-ning, Set our hearts at lib - er - ty.
Pray, and praise Thee with - out ceas - ing, Glo - ry in Thy per - fect love.
Till we cast our crowns be - fore Thee, Lost in won-der, love, and praise.

Calvary Covers It All

Mrs. Walter G. Taylor
Mrs. Walter G. Taylor
1. Far dear-er than all that the world can im-part Was the mes-sage that
2. The stripes that He bore and the thorns that He wore Told His mer-cy and
3. How matchless the grace, when I looked in the face Of this Je-sus, my
4. How bless-ed the thought, that my soul by Him bought, Shall be His in the
came to my heart (to my heart); How that Je-sus a-lone for my
love ev-er-more (ev-er-more); And my heart bowed in shame as I
cru-ci-fied Lord (of my Lord); My re-demp-tion com-plete I then
glo-ry on high (His on high); Where with gladness and song I'll be
sin did a-tone, And Cal-va-ry cov-ers it all. . . . .
called on His name, And Cal-va-ry cov-ers it all. . . . .
found at His feet, And Cal-va-ry cov-ers it all. . . . .
one of the throng, And Cal-va-ry cov-ers it all. . . . .
cov-ers it all.
Chorus
Cal-va-ry cov-ers it all, My past with its sin and stain; My
guilt and de-spair Je-sus took on Him there, And Cal-va-ry cov-ers it all.

Copyright, 1932, by Mrs. Walter G. Taylor. International Copyright secured. Used by permission

24 Throw Out the Life-Line

EDWARD S. UFFORD

E. S. UFFORD
Arr. by GEORGE C. STEBBINS

1. Throw out the Life-Line a - cross the dark wave, There is a broth - er whom
2. Throw out the Life-Line with hand quick and strong: Why do you tar - ry, why
3. Throw out the Life-Line to dan-ger-fraught men, Sink-ing in an-guish where
4. Soon will the sea - son of res - cue be o'er, Soon will they drift to e-

some one should save; Somebody's broth-er! oh, who then, will dare To throw out the
lin - ger so long? See! he is sink-ing; oh; has-ten to-day—And out with the
you've nev-er been: Winds of temp-ta-tion and bil-lows of woe Will soon hurl them
ter - ni - ty's shore, Haste then, my brother, no time for de-lay, But throw out the

CHORUS.

Life-Line, his per - il to share?
Life-Boat! a-way, then, a-way! Throw out the Life-Line! Throw out the Life-Line!
out where the dark wa-ters flow.
Life-Line and save them to-day.

Some one is drift-ing a - way; Some one is sink-ing to - day. A - MEN.

Closer to Jesus

H. J. HEYDT B. F. LUTZ

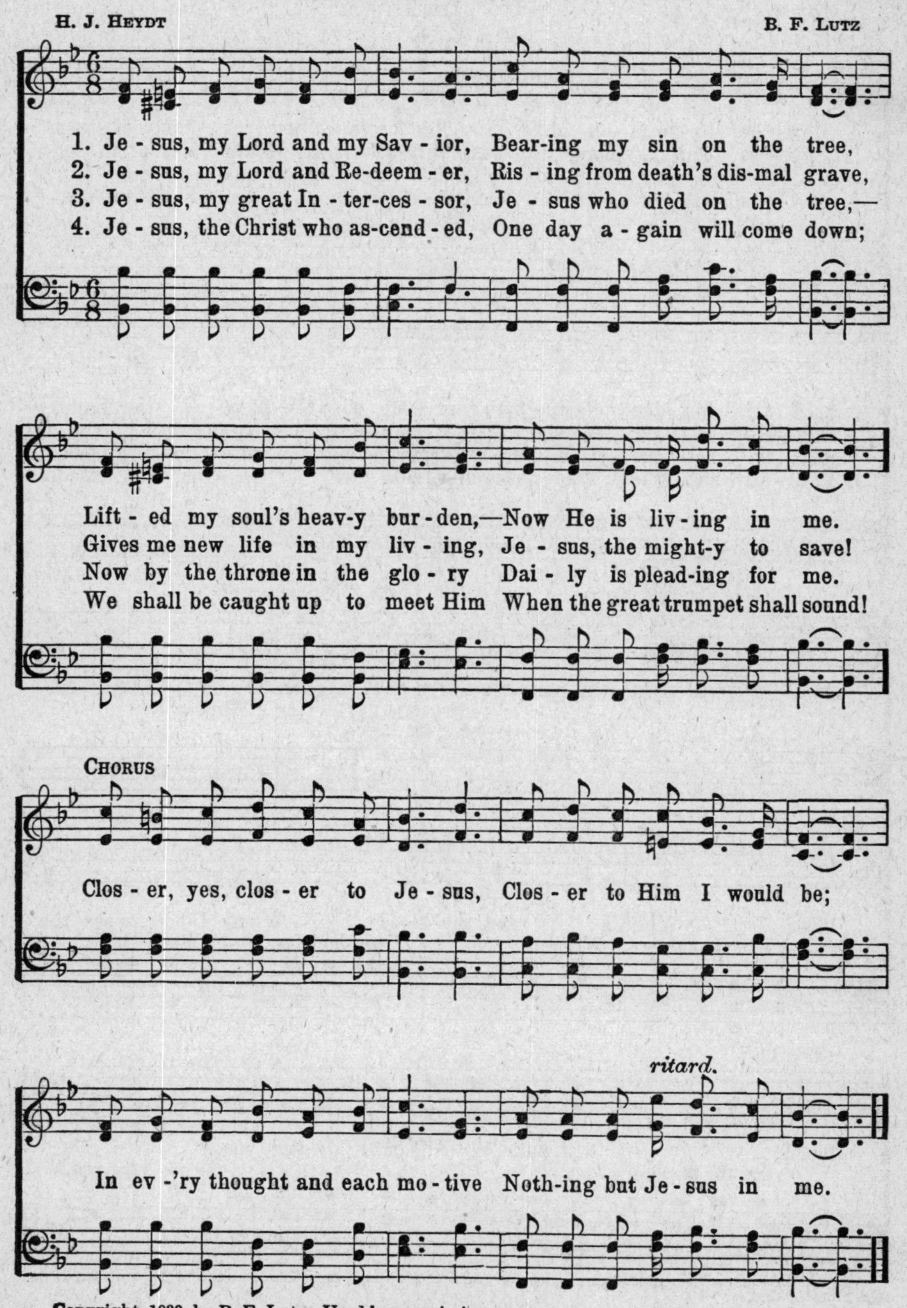
1. Je - sus, my Lord and my Sav - ior, Bear-ing my sin on the tree,
2. Je - sus, my Lord and Re-deem - er, Ris - ing from death's dis-mal grave,
3. Je - sus, my great In - ter-ces - sor, Je - sus who died on the tree,—
4. Je - sus, the Christ who as-cend - ed, One day a - gain will come down;
Lift - ed my soul's heav-y bur - den,—Now He is liv - ing in me.
Gives me new life in my liv - ing, Je - sus, the might-y to save!
Now by the throne in the glo - ry Dai - ly is plead-ing for me.
We shall be caught up to meet Him When the great trumpet shall sound!
CHORUS
Clos - er, yes, clos - er to Je - sus, Clos - er to Him I would be;
ritard.
In ev -'ry thought and each mo - tive Noth-ing but Je - sus in me.

Copyright, 1939, by B. F. Lutz Used by permission

26 When I See the Blood

J. F. G. and E. A. H.
J. F. H.
1. Christ our Re-deem-er died on the cross, Died for the sin-ner, paid all his due; Sprin-kle your soul with the blood of the Lamb,
2. Chief-est of sin-ners, Je-sus will save; All He has prom-ised, that He will do; Wash in the foun-tain o-pened for sin,
3. Judg-ment is com-ing, all will be there, Each one re-ceiv-ing just-ly his due; Hide in the sav-ing sin-cleans-ing blood,
4. O great com-pas-sion! O bound-less love! O lov-ing kind-ness, faith-ful and true! Find peace and shel-ter un-der the blood,
And I will pass, will pass o-ver you.
CHORUS
When I see the blood, When I see the blood, When I see the blood,
When I see the blood, When I see the blood, When I see the blood,
I will pass, I will pass o-ver you.
o-ver you.
rit.

By Foot Bros., not copyrighted. Let no one do so. May this song ever be free to be published for the glory of God.

By the Way of Redeeming Love

Albert Simpson Reitz

Albert Simpson Reitz

1. Oh, the love so full and free That the Lord be-stowed on
2. On the cross His life He gave, Ev - 'ry dy - ing soul to
3. I will praise the Lord in song Till I join that blood-washed
me, When He bade me come To my heav'n - ly home By the
save, And He points the way To the realms of day By the
throng, Nev - er - more to roam When I reach my home By the
way of re-deem - ing love.
Chorus
By the way of re - deem - ing love,
By the way of re - deem - ing love; I'm go - ing
home to glo - ry By the way of re - deem - ing love.

Copyright, 1918. Hope Publishing Company, owner

28 Yes, Lord, I Will Say Yes!

MERRILL DUNLOP
MERRILL DUNLOP
1. Call-ing, pleading, comest Thou, Lord; Sin-ful, need-y, my heart is stirred;
2. Con-trite, bow-ing low at Thy feet, Ask-ing, seek-ing vic-t'ry com-plete,
3. Grant me, Spir-it, unction and pow'r, Bless-ing, glo-ry, one might-y shower!
Wea-ry, help-less, heed-ing Thy Word, Now I say yes to Thee.
Strug-gling vain-ly sin to de-feat, I will say yes to Thee.
Find me wait-ing, yield-ed this hour As I say yes to Thee.
CHORUS
Yes, Lord, I will say yes, Yes to the Spir-it's call; Yes, Lord, I will say yes, And
give Thee my all in all; Thou in Thy beauty hast won my heart; Sweet is Thy
presence so precious Thou art; Yes, Lord, I will say yes, And follow what-e'er be-fall.

Copyright, 1936, by Merrill Dunlop. Used by permission

As a Volunteer

W. S. Brown — Chas. H. Gabriel

1. A call for loy-al sol-diers Comes to one and all; Sol-diers for the con-flict,
2. Yes, Jesus calls for soldiers Who are filled with pow'r, Soldiers who will serve Him
3. He calls you, for He loves you With a heart most kind, He whose heart was broken,
4. And when the war is o-ver, And the vic-t'ry won, When the true and faith-ful
Will you heed the call! Will you an-swer quick-ly, With a read-y cheer,
Ev-'ry day and hour; He will not for-sake you, He is ev-er near;
Bro-ken for man-kind; Now, just now He calls you, Calls in ac-cents clear,
Gath-er one by one, He will crown with glo-ry All who there ap-pear;
Chorus.
Will you be en-list-ed As a vol-un-teer? A vol-un-teer for Je-sus, A sol-dier
true! Oth-ers have enlisted, Why not you? Je-sus is the Cap-tain,
O why not?
We will nev-er fear; Will you be en-list-ed As a vol-un-teer? A-men.

Copyright, 1935. Renewal. Homer A. Rodeheaver, owner. Used by permission

30 I'll Go Where You Want Me to Go

Mary Brown — Carrie E. Rounsefell

1. It may not be on the mountain's height, Or o - ver the storm - y sea;
2. Per-haps to - day there are lov - ing words Which Jesus would have me speak;
3. There's surely somewhere a low - ly place In earth's harvest-fields so wide,
It may not be at the bat - tle's front My Lord will have need of me;
There may be now, in the paths of sin, Some wand'rer whom I should seek.
Where I may la - bor thro' life's short day For Je - sus, the Cru - ci - fied.
But if by a still, small voice He calls To paths I do not know,
O Sav - ior, if Thou wilt be my Guide, Tho' dark and rug-ged the way,
So, trust-ing my all un - to Thy care, I know Thou lov - est me!
I'll answer, dear Lord, with my hand in Thine, I'll go where you want me to go.
My voice shall ech - o the mes-sage sweet, I'll say what you want me to say.
I'll do Thy will with a heart sin-cere, I'll be what you want me to be.
Refrain
I'll go where you want me to go, dear Lord, O'er mountain, or plain, or sea;

Copyright, 1922, by C. E. Rounsefell, Renewal. Homer A. Rodeheaver, owner. Used by permission.

I'll Go Where You Want Me to Go

I'll say what you want me to say, dear Lord, I'll be what you want me to be.

Bring Them In 31

Alexcenah Thomas | W. A. Ogden

1. Hark! 'tis the Shepherd's voice I hear, Out in the des-ert dark and drear,
2. Who'll go and help this Shepherd kind, Help Him the wand'ring ones to find?
3. Out in the des - ert hear their cry, Out on the mountains wild and high;

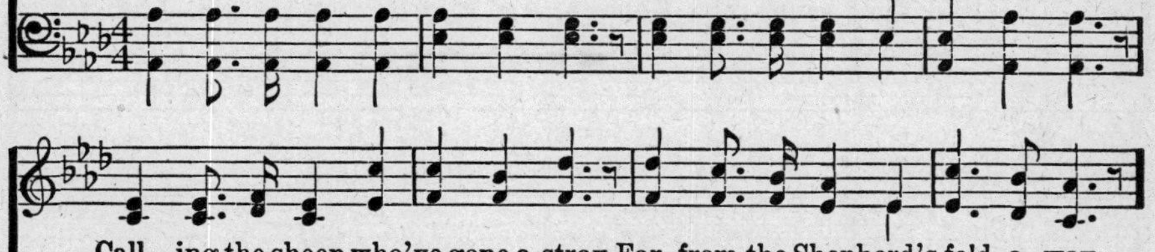

Call - ing the sheep who've gone a-stray Far from the Shepherd's fold a- way.
Who'll bring the lost ones to the fold, Where they'll be sheltered from the cold?
Hark! 'tis the Mas - ter speaks to thee, "Go find my sheep wher-e'er they be."

Chorus

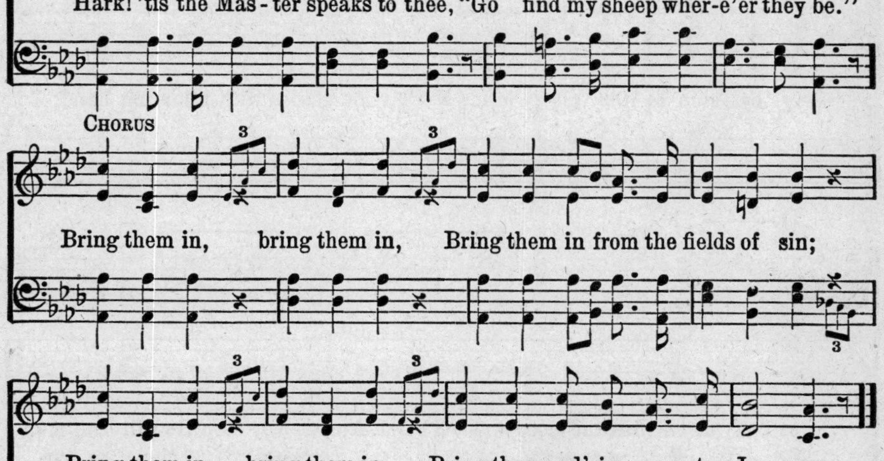
Bring them in, bring them in, Bring them in from the fields of sin;
Bring them in, bring them in, Bring the wand'ring ones to Je - sus.

Step By Step

Jennie Wilson

D. B. Towner
Descant (small notes) Fred Jacky

1. I need not ask what time will bring While to my Sav-ior's hand I cling;
2. I need not fear tho' dark the way, For Je - sus close to me doth stay;
3. Oft on my path falls gold-en light, And bloom-ing flow-ers greet my sight;
4. I shall not have to go a - lone From earth in - to the realms un-known;
A song of trust my soul can sing, For step by step He will lead me.
Un - til the dawn of per - fect day Still step by step He will lead me.
My Savior's love makes all scenes bright, And step by step He will lead me.
My Lord doth ne'er for-sake His own, And step by step He will lead me.
Chorus
Descant
Ah! . . .
Step by step to the glo-ry land, My Sav-ior guides with a lov-ing hand; I
go to dwell with the blood-washed band, And step by step He will lead me.

Copyright, 1933. Renewal. Arr. Copyright, 1941. Hope Publishing Co., owner

Note: Descant in grace notes not to be sung, but rather vocalized to syllable "Ah".

Saved, Saved!

J. P. S. — J. P. Scholfield

1. I've found a friend who is all to me,.... His love is ev - er true; .... I love to tell how He lift - ed me.... And what His grace can do for you. . .
2. He saves me from ev - 'ry sin and harm,. Se- cures my soul each day; .... I'm lean - ing strong on His might - y arm;.. I know He'll guide me all the way. . .
3. When poor and need - y and all a - lone,... In love He said to me,........ "Come un - to me and I'll lead you home, To live with me e - ter - nal - ly."...
Chorus.
Saved . . . . by His pow'r di - vine, Saved . . . . to new life sub - lime!
Saved by His pow'r,
Saved to new life,
Life now is sweet and my joy is com - plete, For I'm Saved, saved, saved!
rit.

Copyright, 1939. Renewal. Robert H. Coleman, owner. Used by permission.

God Loves Me

H. E. M. Snyder — H. E. M. Snyder

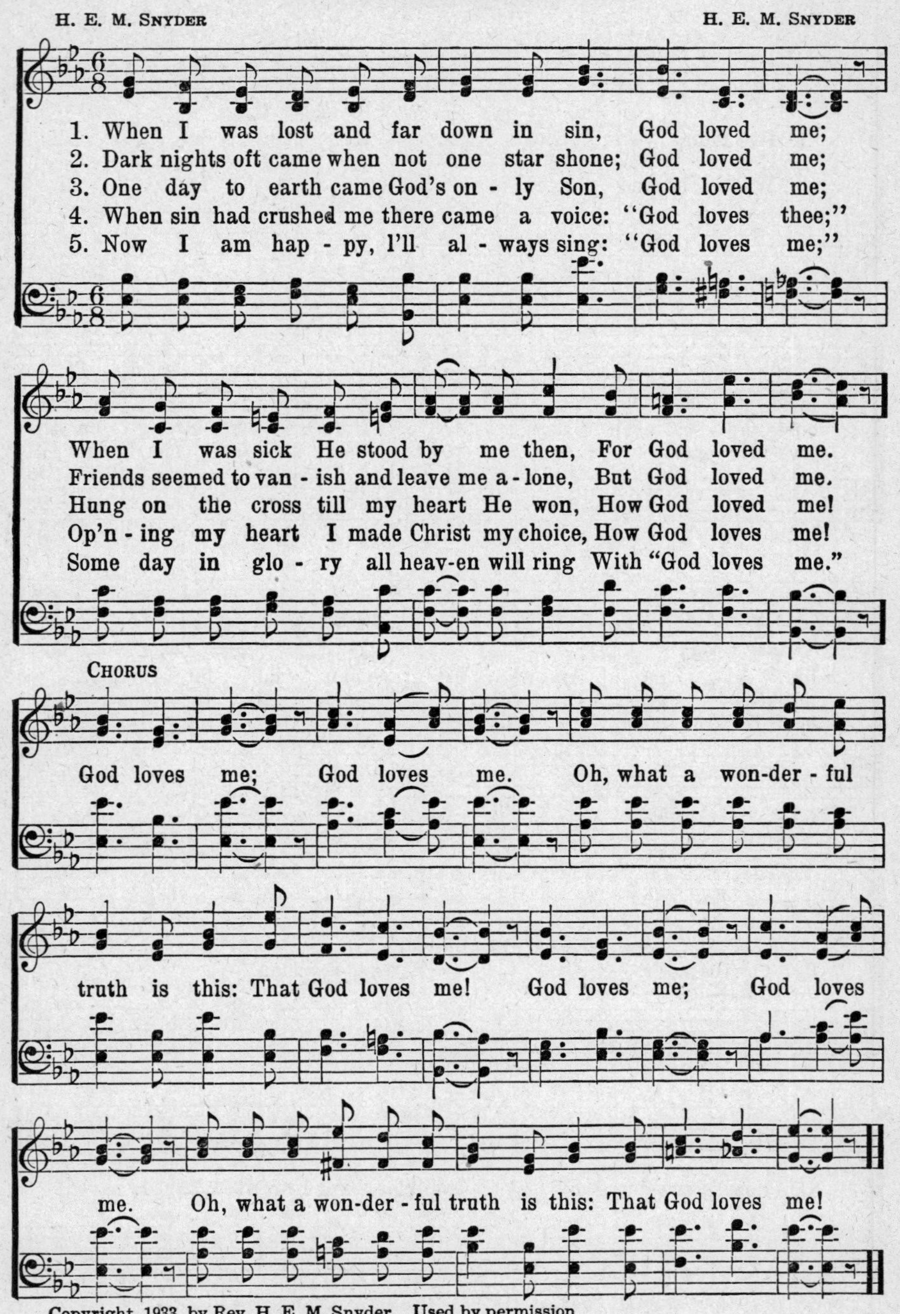
1. When I was lost and far down in sin, God loved me;
2. Dark nights oft came when not one star shone; God loved me;
3. One day to earth came God's on - ly Son, God loved me;
4. When sin had crushed me there came a voice: "God loves thee;"
5. Now I am hap - py, I'll al - ways sing: "God loves me;"
When I was sick He stood by me then, For God loved me.
Friends seemed to van - ish and leave me a - lone, But God loved me.
Hung on the cross till my heart He won, How God loved me!
Op'n - ing my heart I made Christ my choice, How God loves me!
Some day in glo - ry all heav-en will ring With "God loves me."
Chorus
God loves me; God loves me. Oh, what a won-der - ful
truth is this: That God loves me! God loves me; God loves
me. Oh, what a won-der - ful truth is this: That God loves me!

Copyright, 1933, by Rev. H. E. M. Snyder. Used by permission

Since the Savior Found Me

E. J. H.
Edgar J. Haskins
1. Since the Sav-ior found me, Pardoned all my sins, I have had the joy and
2. Since the Sav-ior found me All to Him I owe, For His pre-cious blood has
3. Since the Sav-ior found me I have per-fect rest, Liv-ing in the realms of
liv - ing hope with-in; Gone is all the shame and sor - row of the past,
washed me white as snow; Now no con-dem-na - tion, hap - py as can be,
joy and hap - pi - ness; Lean-ing on my Sav - ior, look - ing for that day
Fine
They're un - der-neath the pre - cious blood of Christ at last.
I'm glad that Je - sus jus - ti - fies and sets me free.
When He shall come to catch His wait - ing bride a - way.
D.S.–saves and keeps and sanc - ti - fies me by His pow'r.
Chorus
Saved, saved, saved, I'm hap - py on the way; Saved, saved, saved, I
D. S.
love Him more each day; Saved, saved, saved, I know He's mine each hour; He

Copyright, 1937, by E. J. Haskins. Used by permission

He's Coming Back

Har. by Mrs. EDWARD BOONE
EDWARD BOONE
1. From Mt. Ol - i - vet our Sav - ior went to heav - en, In a
2. Yes, He's com-ing back a - gain to take the ran - somed To a
3. For a thou-sand years this earth will have no tempt - er, And we'll
4. Then the li - on and the lamb be sweet-ly play - ing, And the
cloud of glo - ry en - tered in the sky; But an an - gel spoke these
home He's now pre-par - ing up on high; So "Let not your heart be
reign down here with Je - sus on the throne; Then the wil - der - ness shall
curse be lift - ed too, for - ev - er - more; U - ni - ver - sal peace be
words of glo-rious com-fort, "In like man-ner He'll be com-ing, bye and bye."
troubled," said the Mas-ter, You'll be ris-ing when you hear the trump-et's cry.
blos - som as the rose-bed, Back to Pal - es - tine the Jews be gathered home.
flow - ing like a riv - er, And His righteousness will go from shore to shore.
CHORUS
He's com-ing back, ... a - gain to reign, ... The prom-ise
He's com-ing back a - gain to reign,
is . . . . I'll come a - gain; . . . . . . "For if I go a-
The prom-ise is I'll come a - gain;

Copyright, 1935, by Edward Boone. Used by permission

He's Coming Back

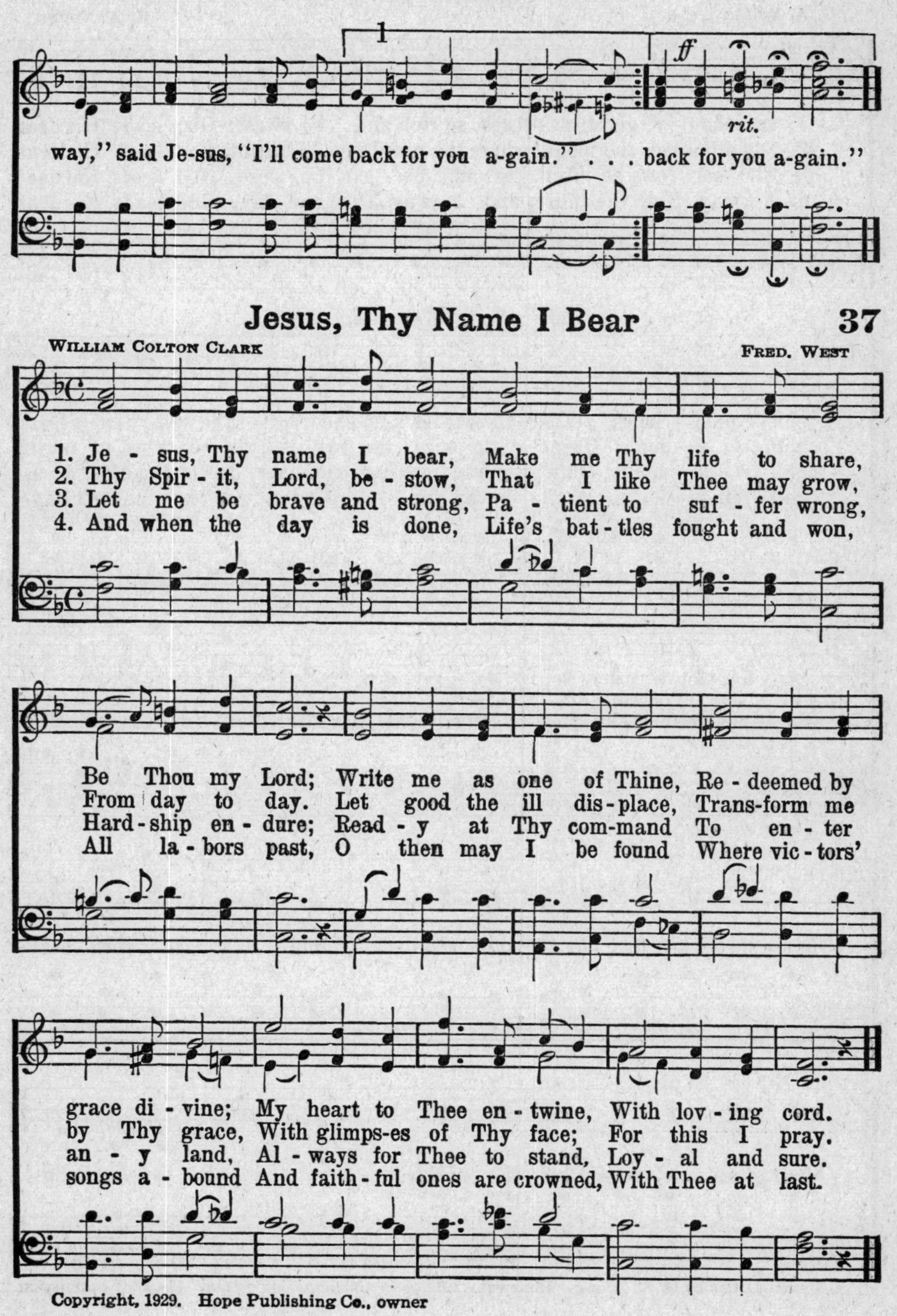

1
ff
rit.
way," said Je-sus, "I'll come back for you a-gain." . . . back for you a-gain."
Jesus, Thy Name I Bear
37
William Colton Clark
Fred. West
1. Je - sus, Thy name I bear, Make me Thy life to share, Be Thou my Lord; Write me as one of Thine, Re - deemed by grace di - vine; My heart to Thee en - twine, With lov - ing cord.
2. Thy Spir - it, Lord, be - stow, That I like Thee may grow, From day to day. Let good the ill dis - place, Trans-form me by Thy grace, With glimps-es of Thy face; For this I pray.
3. Let me be brave and strong, Pa - tient to suf - fer wrong, Hard-ship en - dure; Read - y at Thy com-mand To en - ter an - y land, Al - ways for Thee to stand, Loy - al and sure.
4. And when the day is done, Life's bat - tles fought and won, All la - bors past, O then may I be found Where vic - tors' songs a - bound And faith - ful ones are crowned, With Thee at last.

Copyright, 1929. Hope Publishing Co., owner

38 God Leads Us Along

G. A. YOUNG G. A. YOUNG

1. In shad - y, green pas-tures, so rich and so sweet. God leads His dear
2. Sometimes on the mount where the sun shines so bright, God leads His dear
3. Tho' sor - rows be - fall us, and Sa - tan op - pose, God leads His dear
4. A - way from the mire, and a - way from the clay, God leads His dear
chil-dren a - long; Where the wa-ter's cold flow bathes the wea-ry one's feet,
chil-dren a - long; Some - times in the val - ley, in dark-est of night,
chil-dren a - long; Through grace we can con-quer, de - feat all our foes,
chil-dren a - long; A - way up in glo - ry, e - ter - ni - ty's day,
God leads His dear chil-dren a - long.
CHORUS
Some thro' the waters, some thro' the flood,
Some thro' the fire, but all thro' the blood; Some thro' great sor-row, but
God gives a song, In the night sea - son and all the day long.
rit.

Copyright, 1930, by G. A. Young. Renewal. Lillenas Publishing Co., owner. Used by permission

Under His Blood

H. E. M. Snyder — Mrs. H. E. M. Snyder

1. A riv-er of crim-son flows down from the tree; It springs from the foun-tain of blood. I plunged in that riv-er and Christ set me free; My sins rolled a-way in the flood.
2. 'Twas there on the cross Je-sus suf-fered and died In ag-o-ny, sor-row and woe, That a sol-dier, one day, thrust a spear in His side, And start-ed the life-giv-ing flow.
3. That life-giv-ing stream will con-tin-ue, I'm told, A-down thro' all a-ges of time; Till it car-ries me in-to the cit-y of gold, Re-deemed by the blood of the Lamb.
4. Plunge in then, my broth-er, by faith in God's Word; Let Christ make you whit-er than snow; Trans-formed by His won-der-ful grace you will rise, Sing-ing, "Je-sus has saved me, I know."
Chorus
My sins are all un-der the blood;
My sins are all un-der the blood; From their stain I am clean,
They will nev-er be seen: Hal-le-lu-jah! They're un-der the blood!

Copyright, 1934, by Rev. H. E. M. Snyder. Used by permission

40 Precious Blood

Louise L. Nankivell — Louise L. Nankivell

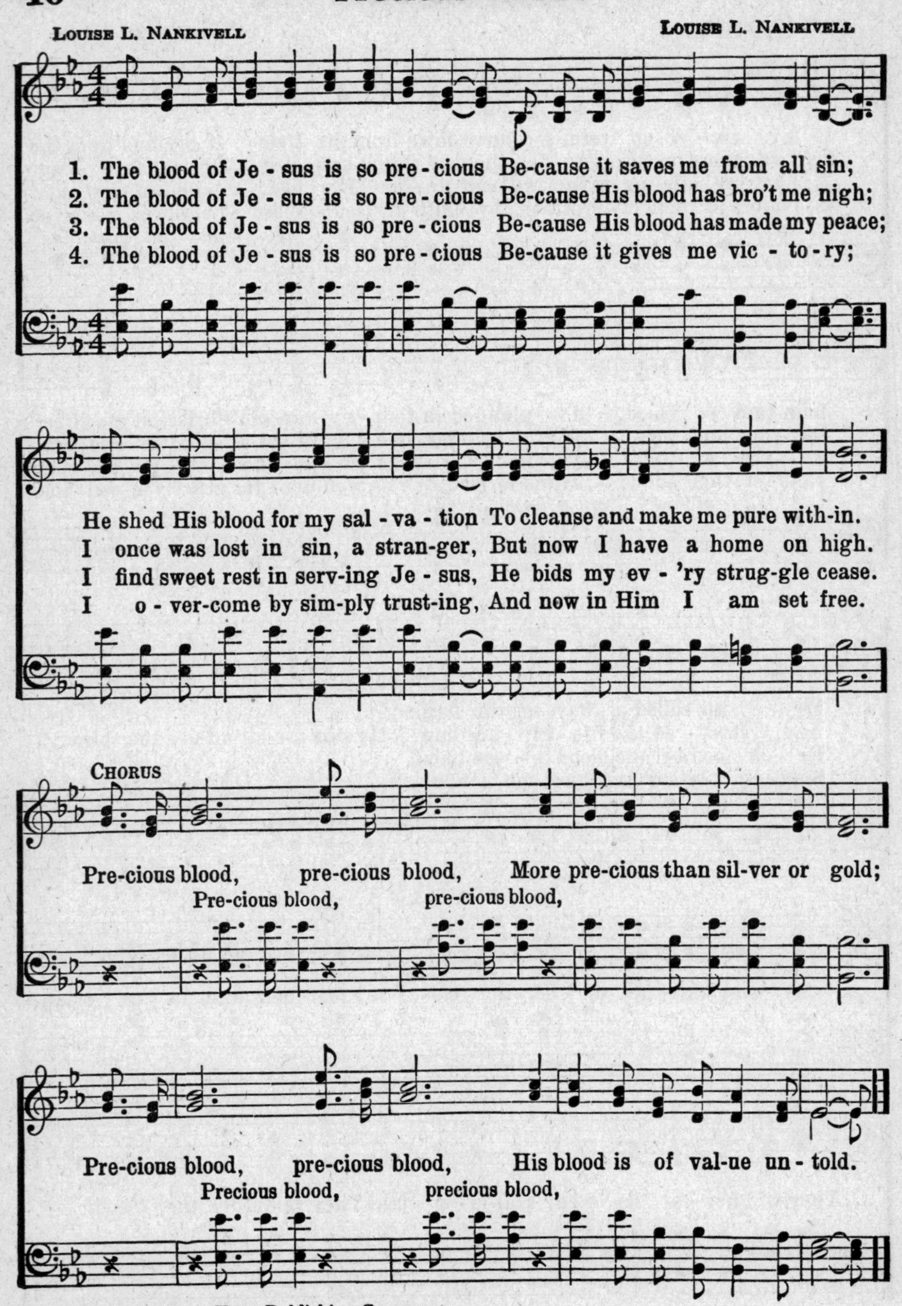
1. The blood of Je - sus is so pre - cious Be-cause it saves me from all sin;
2. The blood of Je - sus is so pre - cious Be-cause His blood has bro't me nigh;
3. The blood of Je - sus is so pre - cious Be-cause His blood has made my peace;
4. The blood of Je - sus is so pre - cious Be-cause it gives me vic - to - ry;
He shed His blood for my sal - va - tion To cleanse and make me pure with-in.
I once was lost in sin, a stran-ger, But now I have a home on high.
I find sweet rest in serv-ing Je - sus, He bids my ev - 'ry strug-gle cease.
I o - ver-come by sim-ply trust-ing, And now in Him I am set free.
CHORUS
Pre-cious blood, pre-cious blood, More pre-cious than sil-ver or gold;
Pre-cious blood, pre-cious blood,
Pre-cious blood, pre-cious blood, His blood is of val-ue un - told.
Precious blood, precious blood,

Copyright, 1941. Hope Publishing Co., owner

Joyfully Serving the King

LIZZIE DE ARMOND — ELTON MENNO ROTH

1. Joy - ful - ly, joy - ful - ly on - ward we tread, Safe-ly and sure-ly by
2. Joy - ful - ly, joy - ful - ly lay - ing a - side All that may hin-der to
3. Joy - ful - ly, joy - ful - ly prais - es we sing, Lift-ing our voic - es to
Je - sus we're led; Where He may call us, we'll go with - out fear,
fol - low our Guide; Faith - ful - ly serv-ing, glad work - ers are we,
Je - sus our King; Friend of all oth - ers, the dear - est and best,
Noth-ing can harm us when He is so near.
Now in life's morn-ing His own we would be.
Those who o - bey Him will sure - ly be blest.
CHORUS
Joy-ful-ly, joy-ful - ly
serv - ing the King, Joy - ful - ly, joy - ful - ly prais-es we sing; Loy - al - ly,
loy - al - ly striv-ing to do Some-thing for Je-sus the whole jour-ney through.
rall.

Copyright, 1941, by Elton M. Roth. Used by permission

42 Christ Jesus Hath the Power

JAMES M. GRAY | D. B. TOWNER

1. Christ Je - sus hath the pow'r, The pow - er to for - give,
2. Christ Je - sus hath the pow'r, The pow - er to re - new,
3. Christ Je - sus hath the pow'r, The pow - er to con - sole,
4. Christ Je - sus hath the pow'r, The pow - er to de - stroy,

The pow'r to quick - en whom He will, And make the sin - ner live.
The pow'r to cleanse your heart from sin, And make you whol - ly true.
The pow'r to car - ry all your care—On Him your bur-dens roll.
The pow'r to bruise your en - e - my Who would your soul an - noy.

Christ Je - sus hath the pow'r, O tell it far and near!
Christ Je - sus hath the pow'r For ev - er - more to keep;
Christ Je - sus hath the pow'r To wipe the tear a - way;
Christ Je - sus hath the pow'r, When on your dy - ing bed,

O bring to Him your guilt - y heart, And grace shall ban - ish fear!
O none can pluck you from His hand, Or rob Him of His sheep!
O place in Him your con - fi - dence! O trust Him, and o - bey!
To give your soul the vic - to - ry, The pow'r to raise the dead!

CHORUS

Christ Je - sus hath the pow'r, The pow'r of God He wields! Christ Je - sus

Copyright, 1931, Renewal. Hope Publishing Co., owner

Christ Jesus Hath the Power
hath the pow'r, My heart sur-ren-der yields! Christ Je-sus hath the pow'r, I
trust Him ev - er-more! Christ Je-sus hath the pow'r, I wor-ship and a-dore!
rit.
Savior, More Than Life
43
FANNY J. CROSBY
W. H. DOANE
1. Sav - ior, more than life to me, I am cling-ing, cling-ing close to Thee;
2. Thro' this chang-ing world be-low, Lead me gen-tly, gen-tly as I go;
3. Let me love Thee more and more, Till this fleet-ing, fleet-ing life is o'er;
FINE
Let Thy pre-cious blood ap-plied, Keep me ev - er, ev - er near Thy side.
Trusting Thee, I can-not stray, I can nev-er, nev - er lose my way.
Till my soul is lost in love, In a bright-er, bright-er world a - bove.
D. S.—May Thy ten - der love to me Bind me clo - ser, clo - ser, Lord, to Thee.
REFRAIN
D. S.
Ev-'ry day, ev - 'ry hour, Let me feel Thy cleans-ing pow'r;
Ev-'ry day and hour, ev - 'ry day and hour,

My Father Knows

S. M. I. Henry
E. O. Excell
Arr. by Fred Jacky
1. I know my heav'nly Father knows The storms that would my way oppose; But He can drive the clouds a - way, And turn the darkness in - to day.
2. I know my heav'nly Father knows The balm I need to soothe my woes; And with His touch of love di - vine He heals this wounded heart of mine.
3. I know my heav'nly Father knows How frail I am to meet my foes; But He my cause will e'er de - fend, Up - hold and keep me to the end.
4. I know my heav'nly Father knows The hour my journey here will close; And may that hour, O faith - ful Guide, Find me safe shel-tered by Thy side,
Chorus
Sop. Solo
Sop. and Ten.
Hum.
He knows, ... He knows . . . . The clouds that would my way oppose;
Hum.
Sop. Solo
Parts
Hum.
He knows, ... He knows, . . . And tem-pers ev - 'ry wind that blows.
Hum.

Copyright, 1924. Renewal. Arr. Copyright, 1941, Hope Publishing Co., owner

He Set Me Free

HALDOR LILLENAS HALDOR LILLENAS

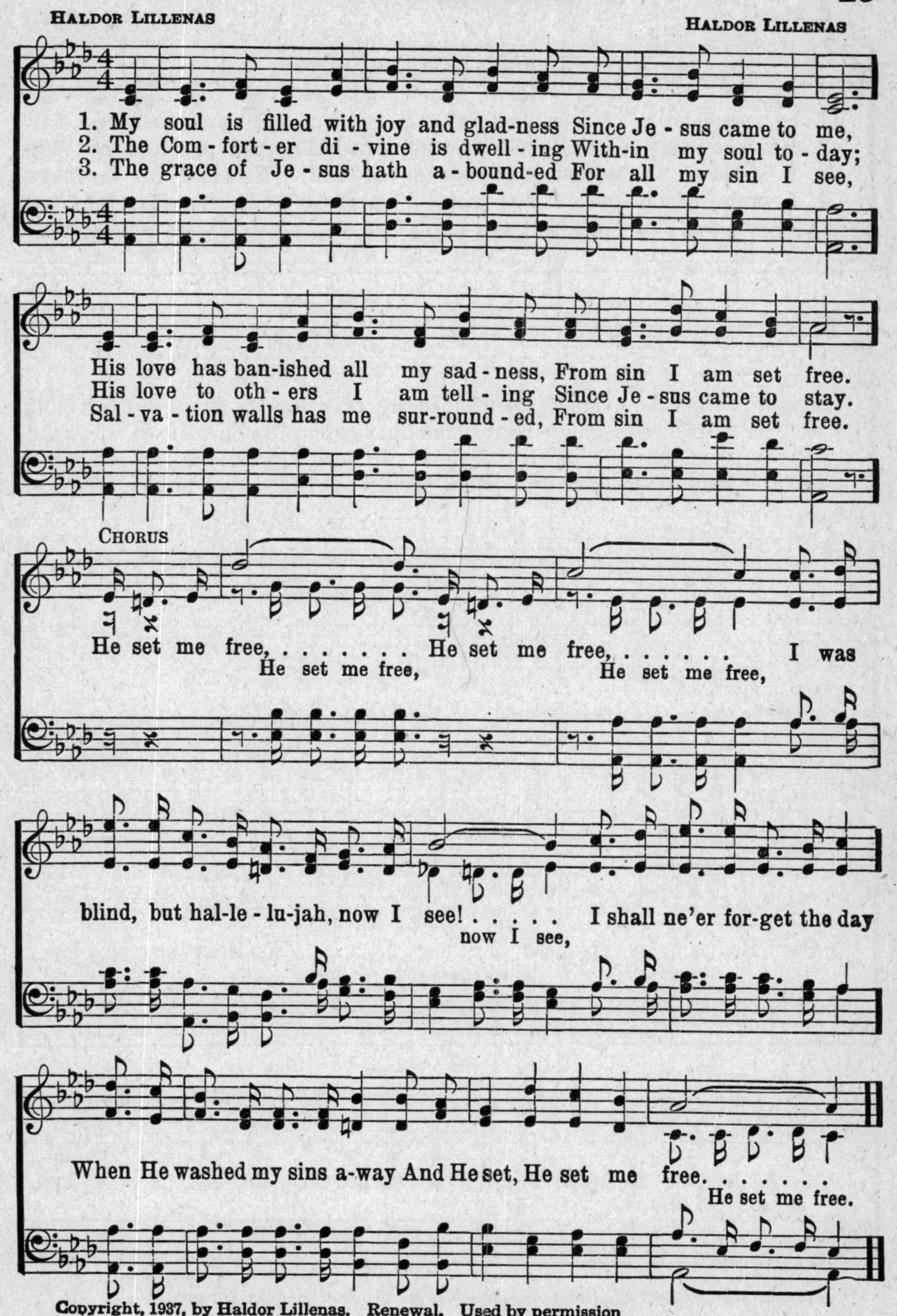
1. My soul is filled with joy and glad-ness Since Je - sus came to me,
2. The Com-fort - er di - vine is dwell - ing With-in my soul to - day;
3. The grace of Je - sus hath a - bound-ed For all my sin I see,
His love has ban-ished all my sad - ness, From sin I am set free.
His love to oth - ers I am tell - ing Since Je - sus came to stay.
Sal - va - tion walls has me sur-round - ed, From sin I am set free.
CHORUS
He set me free, ... He set me free, ... I was
He set me free, He set me free,
blind, but hal-le - lu-jah, now I see! . . . . . I shall ne'er for-get the day
now I see,
When He washed my sins a-way And He set, He set me free. . . . . . .
He set me free.

Copyright, 1937, by Haldor Lillenas. Renewal. Used by permission

46 He is So Precious to Me

C. H. G.
Chas. H. Gabriel.
1. So pre-cious is Je-sus, my Sav-ior, my King, His praise all the day long with rap-ture I sing; To Him in my weak-ness for strength I can cling,
2. He stood at my heart's door 'mid sunshine and rain, And pa-tient-ly wait-ed an en-trance to gain; What shame that so long He en-treat-ed in vain,
3. I stand on the moun-tain of bless-ing at last, No cloud in the heav-ens a shad-ow to cast; His smile is up-on me, the val-ley is past,
4. I praise Him be-cause He ap-point-ed a place Where, some day, thro' faith in His won-der-ful grace, I know I shall see Him—shall look on His face,
For He is so pre-cious to me.
Chorus. Faster.
For He is so pre-cious to me, . . .
so pre-cious to me,
For He is so pre-cious to me; . . . .
so pre-cious to me;
'Tis Heav-en be-low My Re-deem-er to know,
rit. . .
For He is so pre-cious to me.
A-men.

Copyright, 1930. Renewal. Homer A. Rodeheaver, owner. Used by permission.

There is Power in the Blood

L. E. J.
L. E. Jones
1. Would you be free from the bur - den of sin? There's pow'r in the blood,
2. Would you be free from your pas-sion and pride? There's pow'r in the blood,
3. Would you be whit - er, much whiter than snow? There's pow'r in the blood,
4. Would you do serv - ice for Je - sus your King? There's pow'r in the blood,
pow'r in the blood; Would you o'er e - vil a vic - to - ry win? There's
pow'r in the blood; Come for a cleans-ing to Cal - va - ry's tide; There's
pow'r in the blood; Sin-stains are lost in its life - giv - ing flow; There's
pow'r in the blood; Would you live dai - ly His prais - es to sing? There's
won - der-ful pow'r in the blood.
Chorus.
There is pow'r, there is pow'r, Wonder-working pow'r
In the blood In the blood of the Lamb; of the Lamb;
There is pow'r, there is pow'r,
Won - der-work-ing pow'r In the pre - cious blood of the Lamb. A - men.

Copyright, 1927. Renewal. Hope Publishing Co., owner.

48 Grace Greater Than Our Sin

JULIA H. JOHNSTON
D. B. TOWNER
1. Mar-vel-ous grace of our lov-ing Lord, Grace that ex-ceeds our sin and our guilt, Yon-der on Cal-va-ry's mount out-poured, There where the blood of the Lamb was spilt.
2. Sin and de-spair like the sea waves cold, Threat-en the soul with in-fi-nite loss; Grace that is great-er, yes, grace un-told, Points to the Ref-uge, the Might-y Cross.
3. Dark is the stain that we can-not hide, What can a-vail to wash it a-way? Look! there is flow-ing a crim-son tide; Whit-er than snow you may be to-day.
4. Mar-vel-ous, in-fi-nite, match-less grace, Free-ly be-stowed on all who be-lieve; You that are long-ing to see His face, Will you this mo-ment His grace re-ceive?
CHORUS
Grace, grace, God's grace, Grace that will par-don and cleanse with-in; Grace, grace, God's grace, Grace that is great-er than all our sin.
Mar-vel-ous grace, In-fi-nite grace, Mar-vel-ous grace, In-fi-nite grace,

Copyright, 1938. Renewal. Hope Publishing Co., owner.

Kept In Christ, I'm Satisfied

Mrs. Walter G. Taylor
Mrs. Walter G. Taylor
1. Sat - is - fied my soul's deep long-ing, When in Christ my soul doth hide,
2. When life's cares per-plex, dis-tress me, Earth-ly friends all seem to go,
3. So through all life's var - ied path-way, Sweet-est peace is ev - er mine;
When the snares my foot-steps throng-ing, I have Him, there's naught be-side;
Then in Je - sus shall my trust be, For I know He loves me so.
In com - mun-ion with Him dai - ly, He doth give me pow'r di - vine.
Sat - is - fied, O precious knowl-edge, Kept in Christ, I'm sat - is - fied.
Sat - is - fied, O bless - ed com - fort, Kept in Christ, I'm sat - is - fied.
Sat - is - fied, He's mine for - ev - er, Kept in Christ, I'm sat - is - fied.
Chorus
Kept in Christ, I'm sat - is - fied, When in Him my soul doth hide;
Ev - 'ry need by Him sup - plied, Kept in Christ, I'm sat - is - fied.

Copyright, 1925. Mrs. Walter G. Taylor, owner. Used by permission

Count Your Blessings

Rev. JOHNSON OATMAN, JR. — E. O. EXCELL

1. When up-on life's bil-lows you are tem-pest-tossed, When you are dis-
2. Are you ev-er bur-dened with a load of care? Does the cross seem
3. When you look at oth-ers with their lands and gold, Think that Christ has
4. So, a-mid the con-flict, whether great or small, Do not be dis-
cour-aged, think-ing all is lost, Count your man-y bless-ings, name them
heav-y you are called to bear? Count your man-y bless-ings, ev-'ry
prom-ised you His wealth un-told; Count your man-y bless-ings, mon-ey
cour-aged, God is o-ver all; Count your man-y bless-ings, an-gels
one by one, And it will sur-prise you what the Lord hath done.
doubt will fly, And you will be sing-ing as the days go by.
can-not buy Your re-ward in Heav-en, nor your home on high.
will at-tend, Help and com-fort give you to your jour-ney's end.
CHORUS.
Count your bless-ings, Name them one by one; Count your
Count your man-y bless-ings, Name them one by one; Count your man-y
bless-ings, See what God hath done; Count your bless-ings,
bless-ings, See what God hath done; Count your man-y bless-ings,

Copyright, 1925. Renewal. Hope Publishing Co., owner.

Count Your Blessings

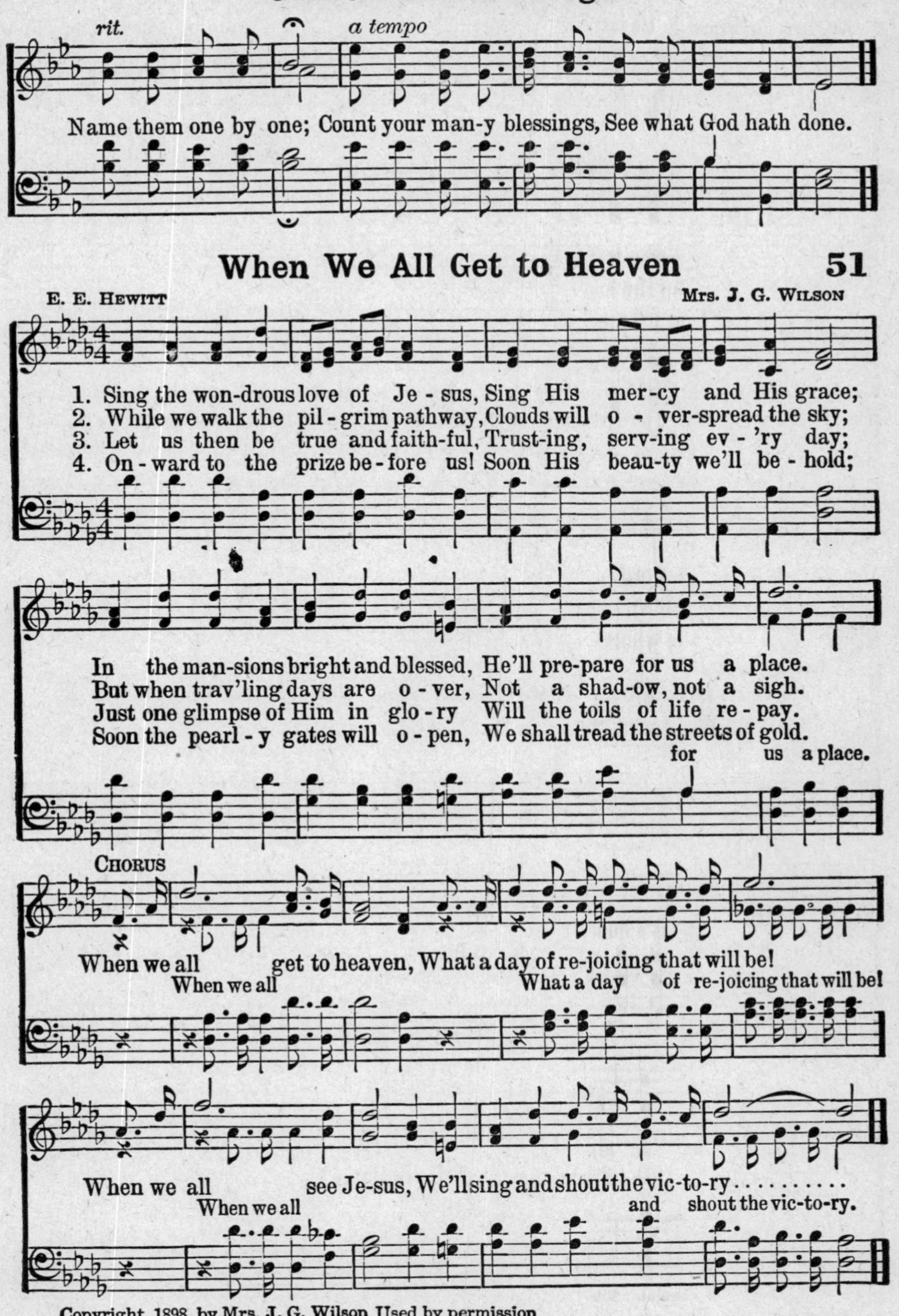
rit.
a tempo
Name them one by one; Count your man-y blessings, See what God hath done.
When We All Get to Heaven
51
E. E. Hewitt
Mrs. J. G. Wilson
1. Sing the won-drous love of Je - sus, Sing His mer-cy and His grace;
2. While we walk the pil - grim pathway, Clouds will o - ver-spread the sky;
3. Let us then be true and faith-ful, Trust-ing, serv-ing ev - 'ry day;
4. On - ward to the prize be - fore us! Soon His beau-ty we'll be - hold;
In the man-sions bright and blessed, He'll pre-pare for us a place.
But when trav'ling days are o - ver, Not a shad-ow, not a sigh.
Just one glimpse of Him in glo - ry Will the toils of life re - pay.
Soon the pearl - y gates will o - pen, We shall tread the streets of gold.
for us a place.
Chorus
When we all get to heaven, What a day of re-joicing that will be!
When we all What a day of re-joicing that will be!
When we all see Je-sus, We'll sing and shout the vic-to-ry..........
When we all and shout the vic-to-ry.

Copyright, 1898, by Mrs. J. G. Wilson Used by permission

52 A New Name in Glory

C. AUSTIN MILES — C. AUSTIN MILES

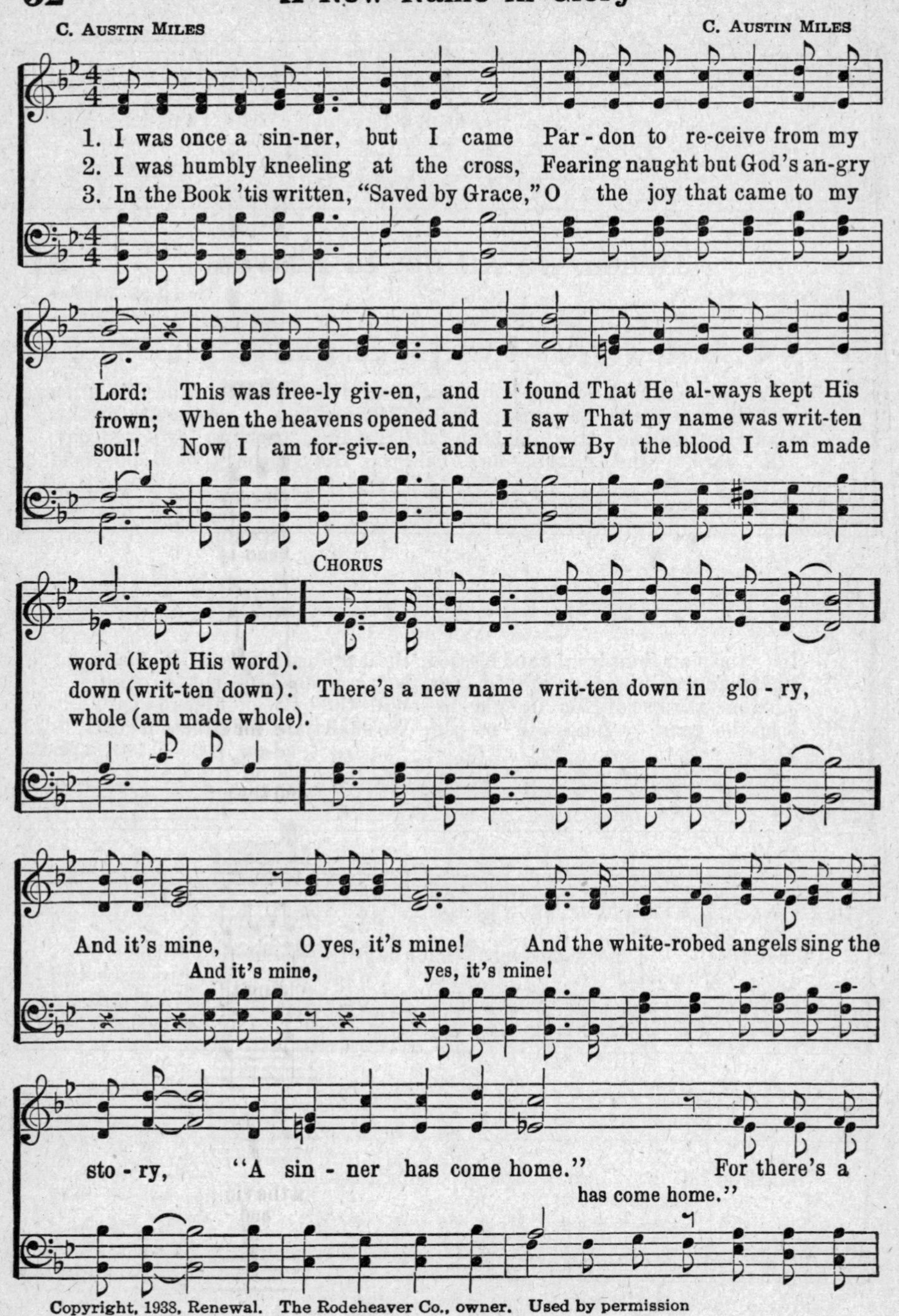
1. I was once a sin-ner, but I came Par-don to re-ceive from my Lord: This was free-ly giv-en, and I found That He al-ways kept His word (kept His word).
2. I was humbly kneeling at the cross, Fearing naught but God's an-gry frown; When the heavens opened and I saw That my name was writ-ten down (writ-ten down).
3. In the Book 'tis written, "Saved by Grace," O the joy that came to my soul! Now I am for-giv-en, and I know By the blood I am made whole (am made whole).
CHORUS
There's a new name writ-ten down in glo-ry, And it's mine, O yes, it's mine!
And it's mine, yes, it's mine!
And the white-robed angels sing the sto-ry, "A sin-ner has come home."
has come home."
For there's a

Copyright, 1938, Renewal. The Rodeheaver Co., owner. Used by permission

A New Name in Glory

new name writ-ten down in glo-ry, And it's mine, O yes, it's mine!
And it's mine, yes, it's mine!
With my sins for-giv - en I am bound for heav-en, Nev - er-more to roam.
Jesus My All in All
53
Chas. P. Jones
Chas. P. Jones
1. Je - sus my Sav - ior, I love and a-dore Thee, Je-sus my all in all;
2. Pre-cious Re-deem-er from sin and from sorrow, Je-sus my all in all;
3. Je - sus who died for my sins, precious Master! Je-sus my all in all;
4. Je - sus my wis-dom and right-eous-ness ev-er, Je-sus my all in all;
Fine
Nothing on earth would I wor-ship be-fore Thee, Je-sus my all in all.
Je - sus the same in the past and to-mor-row, Je-sus my all in all.
Je - sus my com-fort in ev - 'ry dis - as - ter, Je-sus my all in all.
Je - sus my ho - li-ness, fail-ing me nev - er, Je-sus my all in all.
D.S.–How it would grieve Him if e'er I would leave Him, Je - sus my all in all.
Chorus
D. S.
Je - sus my all in all, Je - sus my all in all;

54 Since the Fullness of His Love Came In

E. E. HEWITT | B. D. ACKLEY

1. Once my way was dark and drear - y, For my heart was full of sin,
2. There is grace for all the low - ly, Grace to keep the trust-ing soul:
3. Let me spread a - broad the sto - ry, Oth - er souls to Je - sus win;
But the sky is bright and cheer-y, Since the full-ness of His love came in.
Pow'r to cleanse and make me ho - ly, Je - sus shall my yield-ed life con - trol.
For the cross is now my glo - ry, Since the full-ness of His love came in.
CHORUS
I can nev-er tell how much I love Him, I can nev-er tell His love for me;
For it pass-eth hu-man measure, Like a deep, unfathomed sea;
deep, unfathomed sea;
'Tis re-deeming love in Christ my Sav-ior, In my soul the heav'nly joys be-gin;

Copyright, 1916. Hope Publishing Co., owner

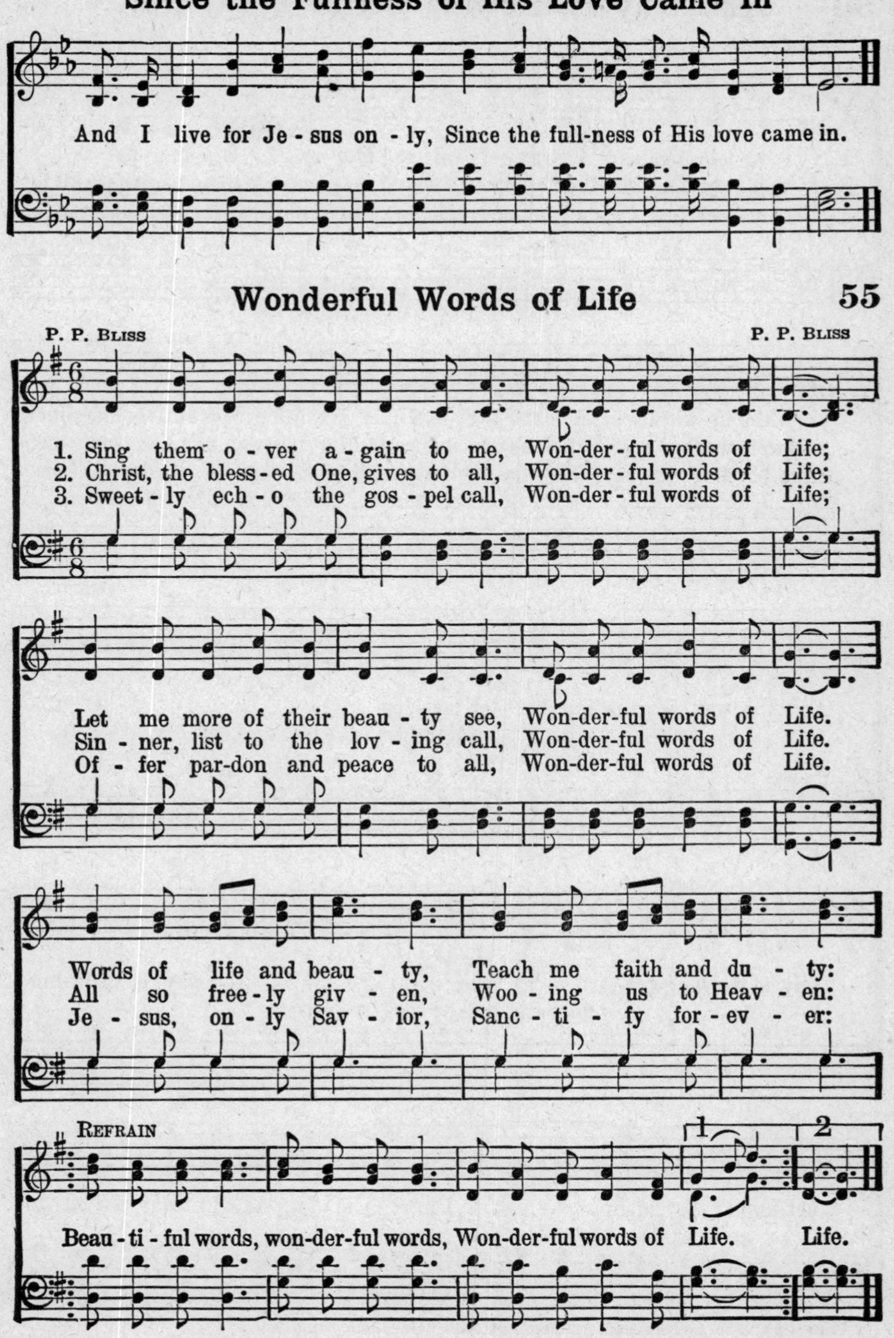
Since the Fullness of His Love Came In
And I live for Je - sus on - ly, Since the full-ness of His love came in.
Wonderful Words of Life
55
P. P. Bliss
P. P. Bliss
1. Sing them o - ver a - gain to me, Won-der - ful words of Life;
2. Christ, the bless - ed One, gives to all, Won-der - ful words of Life;
3. Sweet - ly ech - o the gos - pel call, Won-der - ful words of Life;
Let me more of their beau - ty see, Won-der-ful words of Life.
Sin - ner, list to the lov - ing call, Won-der-ful words of Life.
Of - fer par-don and peace to all, Won-der-ful words of Life.
Words of life and beau - ty, Teach me faith and du - ty:
All so free-ly giv - en, Woo - ing us to Heav - en:
Je - sus, on - ly Sav - ior, Sanc - ti - fy for - ev - er:
Refrain
Beau - ti - ful words, won-der-ful words, Won-der-ful words of Life. Life.

56 The Way Is Growing Better Every Day

FLOYD W. HAWKINS
FLOYD W. HAWKINS
1. I'm re - joic-ing as I trav - el on to glo - ry, I am hap-py as I press the up-ward way; For the Lord has filled my life with countless bless-ings, And the way is grow-ing bet - ter ev - 'ry day. . . . .
2. I can - not for - get the day when I found Je - sus At the cross where all my sins were washed a-way; Nor how gra-cious-ly His lov - ing hand has led me,
3. I am seek-ing for a bet - ter, rich - er treas-ure Than the things of earth that crum-ble and de - cay; Ev - 'ry step I take brings heaven's portals near - er,
grow-ing bet - ter ev - 'ry day.
CHORUS
O the way is growing bet-ter ev - 'ry day; . . . . . . O the way is grow-ing bet-ter ev - 'ry day; . . . . . . I'm re - joic - ing as I trav - el on to
grow-ing bet - ter ev - 'ry day;
grow-ing bet - ter ev - 'ry day;

Copyright, 1936, by Nazarene Publishing House. Used by permission

The Way Is Growing Better Every Day
poco rit.
glo - ry, For the way is grow-ing bet - ter ev - 'ry day. . . . . . .
grow - ing bet - ter ev - 'ry day.
Speak Just a Word!
57
Katherine O. Barker
D. B. Towner
Arr. by Fred Jackey
1. Speak just a word for Je - sus, Tell how He died for you,
2. Speak just a word for Je - sus, Tell how He helps you live,
3. Speak just a word for Je - sus, Do not for oth - ers wait;
4. Speak just a word for Je - sus, Tell of His love for men!
Of - ten re - peat the sto - ry, Won - der - ful, glad, and true!
Tell of the strength and com - fort Which He will free - ly give!
Glad - ly pro - claim the mes - sage Ere it shall be too late!
Some one dis - tressed may lis - ten, Will - ing to trust Him then.
Chorus
Speak, Oh, speak a word for Je - sus! Ev - er to Him be true;
Speak a word for Je - sus,
Speak, Just speak a word for Je-sus! Oh, tell what He's doing for you!
Speak a word for Je - sus,

Copyright, 1936. Renewal. Arr. Copyright, 1941. Hope Publishing Co., owner
Note: This hymn very effective by repeating chorus in almost a whisper.

58 My Anchor Holds

W. C. MARTIN, arr. D. B. TOWNER

1. Tho' the an - gry sur - ges roll On my tem - pest-driv - en soul,
2. Might-y tides a - bout me sweep, Per - ils lurk with - in the deep,
3. I can feel the an - chor fast As I meet each sud - den blast,
4. Troub-les al - most 'whelm the soul; Griefs like bil - lows o'er me roll;
I am peace - ful, for I know, Wild - ly though the winds may blow,
An - gry clouds o'er-shade the sky, And the tem - pest ris - es high;
And the ca - ble, though un - seen, Bears the heav - y strain be - tween;
Tempters seek to lure a - stray; Storms ob - scure the light of day:
I've an an - chor safe and sure, That can ev - er - more en - dure.
Still I stand the tem-pest's shock, For my an - chor grips the Rock.
Thro' the storm I safe - ly ride, Till the turn - ing of the tide.
But in Christ I can be bold, I've an an - chor that shall hold.
CHORUS
And it holds, my an - chor holds; Blow your wild - est, then, O
And it holds,....... my an - chor holds; Blow your wild - - - est,
gale, On my bark so small and frail: By His grace I shall not
then, O gale,

Copyright, 1930. Renewal. Hope Publishing Co., owner.

My Anchor Holds
fail, For my an - chor holds, my an - chor holds.
For my an - chor holds, it firm - ly holds,
Have Thine Own Way, Lord
59
Adelaide A. Pollard
Geo. C. Stebbins
Slowly
1. Have Thine own way, Lord! Have Thine own way!.. Thou art the
2. Have Thine own way, Lord! Have Thine own way!.. Search me and
3. Have Thine own way, Lord! Have Thine own way!.. Wound-ed and
4. Have Thine own way, Lord! Have Thine own way!.. Hold o'er my
Pot - ter; I am the clay... Mould me and make me Aft - er Thy
try me, Mas-ter, to - day!... Whit - er than snow, Lord, Wash me just
wea - ry, Help me, I pray!. Pow - er—all pow - er—Sure - ly is
be - ing Ab - so - lute sway!. Fill with Thy Spir - it Till all shall
will,... While I am wait - ing, Yield - ed and still...
now,... As in Thy pres - ence Hum - bly I bow...
Thine! Touch me and heal me, Sav - ior di - vine!..
see.... Christ on - ly, al - ways, Liv - ing in me!....

Copyright, 1935. Renewal. Hope Publishing Co., owner.

60 # I Find Thee So Precious

JAMES M. GRAY — JAMES MCGRANAHAN

DUET OR SOLO *(Small notes for Solo)*

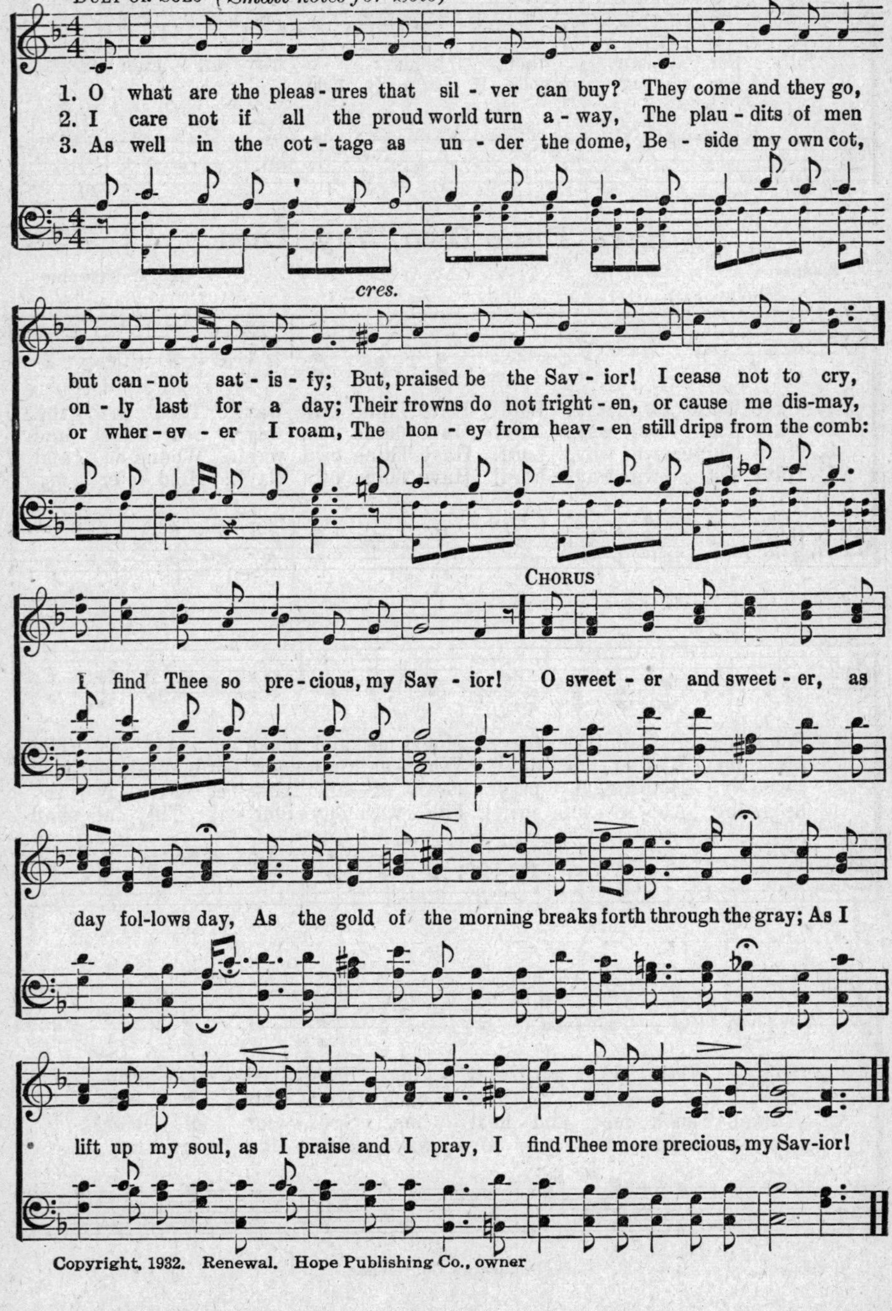

1. O what are the pleas - ures that sil - ver can buy? They come and they go,
2. I care not if all the proud world turn a - way, The plau - dits of men
3. As well in the cot - tage as un - der the dome, Be - side my own cot,

cres.

but can - not sat - is - fy; But, praised be the Sav - ior! I cease not to cry,
on - ly last for a day; Their frowns do not fright - en, or cause me dis - may,
or wher - ev - er I roam, The hon - ey from heav - en still drips from the comb:

I find Thee so pre - cious, my Sav - ior! CHORUS O sweet - er and sweet - er, as

day fol - lows day, As the gold of the morning breaks forth through the gray; As I

lift up my soul, as I praise and I pray, I find Thee more precious, my Sav - ior!

Copyright, 1932. Renewal. Hope Publishing Co., owner

O My Soul, Bless Thou Jehovah

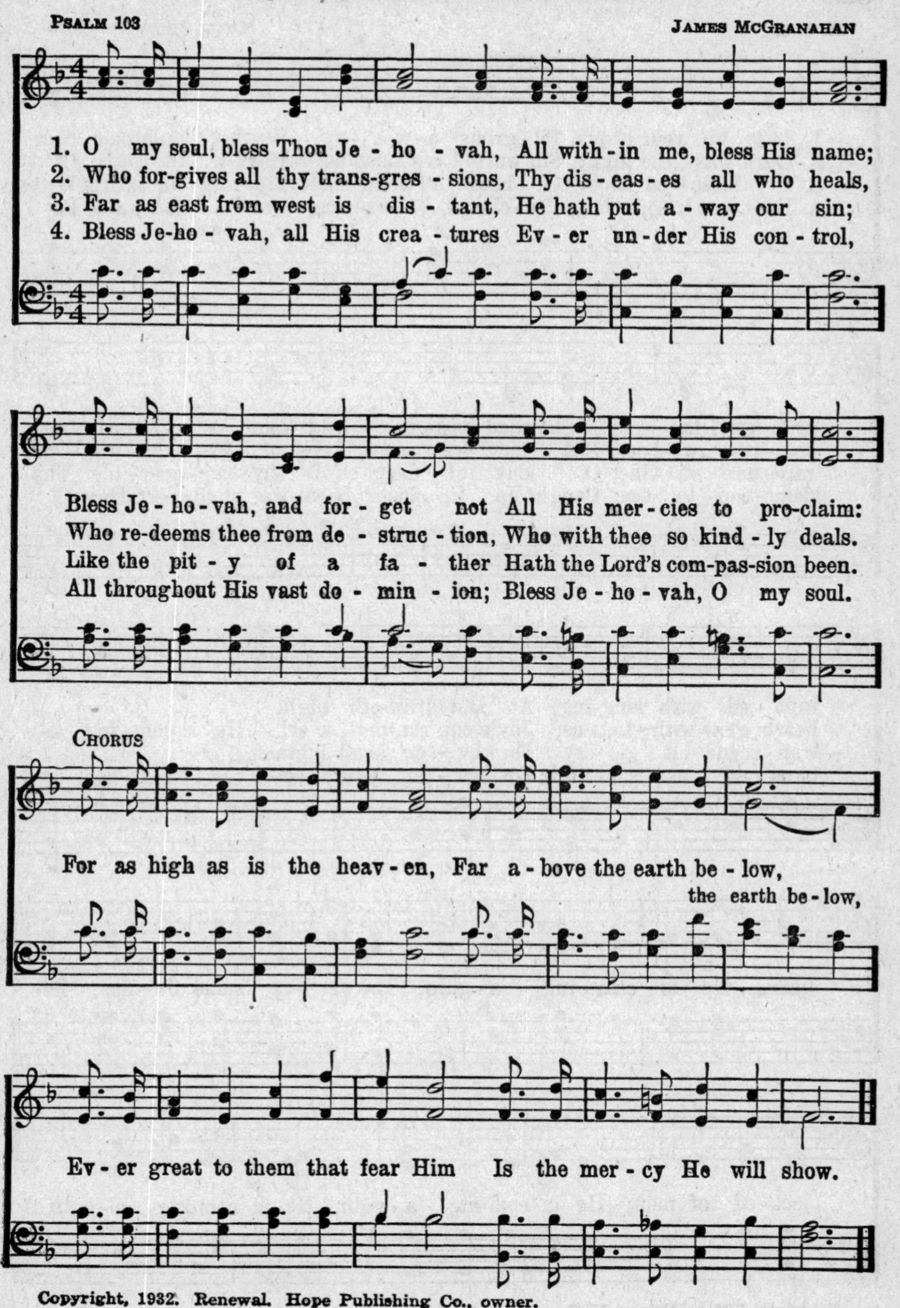
Psalm 103
James McGranahan
1. O my soul, bless Thou Je - ho - vah, All with - in me, bless His name;
2. Who for-gives all thy trans-gres - sions, Thy dis - eas - es all who heals,
3. Far as east from west is dis - tant, He hath put a - way our sin;
4. Bless Je-ho - vah, all His crea - tures Ev - er un - der His con - trol,
Bless Je - ho - vah, and for - get not All His mer - cies to pro-claim:
Who re-deems thee from de - struc - tion, Who with thee so kind - ly deals.
Like the pit - y of a fa - ther Hath the Lord's com-pas-sion been.
All throughout His vast do - min - ion; Bless Je - ho - vah, O my soul.
Chorus
For as high as is the heav - en, Far a - bove the earth be - low,
the earth be - low,
Ev - er great to them that fear Him Is the mer - cy He will show.

Copyright, 1932. Renewal. Hope Publishing Co., owner.

62

He Is Coming Again

M. J. C. Mabel Johnston Camp

1. Lift up your heads, Pil-grims a-wea-ry, See day's ap-proach Now crim-son the sky; Night shad-ows flee, And your Be-lov-ed, A-wait-ed with long-ing, At last draw-eth nigh.
2. Dark was the night, Sin warred a-gainst us; Heav-y the load Of sor-row we bore; But now we see Signs of His com-ing; Our hearts glow with-in us, Joy's cup run-neth o'er!
3. O bless-ed hope! O bliss-ful prom-ise! Fill-ing our hearts With rap-ture di-vine; O day of days! Hail Thy ap-pear-ing! Thy tran-scend-ent glo-ry For-ev-er shall shine.
4. E-ven so, come, Pre-cious Lord Je-sus; Cre-a-tion waits Re-demp-tion to see; Caught up in clouds, Soon we shall meet Thee; O bless-ed as-sur-ance, For-ev-er with Thee!
Chorus
He is com-ing a-gain, He is com-ing a-gain, The ver-y same Je-sus, Re-ject-ed of men; He is com-ing a-gain, He is com-ing a-gain, He is com-ing a-gain,

Copyright, 1913, by Norman H. Camp. Used by permission

He Is Coming Again

Fill Me Now

63

E. R. Stokes. Jno. R. Sweney

With pow'r and great glo - ry, He is com-ing a - gain!
is com-ing a - gain!
1. Hov - er o'er me, Ho - ly Spir - it, Bathe my trem-bling heart and brow;
2. Thou canst fill me, gra-cious Spir - it, Though I can - not tell Thee how;
3. I am weak-ness, full of weak-ness, At Thy sa - cred feet I bow;
4. Cleanse and com-fort, bless and save me, Bathe, O bathe my heart and brow;
Fill me with Thy hal-lowed pres-ence, Come, O come and fill me now.
But I need Thee, great-ly need Thee, Come, O come and fill me now.
Blest, di - vine, e - ter - nal Spir - it, Fill with pow'r, and fill me now.
Thou art com-fort - ing and sav - ing, Thou art sweet - ly fill - ing now.
Chorus
Fill me now, fill me now, Je - sus, come and fill me now;
Fill me with Thy hal-lowed pres-ence, Come, O come and fill me now.

Lead Me, Savior

F. M. D. FRANK M. DAVIS

1. Sav - ior, lead me, lest I stray, Gen - tly lead me all the way;
2. Thou the ref-uge of my soul When life's storm-y bil-lows roll;
3. Sav - ior, lead me, then at last, When the storm of life is past,

1. Sav - ior, lead me, lest I stray, Gen - tly lead me all the way;

I am safe when by Thy side, I would in Thy love a-bide.
I am safe when Thou art nigh, All my hopes on Thee re-ly.
To the land of end-less day, Where all tears are wiped away.

I am safe when by Thy side, I would in Thy love a-bide.

CHORUS

Lead me, lead me, Sav - ior, lead me, lest I stray;......
lest I stray;

Gen-tly down the stream of time, Lead me, Sav-ior, all the way.
stream of time, all the way.

He Keeps Me Singing

L. B. B. — L. B. Bridgers

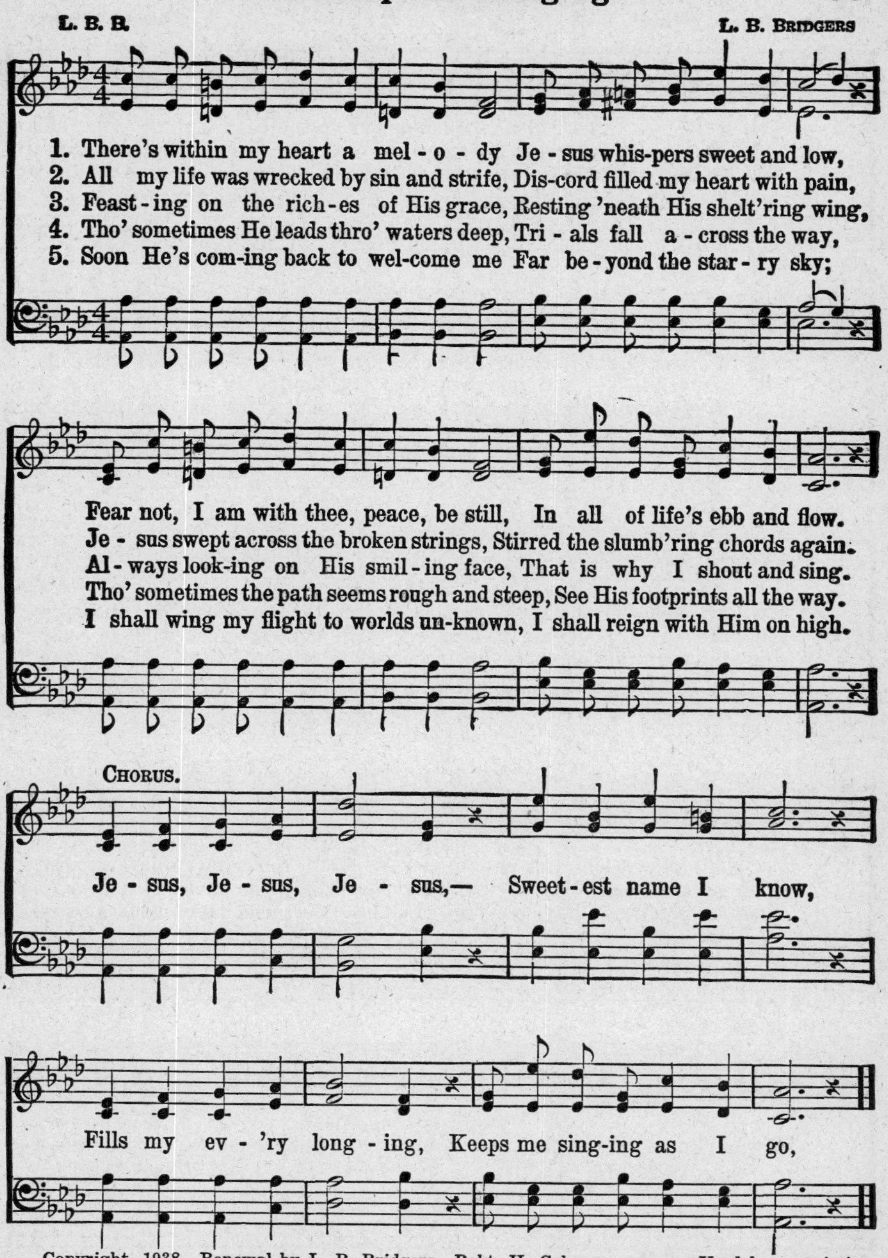
1. There's within my heart a mel - o - dy Je - sus whis-pers sweet and low,
2. All my life was wrecked by sin and strife, Dis-cord filled my heart with pain,
3. Feast - ing on the rich - es of His grace, Resting 'neath His shelt'ring wing,
4. Tho' sometimes He leads thro' waters deep, Tri - als fall a - cross the way,
5. Soon He's com-ing back to wel-come me Far be - yond the star - ry sky;
Fear not, I am with thee, peace, be still, In all of life's ebb and flow.
Je - sus swept across the broken strings, Stirred the slumb'ring chords again.
Al - ways look-ing on His smil - ing face, That is why I shout and sing.
Tho' sometimes the path seems rough and steep, See His footprints all the way.
I shall wing my flight to worlds un-known, I shall reign with Him on high.
Chorus.
Je - sus, Je - sus, Je - sus,— Sweet - est name I know,
Fills my ev - 'ry long - ing, Keeps me sing-ing as I go,

Copyright, 1938. Renewal by L. B. Bridgers. Robt. H. Coleman, owner. Used by permission.

66 When the Mists Have Rolled Away

ANNIE HERBERT. ARR. IRA D. SANKEY

1. When the mists have rolled in splen-dor From the beau-ty of the hills,
2. Oft we tread the path be-fore us With a wea-ry, bur-dened heart;
3. We shall come with joy and glad-ness, We shall gath-er round the throne;
And the sun-light falls in glad-ness On the riv-er and the rills,
Oft we toil a-mid the shad-ows, And our fields are far a-part:
Face to face with those that love us, We shall know as we are known:
We re-call our Fa-ther's prom-ise In the rain-bow of the spray:
But the Sav-ior's "Come, ye bless-ed," All our la-bor will re-pay,
And the song of our re-demp-tion Shall re-sound thro' end-less day,
rit.
We shall know each oth-er bet-ter When the mists have rolled a-way.
When we gath-er in the morning Where the mists have rolled a-way.
When the shad-ows have de-part-ed, And the mists have rolled a-way.
CHORUS
known, as we are known,
We shall know . . . as we are known, . . . Nev-er-more . . . to walk a-
We shall know as we are known, Nev-er-more to walk a-

When the Mists Have Rolled Away

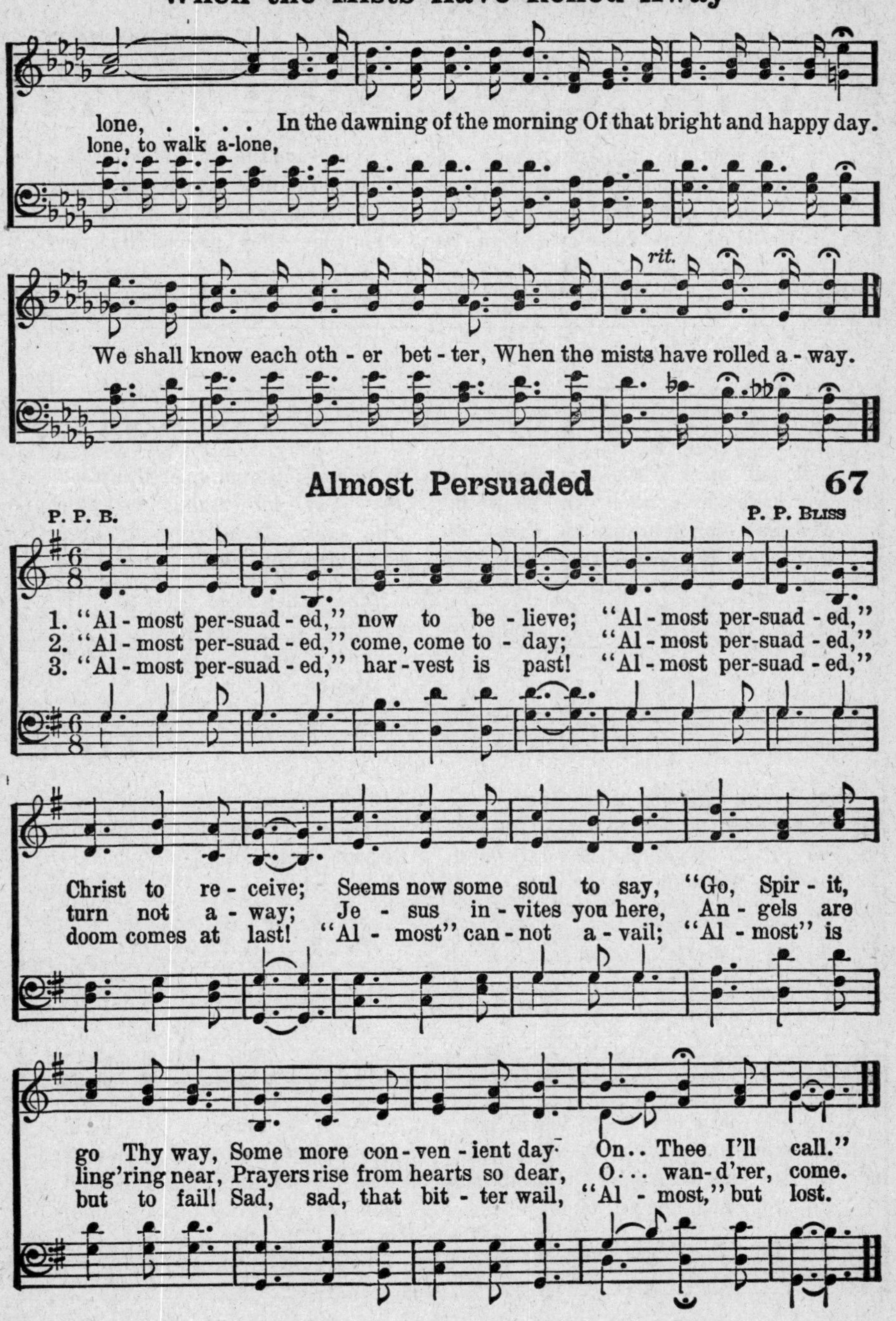
lone, ... In the dawning of the morning Of that bright and happy day.
lone, to walk a-lone,
rit.
We shall know each oth - er bet - ter, When the mists have rolled a - way.
Almost Persuaded
67
P. P. B.
P. P. Bliss
1. "Al - most per-suad - ed," now to be - lieve; "Al - most per-suad - ed,"
2. "Al - most per-suad - ed," come, come to - day; "Al - most per-suad - ed,"
3. "Al - most per-suad - ed," har - vest is past! "Al - most per-suad - ed,"
Christ to re - ceive; Seems now some soul to say, "Go, Spir - it,
turn not a - way; Je - sus in - vites you here, An - gels are
doom comes at last! "Al - most" can - not a - vail; "Al - most" is
go Thy way, Some more con - ven - ient day On.. Thee I'll call."
ling'ring near, Prayers rise from hearts so dear, O... wan - d'rer, come.
but to fail! Sad, sad, that bit - ter wail, "Al - most," but lost.

68 Never Alone!

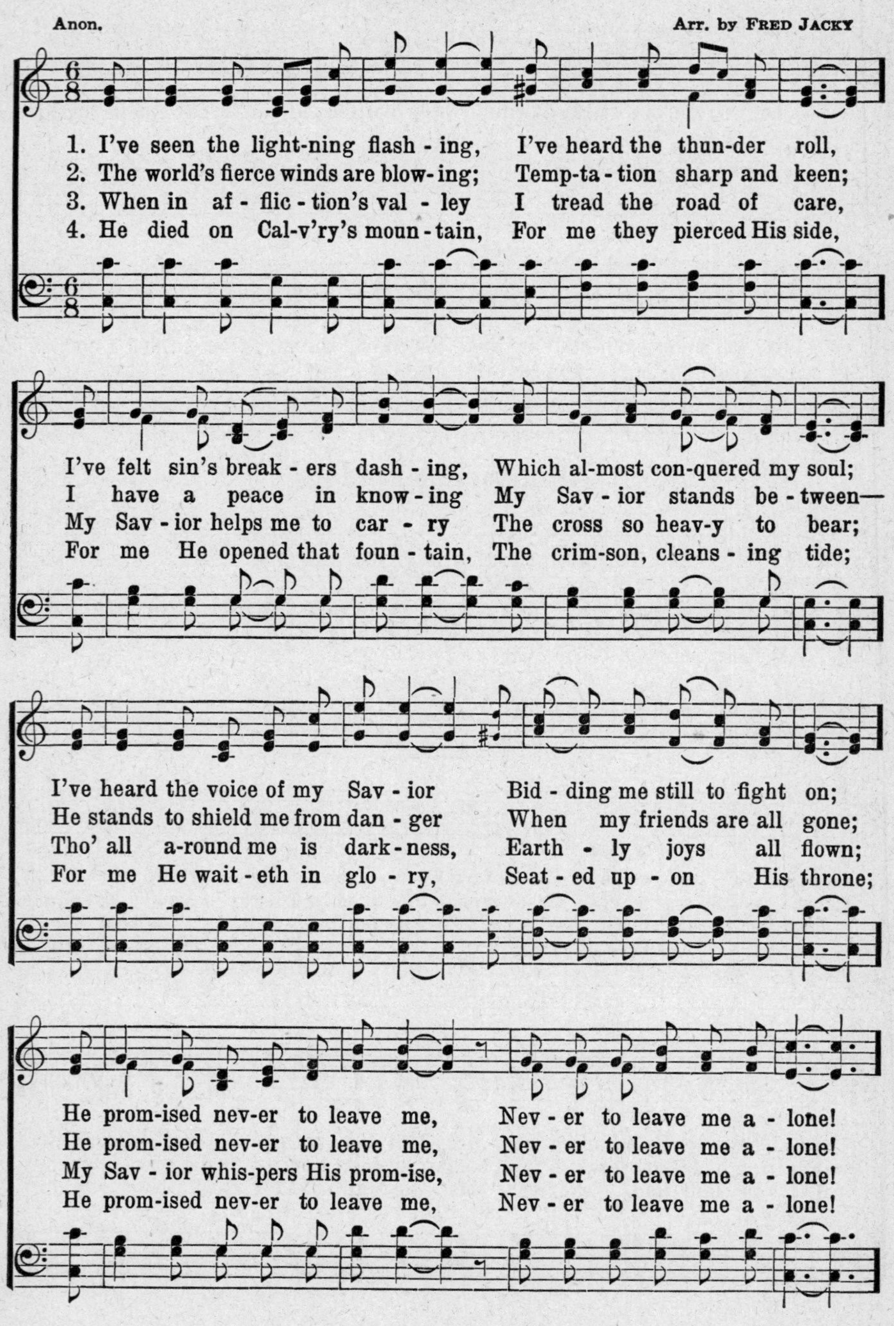
Anon.
Arr. by FRED JACKY
1. I've seen the light-ning flash - ing, I've heard the thun-der roll,
2. The world's fierce winds are blow- ing; Temp-ta - tion sharp and keen;
3. When in af - flic - tion's val - ley I tread the road of care,
4. He died on Cal-v'ry's moun - tain, For me they pierced His side,
I've felt sin's break - ers dash - ing, Which al-most con-quered my soul;
I have a peace in know - ing My Sav - ior stands be - tween—
My Sav - ior helps me to car - ry The cross so heav-y to bear;
For me He opened that foun - tain, The crim-son, cleans - ing tide;
I've heard the voice of my Sav - ior Bid - ding me still to fight on;
He stands to shield me from dan - ger When my friends are all gone;
Tho' all a-round me is dark - ness, Earth - ly joys all flown;
For me He wait - eth in glo - ry, Seat - ed up - on His throne;
He prom-ised nev-er to leave me, Nev - er to leave me a - lone!
He prom-ised nev-er to leave me, Nev - er to leave me a - lone!
My Sav - ior whis-pers His prom-ise, Nev - er to leave me a - lone!
He prom-ised nev-er to leave me, Nev - er to leave me a - lone!

Never Alone!
Chorus
No, nev-er a - lone,.......... No, nev-er a - lone,........ He prom-ised nev-er to
No, never a - lone, No. no, never a - lone,
leave me, He'll claim me for His own. No, nev-er a - lone,...... No, nev-er a-
No, never a - lone, No, no,
lone,...... He prom-ised nev - er to leave me, Nev - er to leave me a - lone.
nev-er a - lone,
When I Survey the Wondrous Cross
69
Isaac Watts
Arr. by Lowell Mason
1. When I sur-vey the won-drous cross, On which the Prince of glo - ry died,
2. For - bid it, Lord, that I should boast, Save in the death of Christ, my God;
3. See, from His head, His hands, His feet, Sor-row and love flow min-gled down;
4. Were the whole realm of na - ture mine, That were a pres - ent far too small;
My rich-est gain I count but loss, And pour con-tempt on all my pride.
All the vain things that charm me most, I sac - ri - fice them to His blood.
Did e'er such love and sor - row meet, Or thorns compose so rich a crown?
Love so a - maz-ing, so di - vine, Demands my soul, my life, my all.

His Way With Thee

C. S. N — Cyrus S. Nusbaum

1. Would you live for Je - sus, and be al-ways pure and good? Would you walk with
2. Would you have Him make you free, and fol-low at His call? Would you know the
3. Would you in His king-dom find a place of con-stant rest? Would you prove Him
Him with - in the nar-row road? Would you have Him bear your burden, car - ry
peace that comes by giv - ing all? Would you have Him save you, so that you need
true in prov - i - den-tial test? Would you in His serv - ice la - bor al-ways
all your load? Let Him have His way with thee.
nev - er fall? Let Him have His way with thee. His pow'r can make you what you
at your best? Let Him have His way with thee.
Chorus.
ought to be; His blood can cleanse your heart and make you free; His love can fill your
soul, and you will see 'Twas best for Him to have His way with thee. A - men.
rit.

The Closet of Prayer

71

E. F. Muir — Alvin A. Rasmussen

1. Have you en-tered your clos-et to-day, my friend? Have you prayed a-lone with your God? Have you wor-shiped the Lord to-day, my friend? Have you told Him the se-crets a-lone?
2. Have you en-tered your clos-et to-day, my friend? Have you told Him all on your heart? Have you thanked Him for love and peace sub-lime, And re-mem-bered that friend by your side?
3. Have you en-tered your clos-et to-day, my friend? Have you called for the help you need? Have you told Him of trou-bles too heav-y to bear? Have you your pe-ti-tions made clear?
4. If you en-ter your clos-et to-day, my friend, You will find the sol-ace you need. He is read-y to hear each lov-ing child, And is will-ing to an-swer him too.
Chorus
It's prayer, ... It is prayer, Yes, 'tis prayer, ... Yes, 'tis prayer, That makes vic-to-ry com-plete; So call, O call up-on Je-sus, It's prayer, O yes, 'tis prayer.

Copyright, 1941, by Alvin A. Rasmussen. Used by permission

72
I Must Tell Jesus
E. A. H.
E. A. Hoffman
1. I must tell Je - sus all of my tri - als; I can - not bear these
2. I must tell Je - sus all of my troub - les; He is a kind, com-
3. Tempted and tried I need a great Sav - ior, One who can help my
4. O how the world to e - vil al - lures me! O how my heart is
bur - dens a - lone; In my dis - tress He kind - ly will help me;
pas - sion - ate Friend; If I but ask Him, He will de - liv - er,
bur - dens to bear; I must tell Je - sus, I must tell Je - sus;
tempt - ed to sin! I must tell Je - sus, and He will help me
He ev - er loves and cares for His own.
Make of my troub - les quick - ly an end.
He all my cares and sor - rows will share.
O - ver the world the vic - t'ry to win.
Chorus
I must tell Je - sus!
I must tell Je - sus! I can - not bear my bur - dens a - lone; I must tell
Je - sus! I must tell Je - sus! Je - sus can help me, Je - sus a - lone.

Copyright, 1926, Renewal. Hope Publishing Co., owner

Over the Top for Jesus

J. V. R.
JAS. V. REID
1. There's a bat-tle rag-ing o-ver the land and sea, True to Christ our Captain we will be; Sa-tan's hosts are might-y, fight-ing for ru-in and sin, But in this great conflict right is sure to win.
2. There's a cry of sor-row rising from hearts oppressed, There's a world in sad-ness and un-rest; But the hope that thrills us, look-ing out in-to the night, Christ, the Lord of bat-tles, leads me in the fight.
3. When the pow'rs of earth before our Redeemer shall kneel, When the joy of tri-umph we shall feel; Then with Christ who conquered, in-to the realms of the blest, We shall march in vic-t'ry to e-ter-nal rest.
REFRAIN
O-ver the top for Je-sus brave-ly we will go: O-ver the top for Je-sus, rout-ing ev-'ry foe,
Nev-er de-lay-ing when we hear the bu-gle blow, (Omit . . . .)
1
2
We'll fight for right with all our might, As o-ver the top we go.

Copyright, 1918, by Jas. V. Reid. Used by permission

74 Lead Me to Calvary

Jennie Evelyn Hussey — Wm. J. Kirkpatrick

1. King of my life, I crown Thee now, Thine shall the glo - ry be;
2. Show me the tomb where Thou wast laid, Ten-der-ly mourned and wept;
3. Let me like Ma - ry, thro' the gloom, Come with a gift to Thee;
4. May I be will - ing, Lord, to bear Dai - ly my cross for Thee;
Lest I for - get Thy thorn-crowned brow, Lead me to Cal - va - ry.
An - gels in robes of light ar - rayed Guarded Thee whilst Thou slept.
Show to me now the emp - ty tomb, Lead me to Cal - va - ry.
E - ven Thy cup of grief to share, Thou hast borne all for me.
Chorus
Lest I for - get Geth-sem - a - ne; Lest I for - get Thine ag - o - ny;
Lest I for - get Thy love for me, Lead me to Cal - va - ry.

Copyright, 1921. The Rodeheaver Company, owner. International Copyright secured.
Used by permission.

The Sunset Gate

JULIA H. JOHNSTON D. B. TOWNER

1. I am trav'ling tow'rd the sun - set gate, I'm a pil-grim go-ing home;
2. There is tran-quil rest when day is done, I shall lay me down in peace;
3. By the side of those most near and dear, I shall drop life's toil and care;
4. I shall rise a - gain at morn - ing dawn, I shall put on glo - ry then;
For the glow of e - ven-tide I wait, I'm a pil-grim go-ing home.
When the end is reached at set of sun, I shall lay me down in peace.
When the Mas-ter's ten - der voice I hear, I shall drop life's toil and care.
With the shad-owy veil of death un-drawn, I shall put on glo - ry then.
REFRAIN
Eve-ning bells . . . . I seem to hear As the sun-set gate draws near!
Eve-ning bells I seem, I seem to hear, draws near!
Eve-ning bells . . . . I seem to hear As the sun - set gate draws near.
Eve-ning bells I seem, I seem to hear,

Copyright, 1931, Renewal. Hope Publishing Co., owner

76 He Ransomed Me

JULIA H. JOHNSTON J. W. HENDERSON

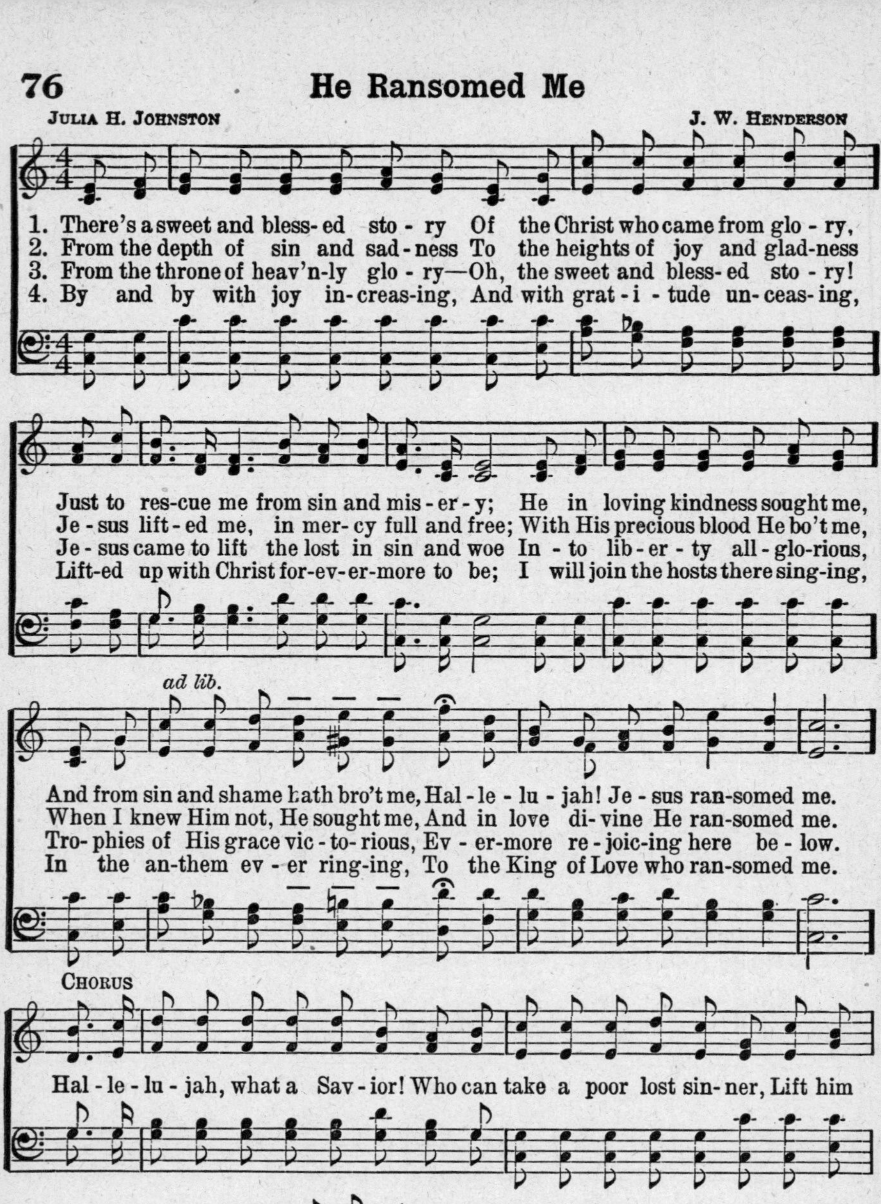
1. There's a sweet and bless-ed sto - ry Of the Christ who came from glo - ry,
2. From the depth of sin and sad-ness To the heights of joy and glad-ness
3. From the throne of heav'n-ly glo - ry—Oh, the sweet and bless-ed sto - ry!
4. By and by with joy in-creas-ing, And with grat - i - tude un-ceas-ing,
Just to res-cue me from sin and mis - er - y; He in loving kindness sought me,
Je - sus lift-ed me, in mer-cy full and free; With His precious blood He bo't me,
Je - sus came to lift the lost in sin and woe In - to lib - er - ty all-glo-rious,
Lift-ed up with Christ for-ev-er-more to be; I will join the hosts there sing-ing,
ad lib.
And from sin and shame hath bro't me, Hal - le - lu - jah! Je - sus ran-somed me.
When I knew Him not, He sought me, And in love di-vine He ran-somed me.
Tro-phies of His grace vic - to-rious, Ev - er-more re - joic-ing here be - low.
In the an-them ev - er ring-ing, To the King of Love who ran-somed me.
CHORUS
Hal - le - lu - jah, what a Sav - ior! Who can take a poor lost sin - ner, Lift him

from the mi - ry clay and set him free; (Hal-le-lu-jah!) I will ev - er tell the sto - ry,

Copyright, 1916, by Homer A. Hammontree

He Ransomed Me
ad lib.
Shout-ing Glo-ry, glo-ry, glo-ry, Hal-le-lu-jah! Je-sus ran-somed me.
'Tis So Sweet to Trust in Jesus
77
Louisa M. R. Stead
Wm. J. Kirkpatrick
1. 'Tis so sweet to trust in Je-sus, Just to take Him at His Word;
2. O how sweet to trust in Je-sus, Just to trust His cleans-ing blood;
3. Yes, 'tis sweet to trust in Je-sus, Just from sin and self to cease;
4. I'm so glad I learned to trust Thee, Pre-cious Je-sus, Sav-ior, Friend;
Just to rest up-on His prom-ise; Just to know, "Thus saith the Lord."
Just in sim-ple faith to plunge me 'Neath the heal-ing, cleans-ing flood!
Just from Je-sus sim-ply tak-ing Life and rest, and joy and peace.
And I know that Thou art with me, Wilt be with me to the end.
Chorus
Je-sus, Je-sus, how I trust Him! How I've proved Him o'er and o'er!
p
Je-sus, Je-sus, pre-cious Je-sus! O for grace to trust Him more!

78 A Passion for Souls

HERBERT G. TOVEY — FOSS L. FELLERS

1. Give me a pas - sion for souls, dear Lord, A pas - sion to save the lost;
2. Though there are dan-gers un-told and stern Con-front-ing me in the way,
3. How shall this pas - sion for souls be mine? Lord, make Thou the an-swer clear;
O that Thy love were by all a-dored, And wel-comed at an - y cost.
Will-ing - ly still would I go, nor turn, But trust Thee for grace each day.
Help me to throw out the old Life-Line To those who are strug-gling near.
CHORUS.
Je - sus, I long, I long to be win - ning Men who are
lost, and con - stant - ly sin - ning; O may this hour be
one of be - gin - ning The sto - ry of par - don to tell.

Copyright, 1914, by Herbert G. Tovey. Used by permission

Count Me

W. C. POOLE — HALDOR LILLENAS

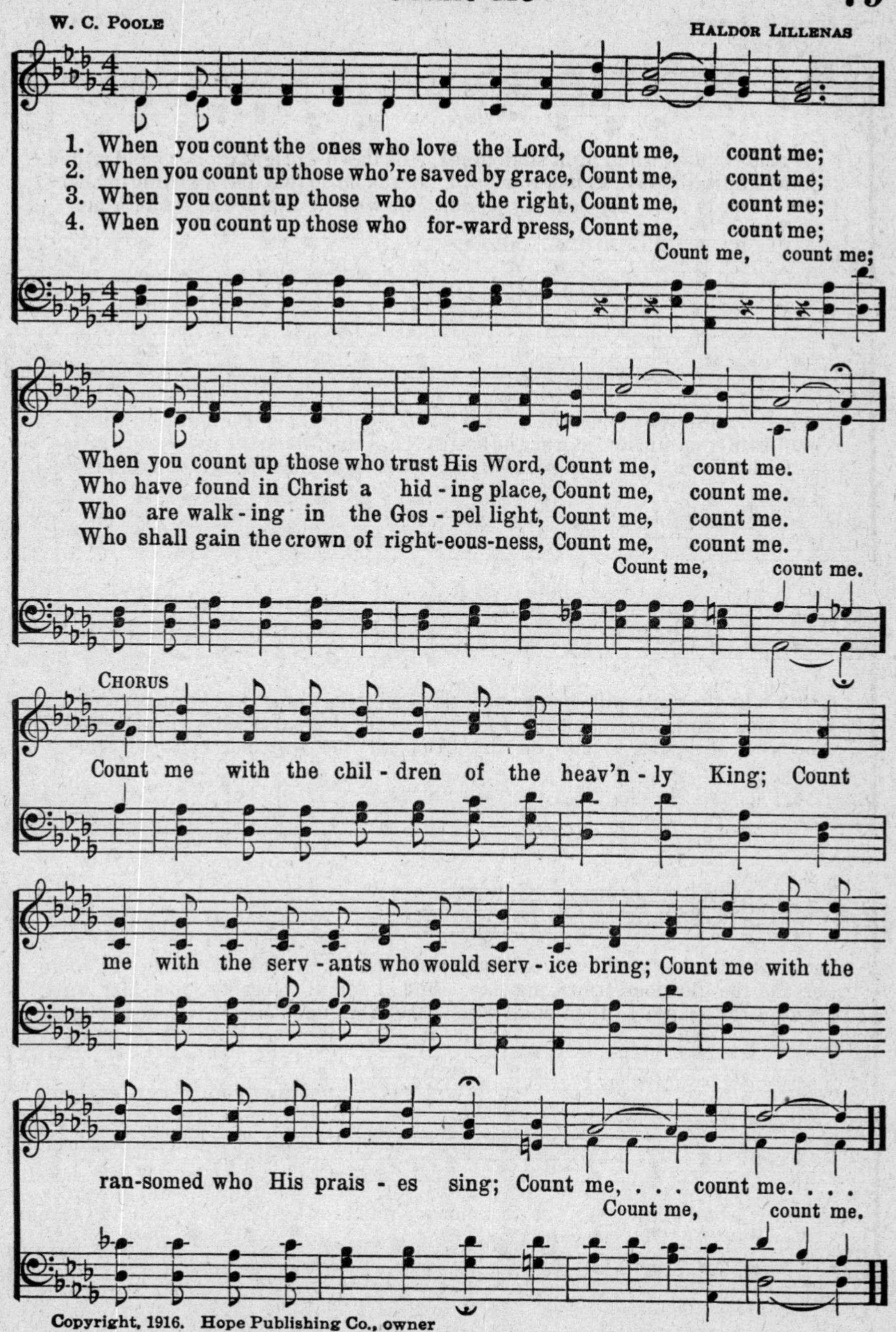

1. When you count the ones who love the Lord, Count me, count me;
2. When you count up those who're saved by grace, Count me, count me;
3. When you count up those who do the right, Count me, count me;
4. When you count up those who for-ward press, Count me, count me;
Count me, count me;
When you count up those who trust His Word, Count me, count me.
Who have found in Christ a hid - ing place, Count me, count me.
Who are walk - ing in the Gos - pel light, Count me, count me.
Who shall gain the crown of right-eous-ness, Count me, count me.
Count me, count me.
CHORUS
Count me with the chil - dren of the heav'n - ly King; Count
me with the serv - ants who would serv - ice bring; Count me with the
ran-somed who His prais - es sing; Count me, . . . count me. . . .
Count me, count me.

Copyright, 1916. Hope Publishing Co., owner

80 Saving Grace

Julia H. Johnston
D. B. Towner
Quickly
1. O gold-en day, when light shall break, And dawn's bright glories shall unfold, . .
2. Life's upward way, a nar-row path, Leads on to that fair dwelling-place, ...
3. I dim-ly see my journey's end, But well I know who guideth me: . . . .
When He who knows the path I take Shall ope for me the gates of gold! . . .
Where, safe from sin, and storm, and wrath, They live who trust redeeming grace. . .
I fol-low Him, that wondrous Friend, Whose matchless love is full and free. . .
rall.
Earth's lit-tle while will soon be past, My pil-grim-song will soon be o'er, The
Sing, sing, my heart, along the way, The grace that saves will keep and guide Till
And when with Him I en-ter in, And all the way look back to trace, The
a tempo
grace that saves shall time out-last, And be my theme on yon-der shore.
breaks the glo-rious crown-ing day, And I shall cross to yon-der side.
con-qu'ror's palm I then shall win, Thro' Christ and His re-deem-ing grace.
Chorus Faster
Then I shall know as I am known, And stand complete be-fore the throne;

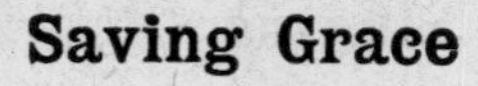

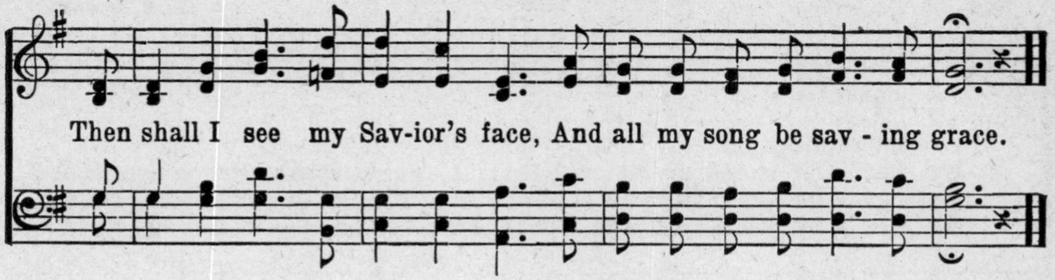

Then shall I see my Sav-ior's face, And all my song be sav - ing grace.

Where Jesus Is, 'Tis Heaven 81

C. F. Butler — J. M. Black

1. Since Christ my soul from sin set free, This world has been a Heav'n to me;
And 'mid earth's sorrows and its woe, 'Tis Heav'n my Je - sus here to know.

2. Once Heav-en seemed a far - off place, Till Je - sus showed His smil-ing face;
Now it's be - gun with - in my soul, 'Twill last while end-less a - ges roll.

3. What mat-ters where on earth we dwell? On moun-tain top, or in the dell,
In cot-tage, or a man-sion fair, Where Je - sus is, 'tis Heav-en there.

Chorus

O hal - le - lu - jah, yes, 'tis Heav'n, 'Tis Heav'n to know my sins for-giv'n;
On land or sea, what matters where? Where Je - sus is, 'tis Heav-en there.

Copyright, 1926, Renewal. Hope Publishing Co., owner

82 Singing Glory!

L. R. M. L. R. Minor

1. I've some-thing in my heart that Je - sus gave to me, It
2. My Sav - ior loosed my tongue that I might speak His praise; Since
3. My Sav - ior took my feet from out the mir - y clay; Since
4. O wea - ry heart and sad, O heav - y - la - den soul, If
makes me feel like sing - ing glo - ry all the day; He found my cap - tive
then I have been sing - ing glo - ry all the day; I love to tell the
then I have been sing - ing glo - ry all the day; He placed them on the
you would feel like sing - ing glo - ry all the day, Just let the Sav - ior
soul and gave me lib - er - ty, And now I feel like sing - ing glo - ry!
lost of Je - sus and His ways, And oh, it keeps me sing - ing glo - ry!
Rock that shall not pass a - way—I can - not keep from sing - ing glo - ry!
in, and let Him take con - trol; Then you will feel like sing - ing glo - ry!
Chorus
He makes the path grow brighter ev - 'ry pass-ing day; He makes the bur-den
light - er all a - long the way; His Word is my de - light, His

Singing Glory!
will I now o-bey, And all the time I'm sing-ing glo-ry!
After
83
N. B. Vandall
N. B. Vandall
1. Aft-er the toil and the heat of the day, Aft-er my troubles are past,
Aft-er the sor-rows are tak-en a-way, I shall see Je-sus at last.
2. Aft-er the heartaches and sighing shall cease, Aft-er the cold winter's blast,
Aft-er the conflict comes glo-ri-ous peace, I shall see Je-sus at last.
3. Aft-er the shadows of eve-ning shall fall, Aft-er my an-chor is cast,
Aft-er I list to my Sav-ior's last call, I shall see Je-sus at last.
Chorus.
Melody here optional large notes
He will be wait-ing for me, Je-sus so kind and true, On His
beau-ti-ful throne, He will welcome me home Aft-er the day is through.

Copyright, 1934, by Harry D. Clarke, Winona Lake, Indiana. Used by permission

84 The Fight is On

C. H. M. Mrs. C. H. Morris

1. The fight is on, the trump-et sound is ring-ing out, The cry "To arms!" is heard a-far and near; The Lord of hosts is march-ing on to vic-to-ry, The tri-umph of the Christ will soon ap-pear.
2. The fight is on, a-rouse, ye sol-diers brave and true! Je-ho-vah leads, and vic-t'ry will as-sure; Go, buck-le on the ar-mor God has giv-en you, And in His strength un-to the end en-dure.
3. The Lord is lead-ing on to cer-tain vic-to-ry; The bow of prom-ise spans the east-ern sky; His glo-rious name in ev-'ry land shall hon-ored be; The morn will break, the dawn of peace is nigh.
CHORUS. Unison
The fight is on, O Chris-tian sol-dier, And face to face in stern ar-ray,... With ar-mor gleaming, and col-ors streaming, The right and wrong engage to-day!

Copyright, 1933. Renewal. Haldor Lillenas, owner. Used by permission

The Fight is On
Harmony
The fight is on, but be not wea-ry; Be strong, and in His might hold fast; If God be
for us, His ban-ner o'er us, We'll sing the vic-tor's song at last!
Vic-t'ry! Vic-t'ry!
Holy Spirit, Faithful Guide
85
Marcus M. Wells
Marcus M. Wells
1. Ho-ly Spir-it, faith-ful Guide, Ev-er near the Chris-tian's side;
Gen-tly lead us by the hand, Pil-grims in a des-ert land;
2. Ev-er pres-ent, tru-est Friend, Ev-er near Thine aid to lend,
Leave us not to doubt and fear, Grop-ing on in dark-ness drear;
3. When our days of toil shall cease, Wait-ing still for sweet re-lease,
Noth-ing left but heav'n and prayer, Wond'ring if our names were there;
Wea-ry souls for-e'er re-joice, While they hear that sweet-est voice,
When the storms are rag-ing sore, Hearts grow faint, and hopes give o'er,
Wad-ing deep the dis-mal flood, Plead-ing naught but Je-sus' blood,
Whis-p'ring soft-ly, "Wand'rer, come! Fol-low Me, I'll guide thee home."
Whis-per soft-ly, "Wand'rer, come! Fol-low Me, I'll guide thee home."
Whis-per soft-ly, "Wand'rer, come! Fol-low Me, I'll guide thee home."

86 Praise Him! Praise Him!

Fanny J. Crosby — Chester G. Allen

1. Praise Him! praise Him! Je-sus, our bless-ed Re-deem-er! Sing, O Earth, His
2. Praise Him! praise Him! Je-sus, our bless-ed Re-deem-er! For our sins He
3. Praise Him! praise Him! Je-sus, our bless-ed Re-deem-er! Heav'nly por - tals
won-der-ful love pro-claim! Hail Him! hail Him! highest archangels in glo-ry;
suffered, and bled, and died; He our Rock, our hope of e - ter-nal sal-va-tion,
loud with ho-san-nas ring! Je - sus, Sav - ior, reigneth for-ev - er and ev - er;
Strength and hon - or give to His ho - ly name! Like a shep-herd, Je-sus will
Hail Him! hail Him! Je-sus the Cru - ci - fied. Sound His praises! Je-sus who
Crown Him! crown Him! Prophet, and Priest, and King! Christ is com-ing! o - ver the
Refrain
guard His children, In His arms He carries them all day long:
bore our sorrows, Love unbounded, wonderful, deep and strong: Praise Him! praise Him!
world vic-to-rious, Pow'r and glo-ry un - to the Lord be-long:
tell of His ex-cel-lent greatness; Praise Him! praise Him! ev-er in joy-ful song!

The Cross Is Not Greater

B. B. BALLINGTON BOOTH

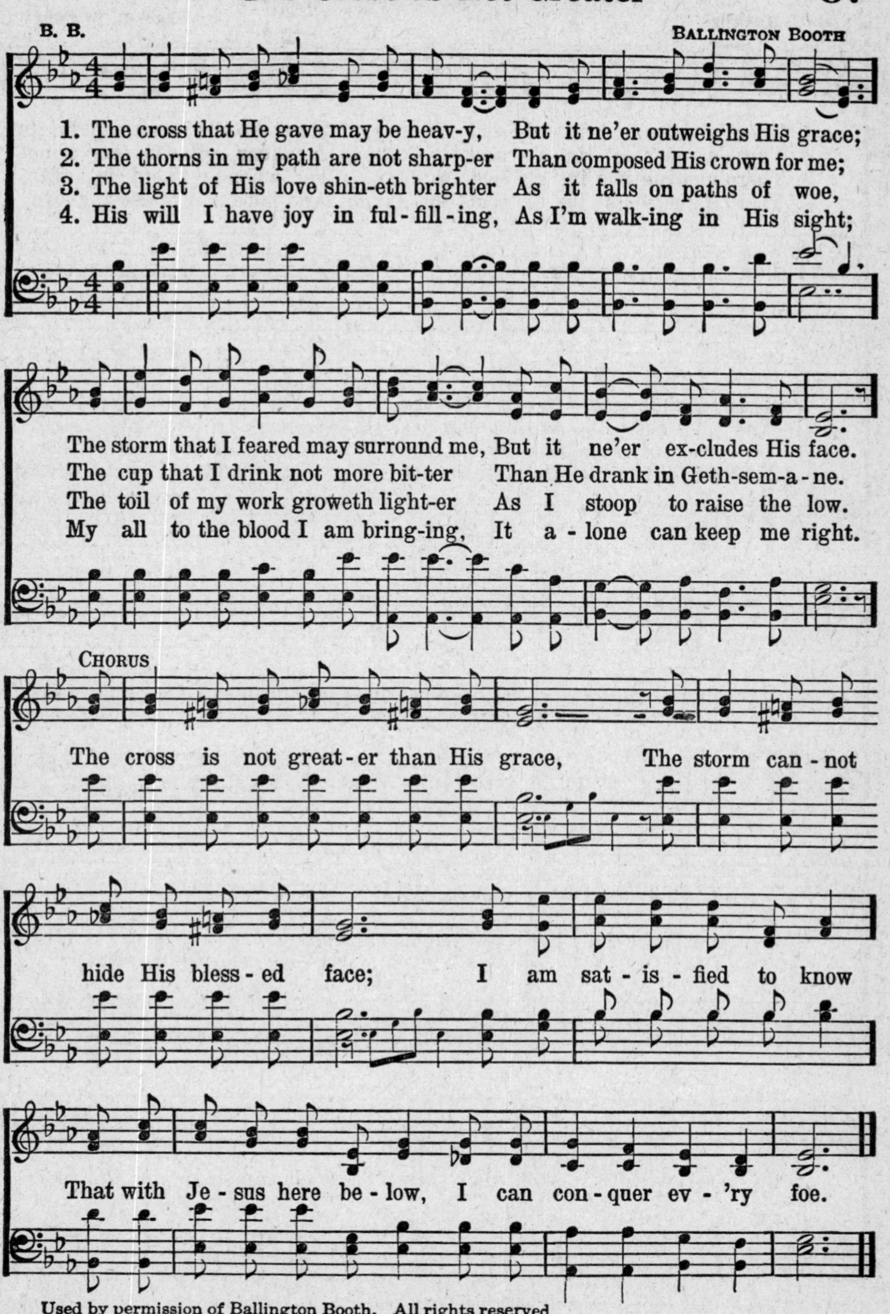
1. The cross that He gave may be heav-y, But it ne'er outweighs His grace;
2. The thorns in my path are not sharp-er Than composed His crown for me;
3. The light of His love shin-eth brighter As it falls on paths of woe,
4. His will I have joy in ful-fill-ing, As I'm walk-ing in His sight;
The storm that I feared may surround me, But it ne'er ex-cludes His face.
The cup that I drink not more bit-ter Than He drank in Geth-sem-a-ne.
The toil of my work groweth light-er As I stoop to raise the low.
My all to the blood I am bring-ing, It a-lone can keep me right.
CHORUS
The cross is not great-er than His grace, The storm can-not
hide His bless-ed face; I am sat-is-fied to know
That with Je-sus here be-low, I can con-quer ev-'ry foe.

Used by permission of Ballington Booth. All rights reserved

88 Sunshine In the Soul

E. E. Hewitt — Jno. R. Sweney

1. There's sun-shine in my soul to-day, More glo-ri-ous and bright
2. There's mu-sic in my soul to-day, A car-ol to my King,
3. There's springtime in my soul to-day, For, when the Lord is near,
4. There's glad-ness in my soul to-day, And hope and praise and love,

Than glows in an-y earth-ly sky, For Je-sus is my light.
And Je-sus, lis-ten-ing, can hear The songs I can-not sing.
The dove of peace sings in my heart, The flow'rs of grace ap-pear.
For bless-ings which He gives me now, For joys "laid up" a-bove.

REFRAIN

O there's sun - - - shine, bless-ed sun - - - shine,
O there's sun-shine in the soul, bless-ed sun-shine in the soul,
When the peace-ful, hap-py mo-ments roll;
hap-py mo-ments roll;
When Je-sus shows His smil-ing face, There is sun-shine in the soul.

Copyright, 1915, Renewal. Hope Publishing Co., owner

Some Golden Daybreak

C. A. Blackmore — Carl Blackmore

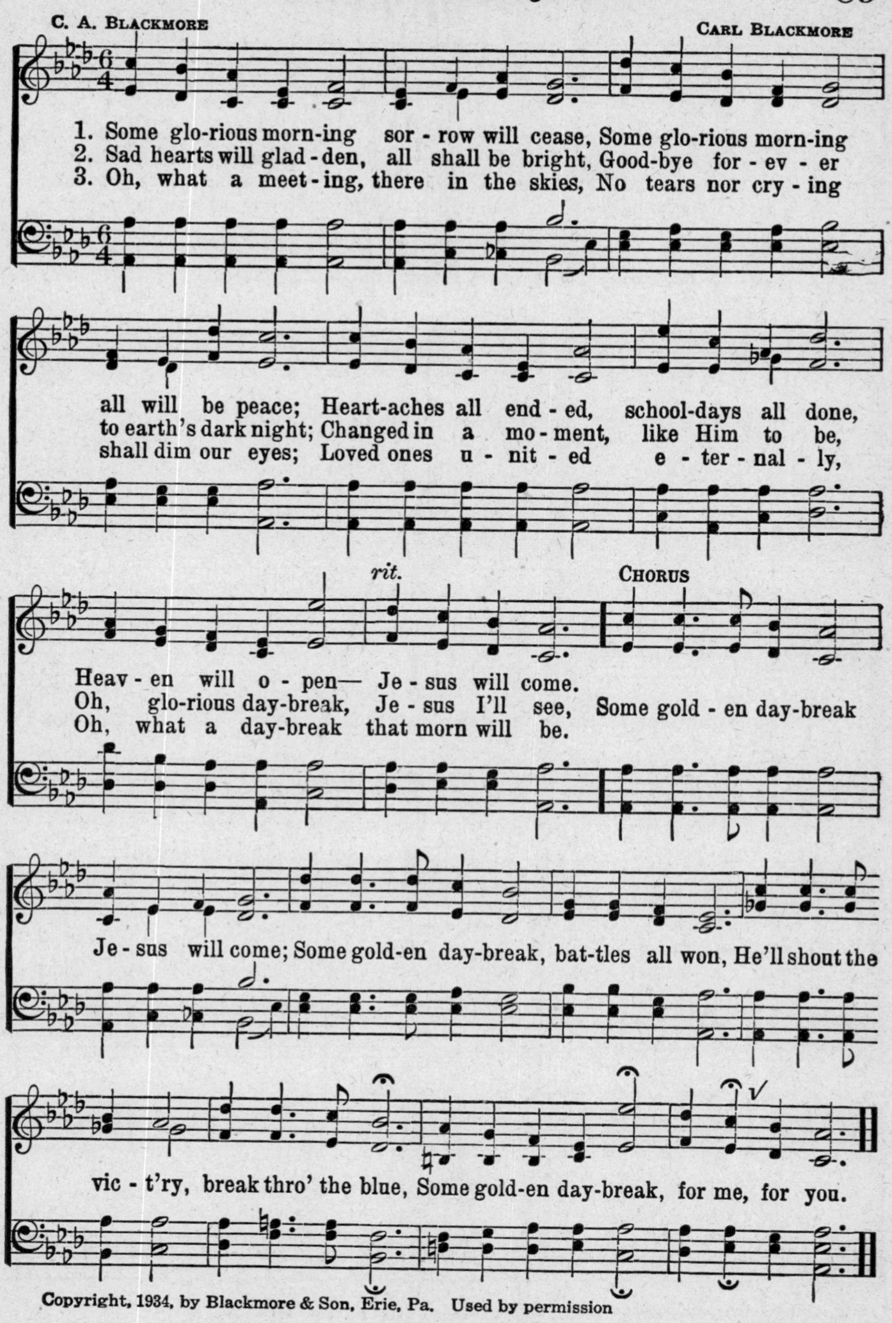
1. Some glo-rious morn-ing sor - row will cease, Some glo-rious morn-ing
2. Sad hearts will glad - den, all shall be bright, Good-bye for - ev - er
3. Oh, what a meet - ing, there in the skies, No tears nor cry - ing
all will be peace; Heart-aches all end - ed, school-days all done,
to earth's dark night; Changed in a mo - ment, like Him to be,
shall dim our eyes; Loved ones u - nit - ed e - ter - nal - ly,
rit.
Chorus
Heav - en will o - pen— Je - sus will come.
Oh, glo-rious day-break, Je - sus I'll see, Some gold - en day-break
Oh, what a day-break that morn will be.
Je - sus will come; Some gold-en day-break, bat-tles all won, He'll shout the
vic - t'ry, break thro' the blue, Some gold-en day-break, for me, for you.

Copyright, 1934, by Blackmore & Son, Erie, Pa. Used by permission

90 **Thy Word Have I Hid In My Heart**

Adapted by E. O. S. E. O. SELLERS

1. Thy Word is a lamp to my feet, A light to my path al - way,
2. For - ev - er, O Lord, is Thy Word Es-tab-lished and fixed on high;
3. At morn-ing, at noon, and at night I ev - er will give Thee praise;
4. Thro' Him whom Thy Word hath foretold, The Sav-ior and Morn-ing Star,
To guide and to save me from sin, And show me the heav'n-ly way.
Thy faith-ful-ness un-to all men A - bid-eth for - ev - er nigh.
For Thou art my por-tion, O Lord, And shall be thro' all my days!
Sal - va-tion and peace have been bro't To those who have strayed a - far.
CHORUS—Ps. 119: 11.
Thy Word have I hid in my heart (in my heart), That I might not
sin a - gainst Thee (a - gainst Thee); That I might not sin, That
ad lib.
I might not sin, Thy Word have I hid in my heart.

Copyright, 1936. Renewal. E. O. Sellers, owner. Used by permission

At the Foot of the Cross

Robert Harkness
Robert Harkness
1. I met Je-sus at the foot of the cross When I was bound by sin;
2. I found par-don at the foot of the cross, For-give-ness full and free;
3. I met Je-sus when I need-ed Him most, De-spair pos-sessed my soul;
Je-sus met me, cleansed my heart of its dross, He gave sweet peace with-in. . . .
Now I love Him on-ly, all else is loss, His grace a-vailed for me. . .
I was un-der con-dem-na-tion and lost, When Je-sus made me whole. .
Chorus
I met Je-sus at the foot of the cross, I met Je-sus at the
foot of the cross; All my sins were washed a-way; Sin's dark night turned
in-to day When I met Je-sus at the foot of the cross.

Copyright, 1922, by Robert H. Coleman and Robert Harkness. International Copyright secured
Used by permission

92 Hallelujah! Praise His Name

J. Edwin McConnell | J. Edwin McConnell

1. I once was load-ed down with sin, but Je-sus came a-long; Hal-le-lu-jah, Hal-le-lu-jah! Now I am free and in my heart I have a hap-py song; Hal-le-lu-jah, praise His name!
2. How man-y times I stum-bled, bear-ing such a heav-y load; Hal-le-lu-jah, Hal-le-lu-jah! But Je-sus took my bur-dens, led me to the nar-row road; Hal-le-lu-jah, praise His name!
3. The grace of God is flow-ing from the Cross of Cal-va-ry: Hal-le-lu-jah, Hal-le-lu-jah! I'm hap-py, for I know that there is grace e-nough for me; Hal-le-lu-jah, praise His name!
Chorus
Hal-le-lu-jah!
His name!
Praise His ho-ly name! Hal-le-lu-jah! He's ev-'ry day the same; My sins are all for-giv-en, I'm on my way to heaven, I'll shout His name for-ev-er: Praise His name!
rit.

Copyright, 1921. Hope Publishing Co., owner

Our Great Savior

J. Wilbur Chapman

Arr. by Robert Harkness

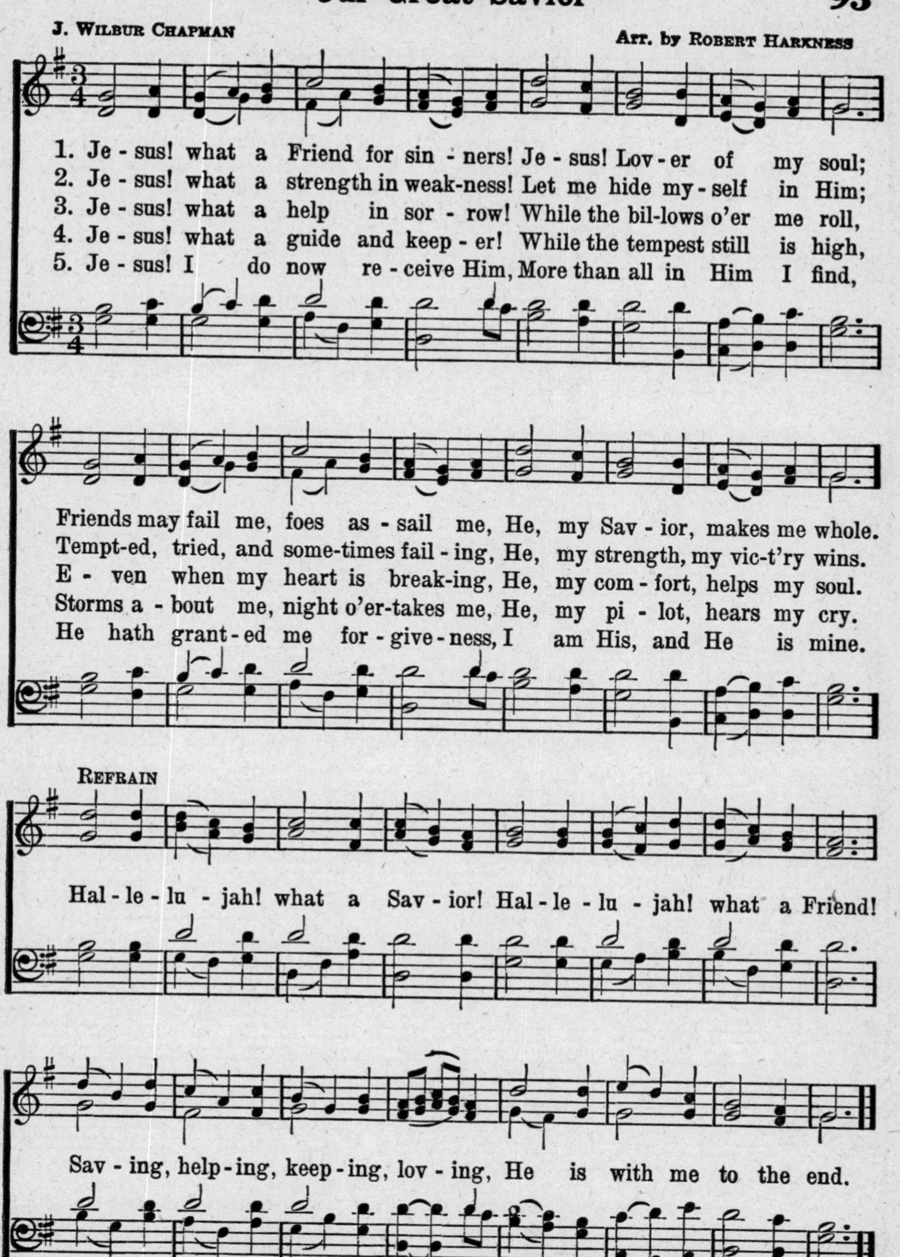
1. Je - sus! what a Friend for sin - ners! Je - sus! Lov - er of my soul;
2. Je - sus! what a strength in weak-ness! Let me hide my - self in Him;
3. Je - sus! what a help in sor - row! While the bil-lows o'er me roll,
4. Je - sus! what a guide and keep - er! While the tempest still is high,
5. Je - sus! I do now re - ceive Him, More than all in Him I find,
Friends may fail me, foes as - sail me, He, my Sav - ior, makes me whole.
Tempt-ed, tried, and some-times fail - ing, He, my strength, my vic-t'ry wins.
E - ven when my heart is break-ing, He, my com - fort, helps my soul.
Storms a - bout me, night o'er-takes me, He, my pi - lot, hears my cry.
He hath grant - ed me for - give - ness, I am His, and He is mine.
Refrain
Hal - le - lu - jah! what a Sav - ior! Hal - le - lu - jah! what a Friend!
Sav - ing, help - ing, keep - ing, lov - ing, He is with me to the end.

Copyright, 1938. Renewal. Hope Publishing Co., owner.

94 My Redeemer

P. P. Bliss | James McGranahan

1. I will sing of my Re-deem-er, And His won-drous love to me;
2. I will tell the won-drous sto-ry, How my lost es-tate to save,
3. I will praise my dear Re-deem-er, His tri-um-phant pow'r I'll tell,
4. I will sing of my Re-deem-er, And His heav'n-ly love to me;
On the cru-el cross He suf-fered, From the curse to set me free.
In His bound-less love and mer-cy, He the ran-som free-ly gave.
How the vic-to-ry He giv-eth O-ver sin, and death, and hell.
He from death to life hath bro't me, Son of God with Him to be.
Chorus
Sing, oh, sing . . . . of my Re-deem - er,
of my Re-deem-er, Sing, oh, sing of my Re-deem-er,
With His blood . . . . He pur-chased me, ...
He pur-chased me, With His blood He pur-chased me,
On the cross . . . . He sealed my par - don,
He sealed my par-don, On the cross He sealed my par-don,

Copyright, 1906, Renewal. Hope Publishing Co., owner

My Redeemer

Paid the debt, ... and made me free. . . . .
and made me free, and made me free.

Take the Name of Jesus With You 95

Mrs. Lydia Baxter — W. H. Doane

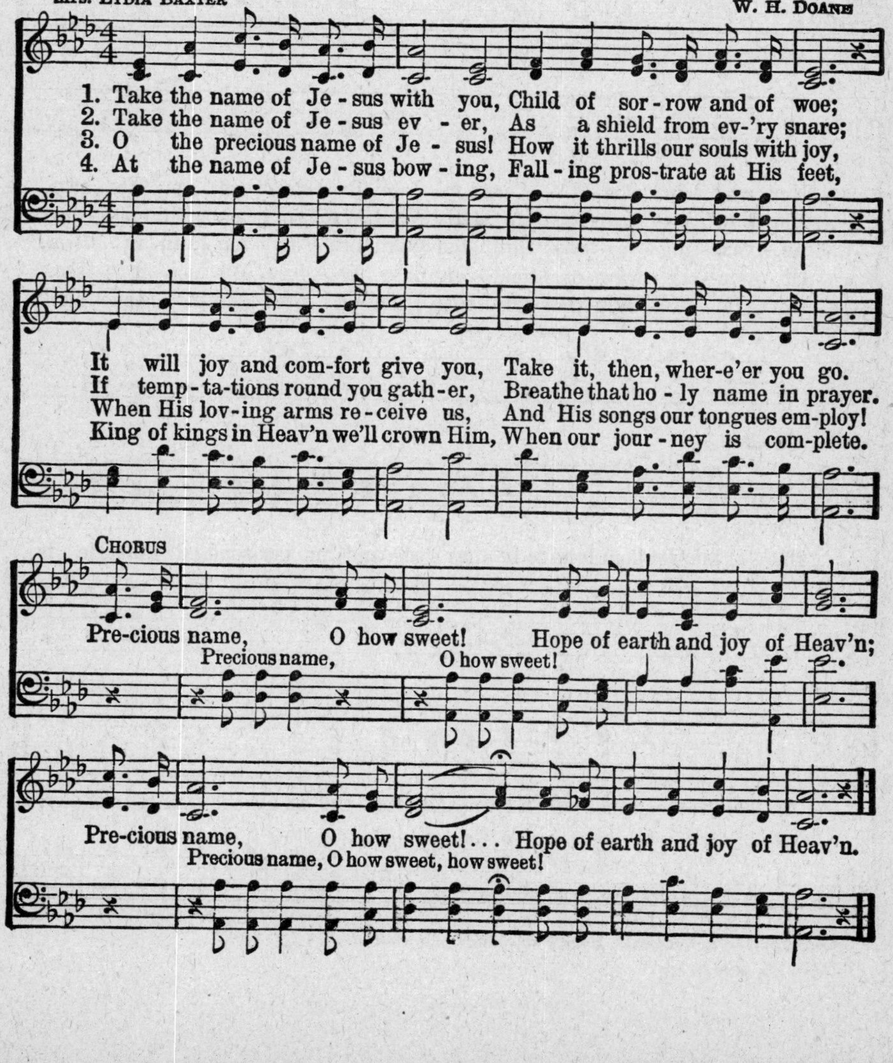

1. Take the name of Je - sus with you, Child of sor - row and of woe;
It will joy and com-fort give you, Take it, then, wher-e'er you go.

2. Take the name of Je - sus ev - er, As a shield from ev-'ry snare;
If temp - ta-tions round you gath - er, Breathe that ho - ly name in prayer.

3. O the precious name of Je - sus! How it thrills our souls with joy,
When His lov-ing arms re - ceive us, And His songs our tongues em-ploy!

4. At the name of Je - sus bow - ing, Fall - ing pros-trate at His feet,
King of kings in Heav'n we'll crown Him, When our jour - ney is com-plete.

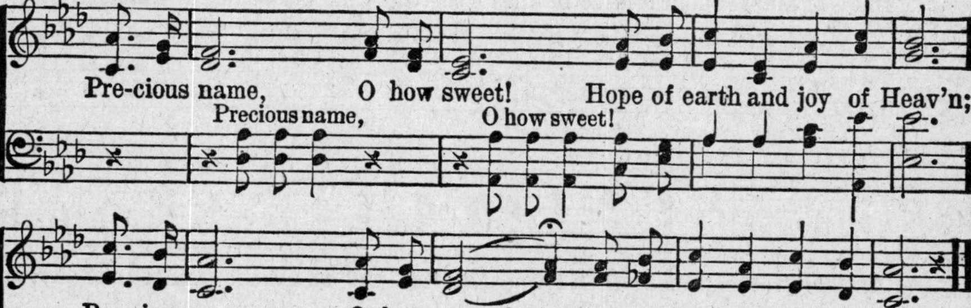

Chorus
Pre-cious name, O how sweet! Hope of earth and joy of Heav'n;
Precious name, O how sweet!
Pre-cious name, O how sweet! . . . Hope of earth and joy of Heav'n.
Precious name, O how sweet, how sweet!

96 I Know Whom I Have Believed

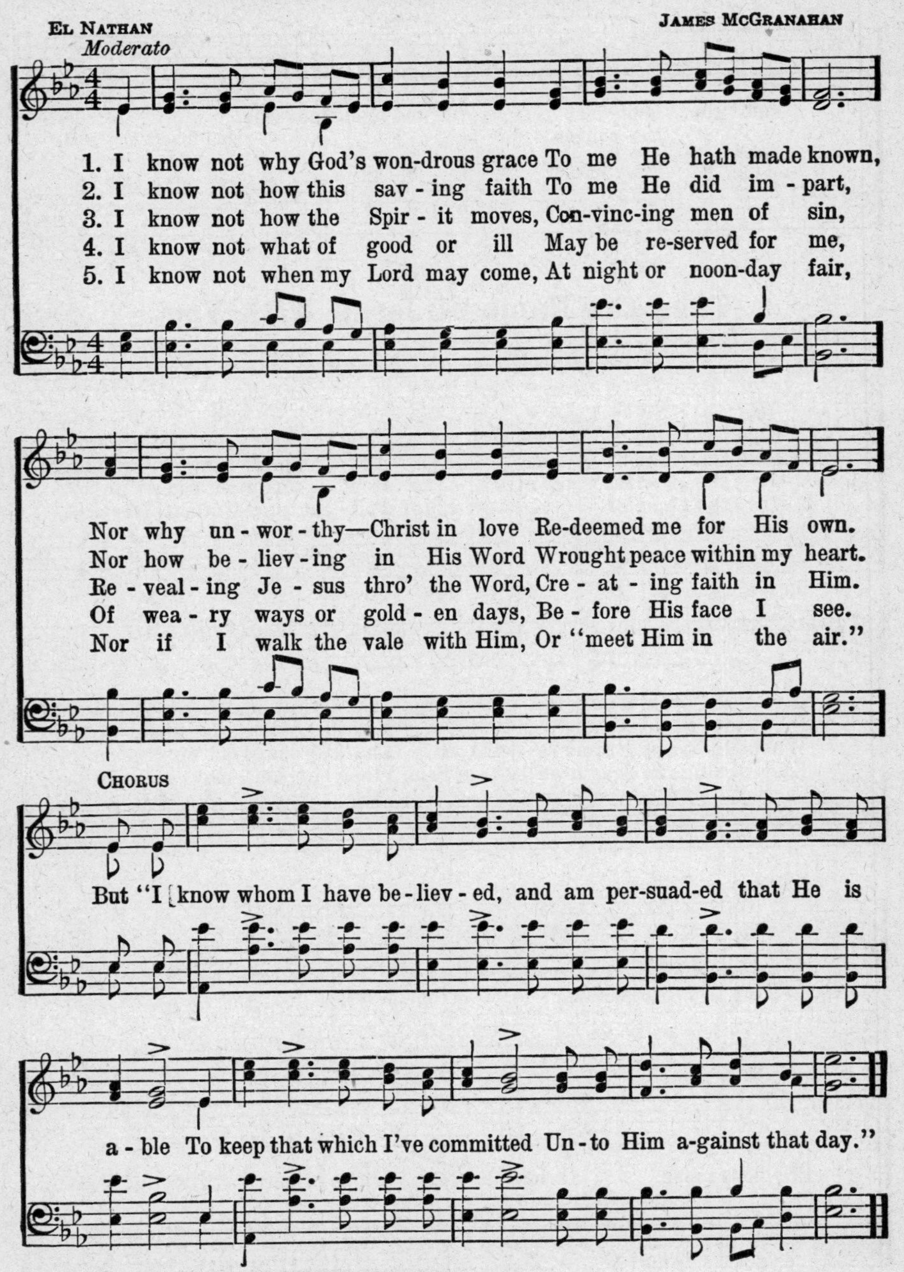
El Nathan
James McGranahan
Moderato
1. I know not why God's won-drous grace To me He hath made known,
2. I know not how this sav - ing faith To me He did im - part,
3. I know not how the Spir - it moves, Con-vinc-ing men of sin,
4. I know not what of good or ill May be re-served for me,
5. I know not when my Lord may come, At night or noon-day fair,
Nor why un - wor - thy—Christ in love Re-deemed me for His own.
Nor how be - liev - ing in His Word Wrought peace within my heart.
Re - veal - ing Je - sus thro' the Word, Cre - at - ing faith in Him.
Of wea - ry ways or gold - en days, Be - fore His face I see.
Nor if I walk the vale with Him, Or "meet Him in the air."
Chorus
But "I know whom I have be - liev - ed, and am per-suad-ed that He is
a - ble To keep that which I've committed Un - to Him a-gainst that day."

Copyright, 1913, Renewal. Hope Publishing Co., owner

Higher Ground

JOHNSON OATMAN, JR. CHAS. H. GABRIEL

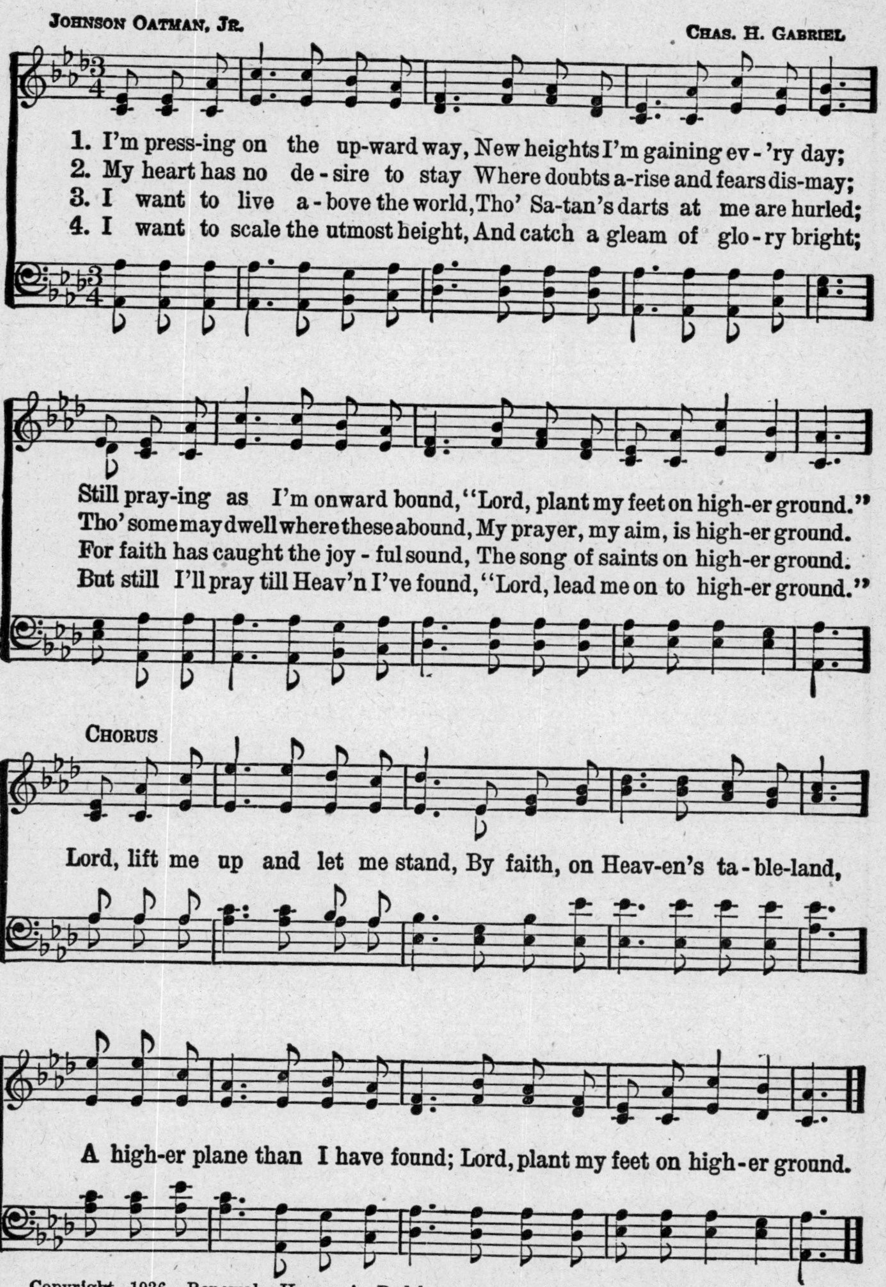
1. I'm press-ing on the up-ward way, New heights I'm gaining ev - 'ry day;
2. My heart has no de - sire to stay Where doubts a-rise and fears dis-may;
3. I want to live a - bove the world, Tho' Sa-tan's darts at me are hurled;
4. I want to scale the utmost height, And catch a gleam of glo - ry bright;
Still pray-ing as I'm onward bound, "Lord, plant my feet on high-er ground."
Tho' some may dwell where these abound, My prayer, my aim, is high-er ground.
For faith has caught the joy - ful sound, The song of saints on high-er ground.
But still I'll pray till Heav'n I've found, "Lord, lead me on to high-er ground."
CHORUS
Lord, lift me up and let me stand, By faith, on Heav-en's ta - ble-land,
A high-er plane than I have found; Lord, plant my feet on high - er ground.

Copyright, 1926. Renewal. Homer A. Rodeheaver, owner. Used by permission.

98 I Will Sing the Wondrous Story

F. H. ROWLEY

PETER P. BILHORN

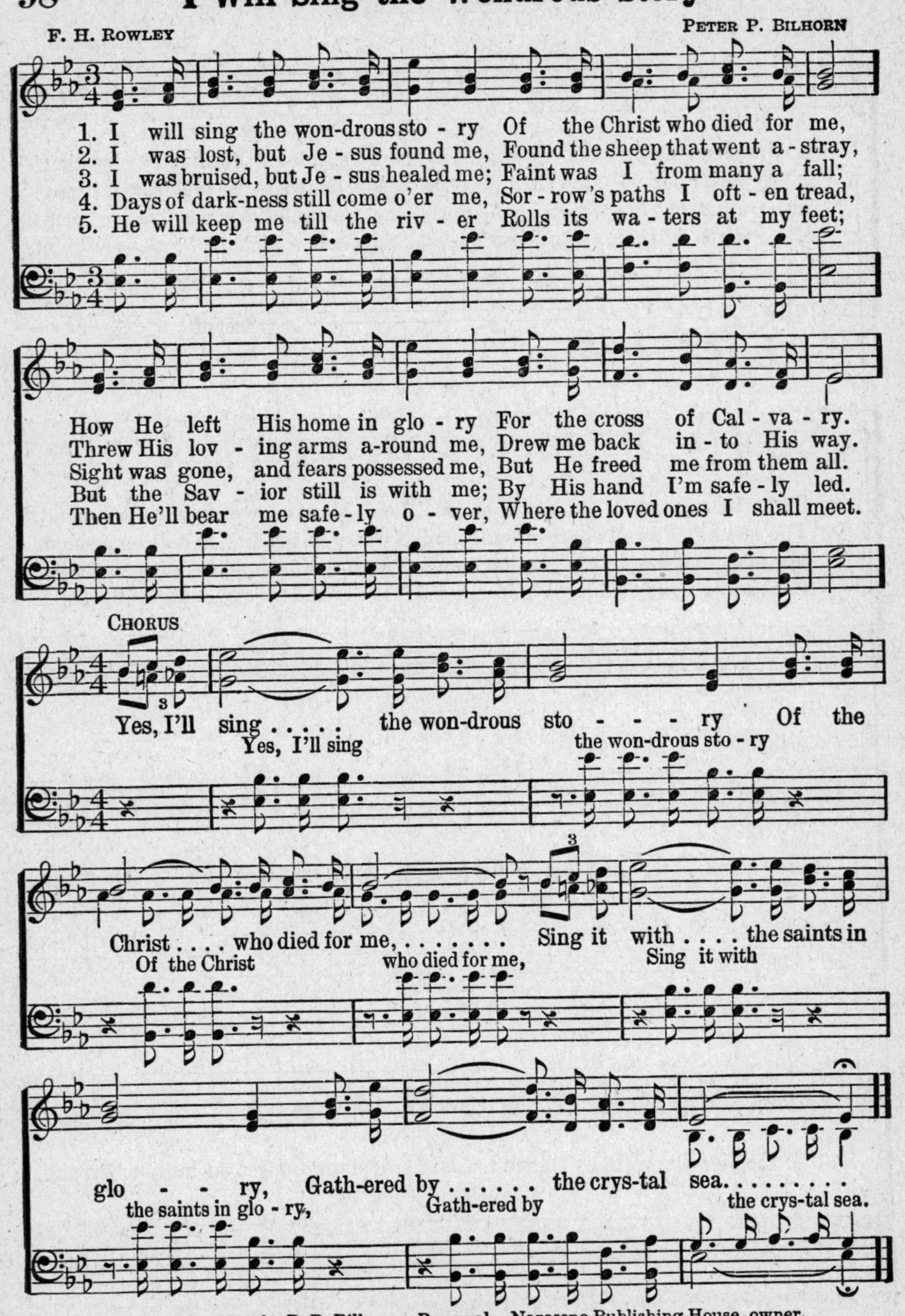
1. I will sing the won-drous sto - ry Of the Christ who died for me,
2. I was lost, but Je - sus found me, Found the sheep that went a - stray,
3. I was bruised, but Je - sus healed me; Faint was I from many a fall;
4. Days of dark-ness still come o'er me, Sor - row's paths I oft - en tread,
5. He will keep me till the riv - er Rolls its wa - ters at my feet;
How He left His home in glo - ry For the cross of Cal - va - ry.
Threw His lov - ing arms a-round me, Drew me back in - to His way.
Sight was gone, and fears possessed me, But He freed me from them all.
But the Sav - ior still is with me; By His hand I'm safe - ly led.
Then He'll bear me safe - ly o - ver, Where the loved ones I shall meet.
CHORUS
Yes, I'll sing . . . . . the won-drous sto - - - - ry Of the
Yes, I'll sing
the won-drous sto - ry
Christ . . . . who died for me, ... Sing it with . . . . the saints in
Of the Christ
who died for me,
Sing it with
glo - - ry, Gath-ered by . . . . . . the crys-tal sea. . . . .
the saints in glo - ry,
Gath-ered by
the crys-tal sea.

Copyright, 1914, by P. P. Bilhorn. Renewal. Nazarene Publishing House, owner.
Used by permission

It is Glory Just to Walk With Him 99

Avis M. Burgeson | Haldor Lillenas

1. It is glo - ry just to walk with Him whose blood has ransomed me; It is rap-ture for my soul each day; It is joy di-vine to feel Him near wher-e'er my path may be; Bless the Lord, it's glo-ry all the way!
2. It is glo - ry when the shad-ows fall, to know that He is near; Oh! what joy to sim-ply trust and pray! It is glo-ry to a-bide in Him when skies a-bove are clear; Yes, with Him, it's glo-ry all the way!
3. 'Twill be glo - ry when I walk with Him on heav-en's gold-en shore, Nev-er from His side a-gain to stray; 'Twill be glo-ry, wondrous glo-ry with the Sav-ior ev - er-more, Ev - er - last-ing glo-ry all the way!
Chorus
It is glo-ry just to walk with Him, ... It is glo-ry just to walk with Him; . . . . He will guide my steps aright,
walk with Him, walk with Him;
Thro' the vale and o'er the height; It is glo - ry just to walk with Him . . . . . .
walk with Him.

Copyright, 1918. Hope Publishing Co., owner

100 Under His Wings

WILLIAM O. CUSHING IRA D. SANKEY

1. Un - der His wings I am safe - ly a - bid - ing; Tho' the night
2. Un - der His wings, what a ref - uge in sor - row! How the heart
3. Un - der His wings, O what pre-cious en - joy - ment! There will I

deep - ens and tem - pests are wild, Still I can trust Him; I
yearn - ing - ly turns to His rest! Oft - en when earth has no
hide till life's tri - als are o'er; Shel-tered, pro - tect - ed, no

know He will keep me; He has re-deemed me, and I am His child.
balm for my heal - ing, There I find com - fort, and there I am blest.
e - vil can harm me; Rest - ing in Je - sus I'm safe ev - er - more.

CHORUS

Un-der His wings, un-der His wings, Who from His love can sev - er?

Un-der His wings my soul shall a - bide, Safe - ly a - bide for - ev - er.

Copyright, 1924, by G. V. Sankey. Renewal. Hope Publishing Company, owner

The Touch of His Hand On Mine

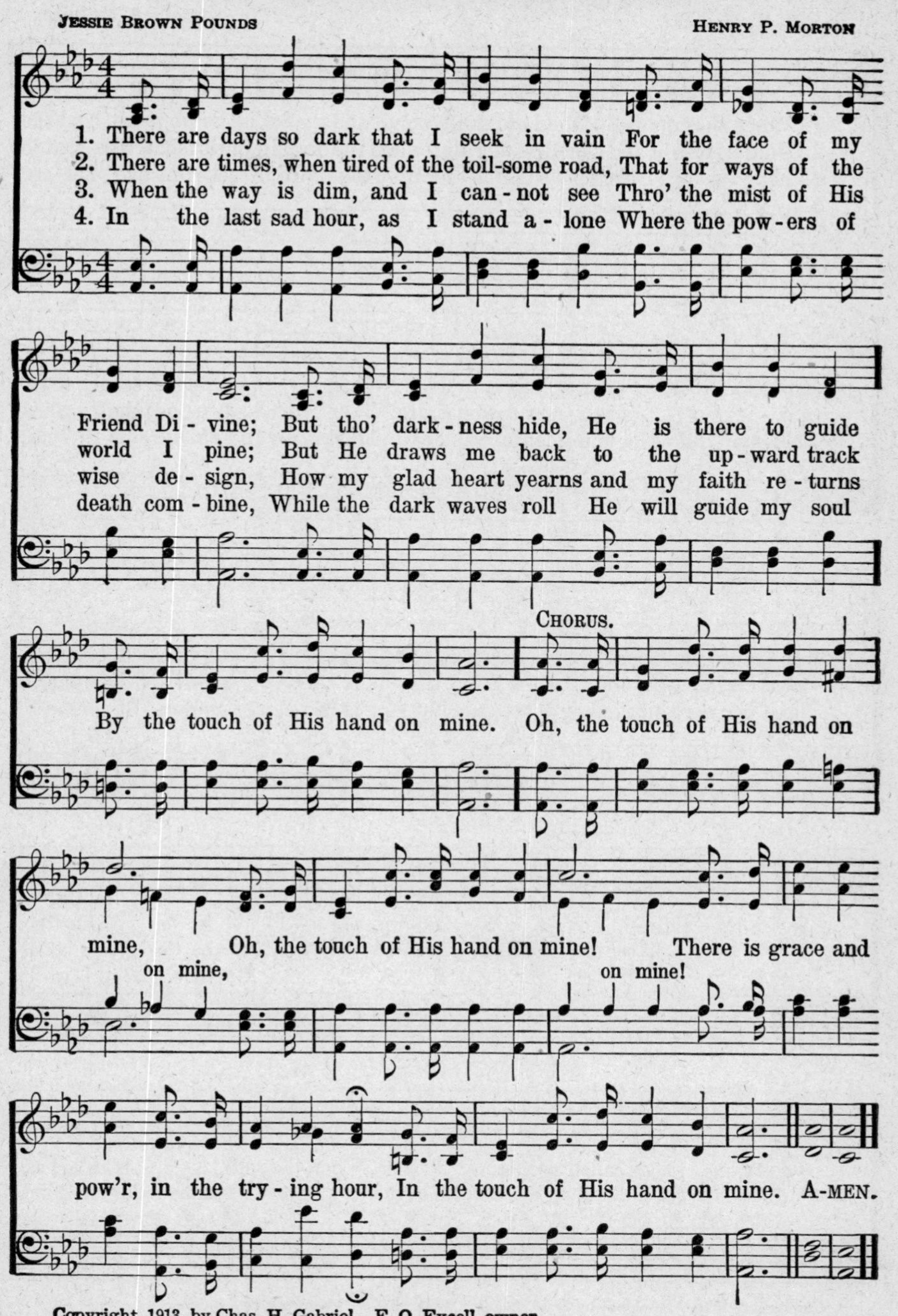
JESSIE BROWN POUNDS
HENRY P. MORTON
1. There are days so dark that I seek in vain For the face of my Friend Di - vine; But tho' dark - ness hide, He is there to guide
2. There are times, when tired of the toil-some road, That for ways of the world I pine; But He draws me back to the up - ward track
3. When the way is dim, and I can - not see Thro' the mist of His wise de - sign, How my glad heart yearns and my faith re - turns
4. In the last sad hour, as I stand a - lone Where the pow - ers of death com - bine, While the dark waves roll He will guide my soul
By the touch of His hand on mine.
CHORUS.
Oh, the touch of His hand on mine, on mine, Oh, the touch of His hand on mine! on mine! There is grace and pow'r, in the try - ing hour, In the touch of His hand on mine.
A-MEN.

Copyright, 1913, by Chas. H. Gabriel. E. O. Excell, owner

102 When the Roll is Called Up Yonder

J. M. B. J. M. BLACK

1. When the trumpet of the Lord shall sound, and time shall be no more, And the morning breaks, e-ter-nal, bright and fair; When the saved of earth shall gather o - ver on the oth-er shore, And the roll is called up yon-der, I'll be there.
2. On that bright and cloudless morning when the dead in Christ shall rise, And the glo - ry of His res - ur-rec-tion share; When His cho-sen ones shall gather to their home beyond the skies, And the roll is called up yon-der, I'll be there.
3. Let us la - bor for the Mas - ter from the dawn till set - ting sun, Let us talk of all His wondrous love and care; Then when all of life is o - ver, and our work on earth is done, And the roll is called up yon-der, I'll be there.
CHORUS.
When the roll . . . . . . is called up yon - - - - der, When the roll . . . . is called up yon - - der, When the roll . . . . is called up
When the roll is called up yon - der, I'll be there,
When the roll is called up yon-der, I'll be there,
When the roll is called up

Copyright, 1921. Renewal by J. M. Black. Tabernacle Publishing Co., owner

When the Roll is Called Up Yonder

yon - der, When the roll is called up yon - der, I'll be there.
Leaning On the Everlasting Arms
103
E. A. Hoffman
A. J. Showalter
1. What a fel-low-ship, what a joy di-vine, Leaning on the ev-er-last-ing arms;
2. Oh, how sweet to walk in this pilgrim way, Leaning on the ev-er-last-ing arms;
3. What have I to dread, what have I to fear, Leaning on the ev-er-last-ing arms?
What a bless-ed-ness, what a peace is mine, Leaning on the ev-er-last-ing arms.
Oh, how bright the path grows from day to day, Leaning on the ev-er-last-ing arms.
I have bless-ed peace with my Lord so near, Leaning on the ev-er-last-ing arms.
Refrain
Lean - ing, lean - ing, Safe and se-cure from all a-larms;
Lean-ing on Je - sus, lean-ing on Je - sus,
Lean - ing, lean - ing, Lean-ing on the ev-er-last-ing arms.
Lean-ing on Je - sus, lean-ing on Je - sus,

The Banner of the Cross

D. W. WHITTLE

JAMES McGRANAHAN

1. There's a roy - al ban - ner giv - en for dis-play To the sol - diers of the King; As an en - sign fair we lift it up to-day, While as ran-somed ones we sing.
2. Though the foe may rage and gath - er as the flood, Let the stand-ard be dis-played; And be-neath its folds, as sol-diers of the Lord, For the truth be not dis-mayed!
3. O - ver land and sea, wher-ev - er man may dwell, Make the glo - rious ti - dings known; Of the crim-son ban - ner now the sto - ry tell, While the Lord shall claim His own!
4. When the glo - ry dawns—'tis draw-ing ver - y near—It is has-t'ning day by day— Then be-fore our King the foe shall dis - ap-pear, And the cross the world shall sway!

CHORUS

March-ing on, . . . march-ing on, . . For Christ count ev - 'ry-thing but loss! . . . . And to crown Him King, toil and sing 'Neath the ban-ner of the cross!

on, on, on, on, ev - 'ry-thing, ev - 'ry - thing but loss! we'll Be - neath

What a Savior! 105

CHARLOTTE G. HOMER — CHAS. H. GABRIEL

1. What a Sav - ior Je - sus is! He is mine, and I am His;
2. What a Sav - ior! praise His name, That to earth for me He came;
3. What a Sav - ior! all the way Walk-ing with me, day by day,
4. What a Sav - ior! and I know When to that bright world I go,
5. What a Sav - ior! how He loves, Ev - 'ry hour His mer - cy proves;
He the price of sin has paid, And for me a - tone-ment made.
Not the least, but all He gave, My im - mor - tal soul to save.
Guid - ing by His ho - ly will, Guard-ing me from ev - 'ry ill.
Saved by His re - deem-ing grace, I shall see Him face to face.
Lis - ten, for He speaks to thee: "Take thy cross, and fol - low Me."
CHORUS
What a Sav - - ior, what a Sav - ior, What a
What a Sav - - ior, what a pre-cious Sav-ior, What a
Sav - - - ior Je - sus is! . . . . . . I will praise Him, ev - er
Sav-ior Je-sus is, What a Sav-ior Je-sus is! I will praise Him,
praise Him, He is mine, ... and I am His! . . . . . .
ev - er praise Him, He is mine, and I am His, He is mine, and I am His!

Copyright, 1933. Renewal. Homer A. Rodeheaver, owner. Used by permission

106 The Homeland

HUGH R. HAWEIS
GEO. C. STEBBINS
Arr. by Fred Jacky
Solo
(Hum)
(Hum)
1. The Homeland! O the Homeland! The land of the free - born! There's no night in the
2. My Lord is in the Homeland, With an-gels bright and fair; There's no sin in the
3. My loved ones in the Homeland Are wait-ing me to come, Where nei-ther death nor
(Hum)
(Hum)
Parts
Home-land, But aye the fade - less morn; I'm sigh - ing for the Home - land, My
Home-land, And no temp-ta - tion there; The mu - sic of the Home - land Is
sor - row In - vades their ho - ly home; O dear, dear na - tive coun - try! O
heart is ach - ing here; There is no pain in the Home - land To which I'm
ring - ing in my ears; And when I think of the Home - land My eyes are
rest and peace a - bove! Christ bring us all to the Home - land Of Thy re-
Solo
(Hum)
draw - ing near; There is no pain in the Home-land To which I'm draw-ing near.
filled with tears; And when I think of the Home-land My eyes are filled with tears.
deem - ing love; Christ bring us all to the Home-land Of Thy re-deem-ing love!
(Hum)

Copyright, 1921. Renewal. Arr. Copyright, 1941. Hope Publishing Co., owner

Is He Satisfied with Me

GRACE B. MAXWELL
GRACE B. MAXWELL
1. I am sat - is - fied with Je - sus, But a ques-tion comes to me
2. Am I kind in word, and ten - der, Am I all I ought to be,
3. Do I tell the bless - ed sto - ry Of the Christ on Cal - va - ry,
As I pon - der o'er His good-ness, Is He sat - is - fied with me?
Am I al - ways His de - fend - er: Is He sat - is - fied with me?
Do - ing all for His own glo - ry: Is He sat - is - fied with me?
REFRAIN
Is my Mas - - - ter sat - is - fied, Is He
Is my Mas - ter sat - is - fied, sat - is - fied with me?
sat - is - fied with me? I am sat - is - fied with Je - sus;
Is He sat - is - fied with me? . . . .
Is He sat - is - fied with me?

Copyright, 1932, Renewal. Hope Publishing Co., owner

We Have An Anchor

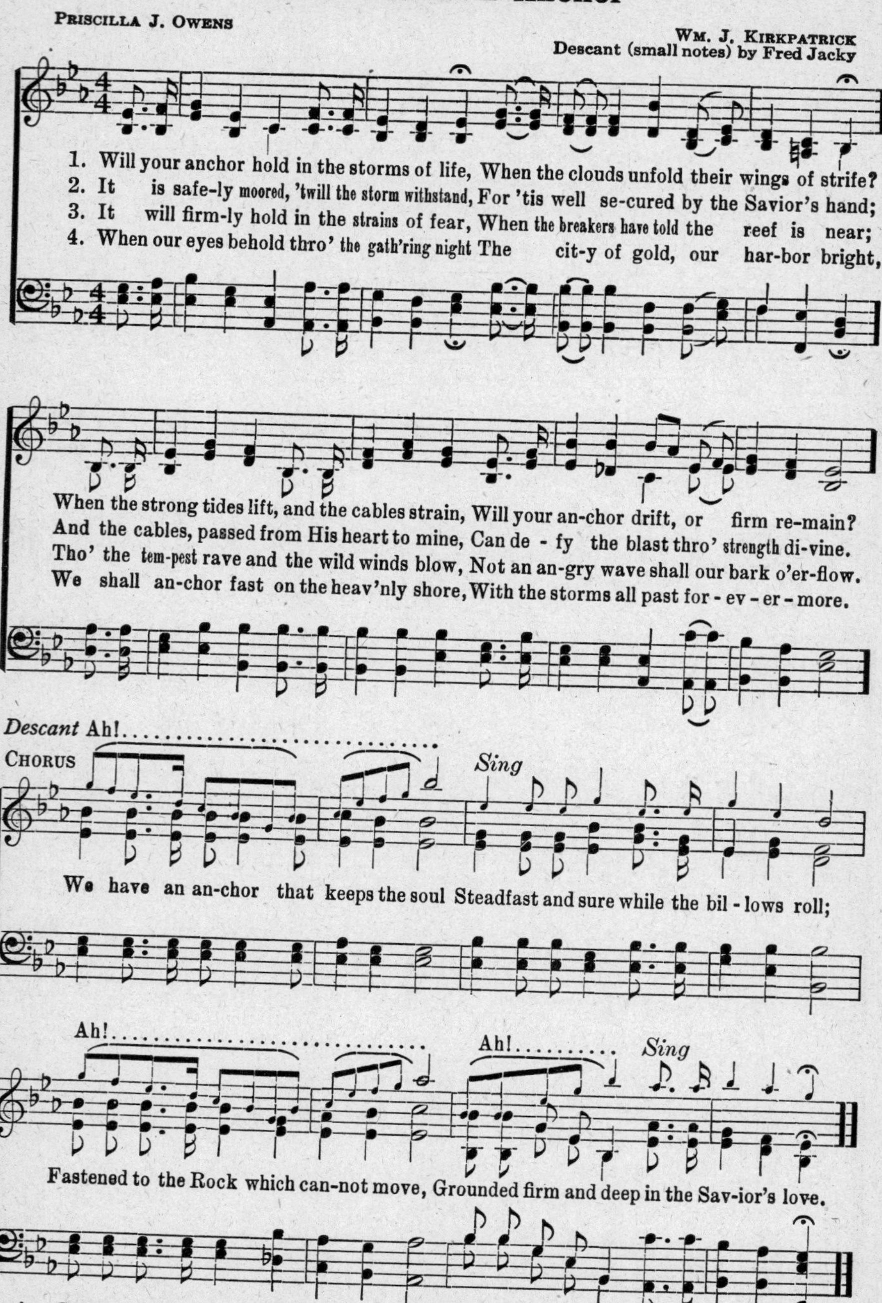
PRISCILLA J. OWENS
WM. J. KIRKPATRICK
Descant (small notes) by Fred Jacky
1. Will your anchor hold in the storms of life, When the clouds unfold their wings of strife? When the strong tides lift, and the cables strain, Will your an-chor drift, or firm re-main?
2. It is safe-ly moored, 'twill the storm withstand, For 'tis well se-cured by the Savior's hand; And the cables, passed from His heart to mine, Can de - fy the blast thro' strength di-vine.
3. It will firm-ly hold in the straits of fear, When the breakers have told the reef is near; Tho' the tem-pest rave and the wild winds blow, Not an an-gry wave shall our bark o'er-flow.
4. When our eyes behold thro' the gath'ring night The cit-y of gold, our har-bor bright, We shall an-chor fast on the heav'nly shore, With the storms all past for - ev - er - more.
Descant Ah!
CHORUS
Sing
We have an an-chor that keeps the soul Steadfast and sure while the bil - lows roll;
Ah!
Ah!
Sing
Fastened to the Rock which can-not move, Grounded firm and deep in the Sav-ior's love.

Arr. Copyright, 1941. Hope Publishing Company, owner

Let the Joy Overflow

E. E. Hewitt — S. B. Jackson

1. There's a clear fountain flowing From the bright throne above, And its waters are glow-ing With the sunshine of love; Take the blest con-so - la - tion, Which the Lord will be - stow, Take the cup of sal - va-tion—Let the joy o - ver-flow.
2. Man - y hearts need the story—Are a-thirst for His grace; Go to them with His glo - ry Shin-ing out from your face; Tell of Je - sus your Sav - ior! If His mer-cies you know, Show the light of His fa - vor—Let the joy o - ver-flow.
3. Be our lives free-ly yield-ed To the Sav-ior's command; By His care ev-er shield-ed And up-held by His hand; In the path-ways of sad-ness, Sweet-est lil - ies may grow; Let us sow seeds of gladness—Let the joy o - ver-flow.
Chorus
O the joy! . . . . With this wondrous salvation Be our hearts all a - glow;
O the joy!
O the joy! . . . . Let the bless-ing run o-ver, And joy o - ver - flow.
O the joy!

Copyright, 1917, by The Rodeheaver Company. Used by permission

110 Mighty Army of the Young

JOHN R. COLGAN — A. F. MYERS

1. Might-y ar-my of the young, Lift the voice in cheer-ful song,
2. Tongues of chil-dren light and free, Tongues of youth all full of glee,
3. Je-sus lives, O bless-ed words! King of kings, and Lord of lords!
Send the wel-come word a-long, Je-sus lives! Once He died for you and me,
Sing to all on land and sea, Je-sus lives! Light for you and all man-kind,
Lift the cross and sheathe the swords, Je-sus lives! See, He breaks the prison wall,
Bore our sins up-on the tree, Now He lives to make us free, Je-sus lives!
Sight for all by sin made blind, Life in Je-sus all may find, Je-sus lives!
Throws a-side the dread-ful pall, Conquers death at once for all, Je-sus lives!
CHORUS
Wait not till the shad-ows lengthen, till you old-er grow, Ral-ly now and
Wait not Sing,
Wait not, wait not, Sing for
sing for Je-sus, ev-'ry-where you go; Lift your joy-ful voi-ces high,
sing,
Je-sus,

Mighty Army of the Young

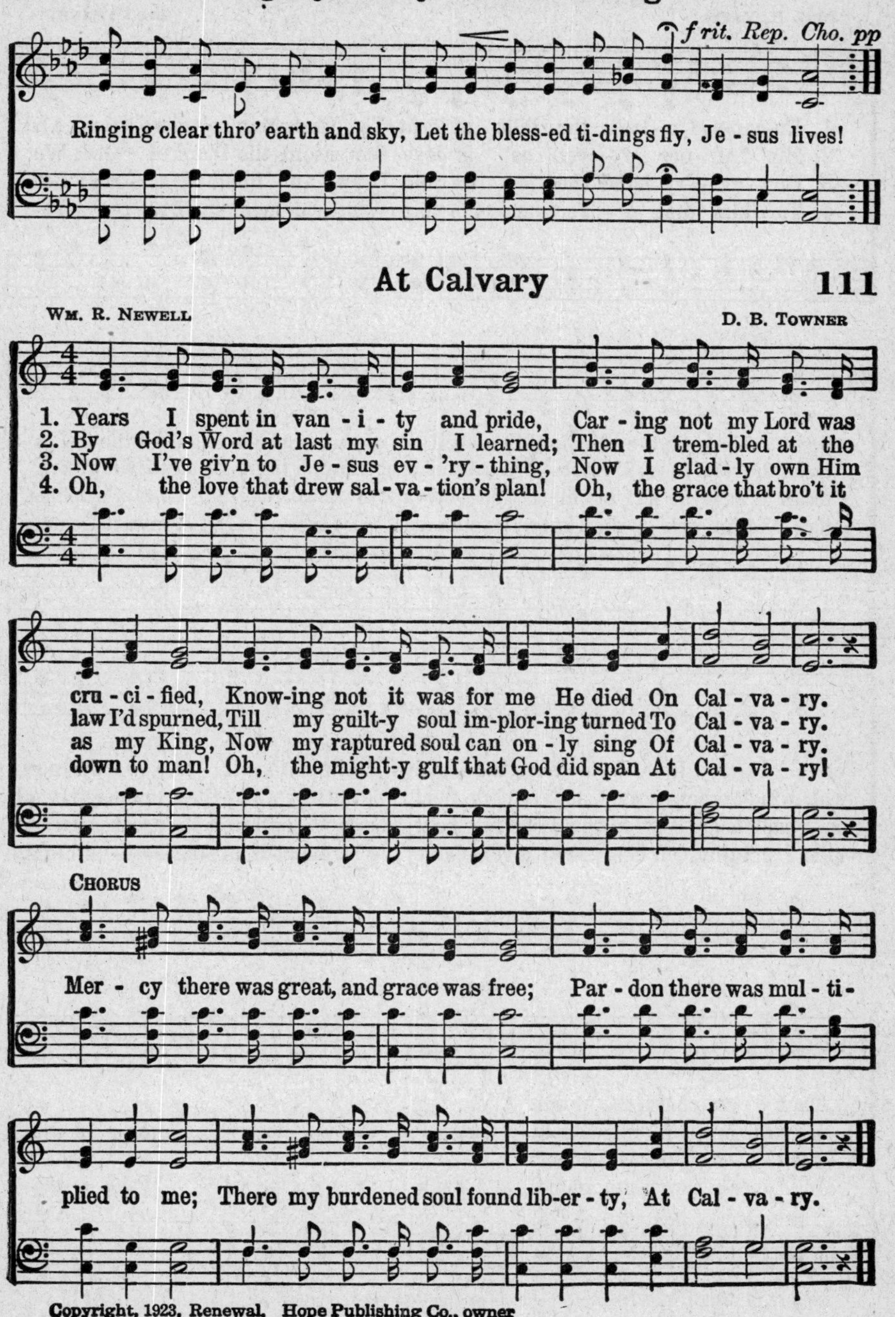
f rit. Rep. Cho. pp
Ringing clear thro' earth and sky, Let the bless-ed ti-dings fly, Je - sus lives!
At Calvary
111
Wm. R. Newell
D. B. Towner
1. Years I spent in van - i - ty and pride, Car - ing not my Lord was cru - ci - fied, Know-ing not it was for me He died On Cal - va - ry.
2. By God's Word at last my sin I learned; Then I trem-bled at the law I'd spurned, Till my guilt-y soul im-plor-ing turned To Cal - va - ry.
3. Now I've giv'n to Je - sus ev - 'ry - thing, Now I glad - ly own Him as my King, Now my raptured soul can on - ly sing Of Cal - va - ry.
4. Oh, the love that drew sal - va - tion's plan! Oh, the grace that bro't it down to man! Oh, the might-y gulf that God did span At Cal - va - ry!
Chorus
Mer - cy there was great, and grace was free; Par - don there was mul - ti - plied to me; There my burdened soul found lib - er - ty, At Cal - va - ry.

Copyright, 1923, Renewal. Hope Publishing Co., owner

112 Faith Is the Victory

JOHN H. YATES — IRA D. SANKEY

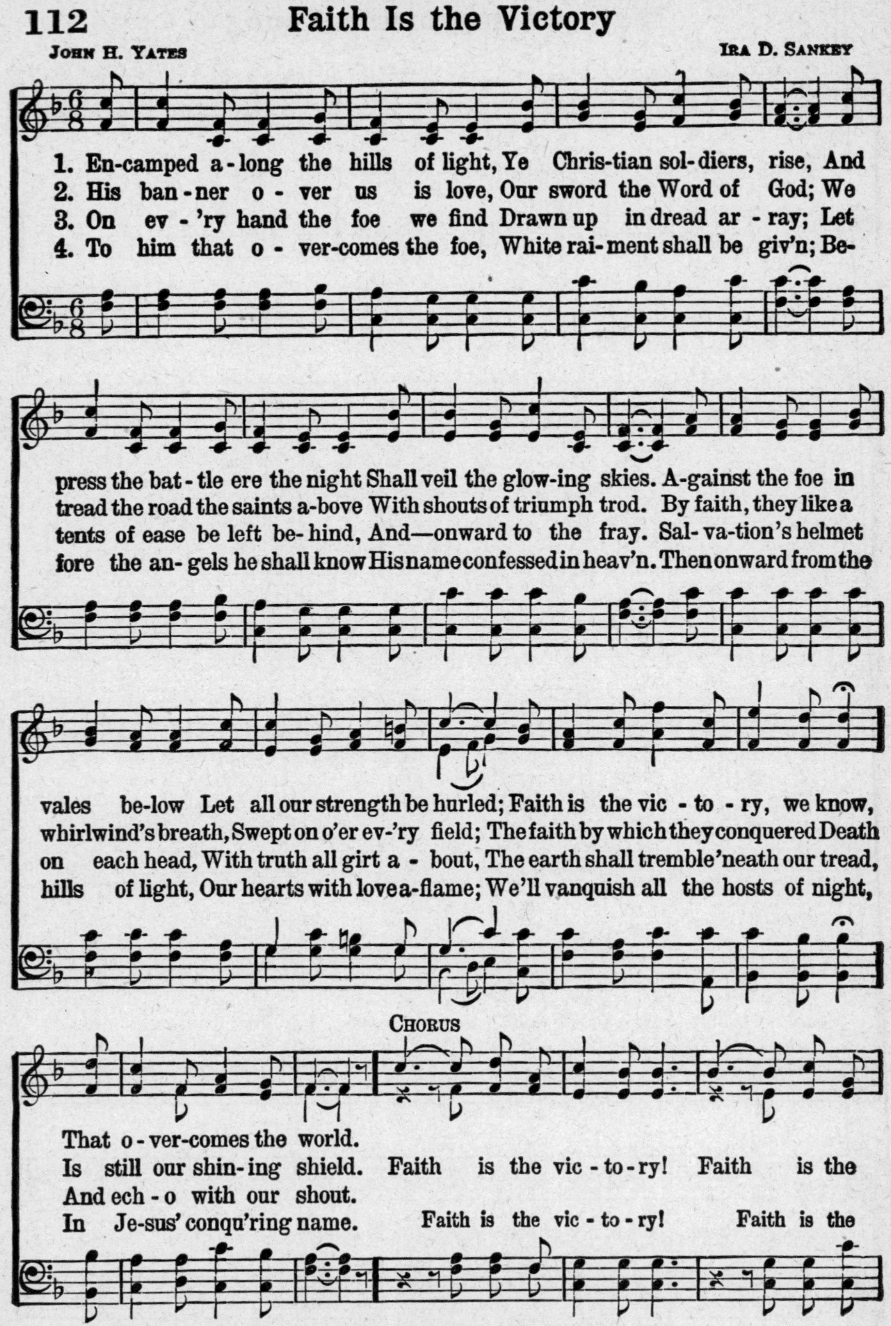
1. En-camped a-long the hills of light, Ye Chris-tian sol-diers, rise, And
2. His ban-ner o - ver us is love, Our sword the Word of God; We
3. On ev - 'ry hand the foe we find Drawn up in dread ar - ray; Let
4. To him that o - ver-comes the foe, White rai-ment shall be giv'n; Be-
press the bat-tle ere the night Shall veil the glow-ing skies. A-gainst the foe in
tread the road the saints a-bove With shouts of triumph trod. By faith, they like a
tents of ease be left be-hind, And—onward to the fray. Sal-va-tion's helmet
fore the an-gels he shall know His name confessed in heav'n. Then onward from the
vales be-low Let all our strength be hurled; Faith is the vic - to - ry, we know,
whirlwind's breath, Swept on o'er ev-'ry field; The faith by which they conquered Death
on each head, With truth all girt a - bout, The earth shall tremble 'neath our tread,
hills of light, Our hearts with love a-flame; We'll vanquish all the hosts of night,
That o-ver-comes the world.
Is still our shin-ing shield.
And ech-o with our shout.
In Je-sus' conqu'ring name.
CHORUS
Faith is the vic-to-ry! Faith is the
Faith is the vic-to-ry! Faith is the

Copyright, 1919. Renewal. Hope Publishing Company, owner.

Faith Is the Victory
vic - to - ry! Oh, glo - ri - ous vic - to - ry, That o - ver-comes the world.
vic - to - ry!
Hiding In Thee
113
Wm O. Cushing
Ira D. Sankey
1. O safe to the Rock that is high-er than I, My soul in its con-flicts and sor-rows would fly; So sin-ful, so wea-ry, Thine, Thine would I be; Thou blest "Rock of A-ges," I'm hid-ing in Thee.
2. In the calm of the noon-tide, in sor-row's lone hour, In times when temp-ta-tion casts o'er me its pow'r; In the tem-pests of life, on its wide, heaving sea, Thou blest "Rock of A-ges," I'm hid-ing in Thee.
3. How oft in the con-flict, when pressed by the foe, I have fled to my Ref-uge and breathed out my woe; How oft-en, when tri-als like sea-bil-lows roll, Have I hid-den in Thee, O Thou Rock of my soul.
Chorus
Hid-ing in Thee, Hiding in Thee, Thou blest "Rock of Ages," I'm hid-ing in Thee.

114 Blessed Be the Fountain

E. R. LATTA H. S. PERKINS

Moderato

1. Bless - ed be the Foun-tain of blood, To a world of sin - ners re-vealed;
Bless - ed be the dear Son of God: On - ly by His stripes we are healed.
Tho' I've wandered far from His fold, Bringing to my heart pain and woe,
Wash me in the blood of the Lamb, And I shall be whit-er than snow,

2. Thorn-y was the crown that He wore, And the cross His bod - y o'er-came;
Griev-ous were the sor-rows He bore, But He suf-fered thus not in vain.
May I to that Fountain be led, Made to cleanse my sins here be-low;
Wash me in the blood that He shed, And I shall be whit-er than snow.

3. Fa - ther, I have wandered from Thee, Oft - en has my heart gone a - stray;
Crim - son do my sins seem to me— Wa-ter can - not wash them a - way.
Je - sus, to that Fountain of Thine, Lean-ing on Thy prom-ise, I go;
Cleanse me by Thy wash-ing di - vine, And I shall be whit-er than snow.

CHORUS

Whit - - - - - er than the snow, ... Whit - - - - er
Whit - er than the snow, whit - er than the snow, Whit-er than the snow,

Blessed Be the Fountain
than the snow; . . . . Wash me in the blood of the
whit - er than the snow;
Lamb, ... And I shall be whit - er than snow. . . .
of the Lamb, than snow.
rit.
Pass Me Not
115
FANNY J. CROSBY
W. H. DOANE
1. Pass me not, O gen - tle Sav - ior, Hear my hum - ble cry; While on oth - ers
2. Let me at a throne of mer - cy Find a sweet re - lief; Kneel - ing there in
3. Trust - ing on - ly in Thy mer - it, Would I seek Thy face; Heal my wounded,
4. Thou the Spring of all my com - fort, More than life to me, Whom have I on
Thou art call - ing, Do not pass me by.
deep con - tri - tion, Help my un - be - lief.
bro - ken spir - it, Save me by Thy grace.
earth beside Thee? Whom in Heav'n but Thee?
CHORUS
Sav - ior, Sav - ior, Hear my humble
cry; While on oth - ers Thou art call - ing, Do not pass me by.

116 Tell Me the Old, Old Story

KATE HANKEY W. H. DOANE

1. Tell me the Old, Old Sto-ry, Of un-seen things a-bove, Of Je-sus and His glo-ry, Of Je-sus and His love; Tell me the sto-ry sim-ply, As to a lit-tle child, For I am weak and wea-ry, And help-less and de-filed.
2. Tell me the sto-ry slow-ly, That I may take it in— That won-der-ful re-demp-tion, God's rem-e-dy for sin; Tell me the sto-ry oft-en, For I for-get so soon, The "ear-ly dew" of morn-ing Has passed a-way at noon.
3. Tell me the sto-ry soft-ly, With ear-nest tones and grave; Re-mem-ber I'm the sin-ner Whom Je-sus came to save; Tell me the sto-ry al-ways, If you would real-ly be, In an-y time of troub-le, A com-fort-er to me.
4. Tell me the same old sto-ry, When you have cause to fear That this world's emp-ty glo-ry Is cost-ing me too dear; Yes, and when that world's glo-ry is dawn-ing on my soul, Tell me the Old, Old Sto-ry: "Christ Je-sus makes thee whole."

CHORUS

Tell me the Old, Old Sto-ry, Tell me the Old, Old Sto-ry, Tell me the Old, Old Sto-ry Of Je-sus and His love.

Believe On the Lord Jesus Christ

Avis B. Christiansen — Harry D. Clarke

1. "What must I do?" the trem-bling jail - or cried, When dazed by fear and won-der; "Be - lieve on Christ!" was all that Paul re - plied, "And thou shalt be saved from sin."
2. What must I do! O wea - ry, trem-bling soul, Just turn to-day to Je - sus; He will re - ceive, for-give and make thee whole— Christ a - lone can set thee free.
3. His blood is all thy plea for sav - ing grace, The pre - cious fount of cleans-ing! O come, ac - cept His love, be - hold His face, And be saved for - ev - er - more.
Chorus
Be - lieve on the Lord Je - sus Christ, Be - lieve on the Lord Je - sus Christ, Be - lieve on the Lord Je - sus Christ, And thou shalt be saved!
Be - lieve
Be - lieve
Be - lieve

Copyright, 1920. Hope Publishing Co., owner

118 My Savior First of All

FANNY J. CROSBY — JNO. R. SWENEY

1. When my life work is end - ed, and I cross the swell-ing tide, When the
2. Oh, the soul-thrill-ing rap-ture when I view His bless-ed face, And the
3. Oh, the dear ones in glo - ry, how they beck-on me to come, And our
4. Thro' the gates to the cit - y in a robe of spot-less white, He will

bright and glorious morning I shall see; I shall know my Re-deem-er when I
lus - ter of His kind-ly beaming eye; How my full heart will praise Him for the
part - ing at the riv - er I re - call; To the sweet vales of E - den they will
lead me where no tears shall ev-er fall; In the glad song of a - ges I shall

reach the oth - er side, And His smile will be the first to wel-come me.
mer - cy, love, and grace, That pre-pares for me a man-sion in the sky.
sing my wel-come home, But I long to meet my Sav - ior first of all.
min - gle with de - light; But I long to meet my Sav - ior first of all.

CHORUS

I shall know . . Him, I shall know Him, As redeemed by His side I shall stand;
I shall know

I shall know . . . Him, I shall know Him By the print of the nails in His hand.
I shall know

Copyright, 1919. Renewal. Hope Publishing Company, owner

To Eternity

Paul Rader
Arthur W. McKee
1. The riv - er of Thy grace is flow - ing free, We launch up - on its
2. The breez - es of Thy love are blow - ing free, They tell Thy love to
3. Thy Spir - it calls to all, "Come home to - day;" Come back and find the
depths to sail to Thee; In the o - cean of Thy love we soon shall
all hu - man - i - ty; They are sing - ing of the blood of Cal - va-
Sav - ior while you may; Find that Je - sus is the Life, the Truth, the
Chorus
be, We are sail - ing to e - ter - ni - ty.
ry, Mak - ing white thro' all e - ter - ni - ty. Earth - ly joys can - not com-
Way, Lead - ing, guid - ing, to e - ter - ni - ty.
pare with all the glo - ry, When our longing eyes shall see Thy face; We shall
have Thy fel - low - ship for - ev - er, In the splendor of the throne of grace.

Copyright, 1916, by Arthur W. McKee. Standard Publishing Co., owner. Used by permission

120 A Shelter in the Time of Storm

Words arranged

IRA D. SANKEY

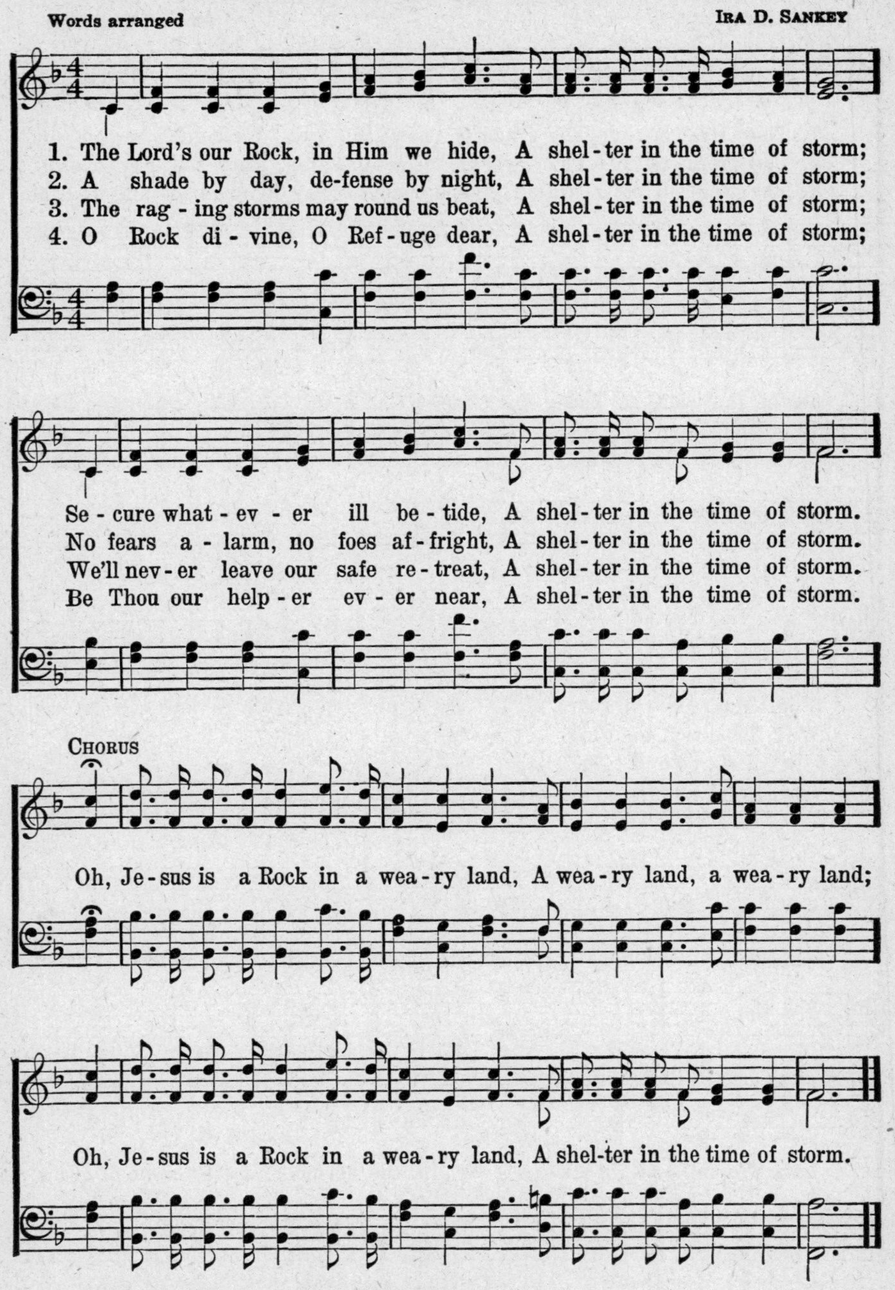
1. The Lord's our Rock, in Him we hide, A shel-ter in the time of storm;
2. A shade by day, de-fense by night, A shel-ter in the time of storm;
3. The rag - ing storms may round us beat, A shel-ter in the time of storm;
4. O Rock di - vine, O Ref-uge dear, A shel-ter in the time of storm;
Se - cure what - ev - er ill be - tide, A shel-ter in the time of storm.
No fears a - larm, no foes af-fright, A shel-ter in the time of storm.
We'll nev - er leave our safe re - treat, A shel-ter in the time of storm.
Be Thou our help - er ev - er near, A shel-ter in the time of storm.
CHORUS
Oh, Je - sus is a Rock in a wea - ry land, A wea - ry land, a wea - ry land;
Oh, Je - sus is a Rock in a wea - ry land, A shel-ter in the time of storm.

Copyright, 1913, Renewal. Hope Publishing Co., owner

Redeemed

FANNY J. CROSBY — WM. J. KIRKPATRICK

1. Redeemed–how I love to pro-claim it! Redeemed by the blood of the Lamb;
2. Redeemed and so happy in Je - sus, No language my rap-ture can tell;
3. I think of my bless-ed Re-deem-er, I think of Him all the day long;
4. I know I shall see in His beau - ty The King in whose law I de - light;

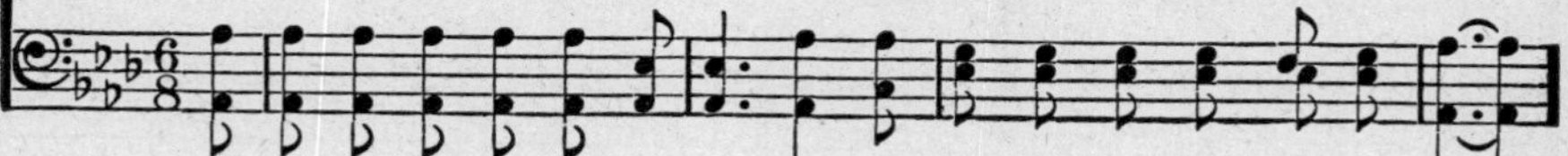

Redeemed thro' His in - fi - nite mer - cy, His child, and for - ev - er, I am.
I know that the light of His presence With me doth con-tin - ual - ly dwell.
I sing, for I can-not be si - lent; His love is the theme of my song.
Who lov - ing - ly guardeth my footsteps, And giv-eth me songs in the night.

CHORUS

Re - deemed, . . re - deemed, . . Redeemed by the blood of the Lamb;
re-deemed, re-deemed,

Re - deemed, . . re - deemed, . . His child, and for - ev - er, I am.
re-deemed, re-deemed,

Trusting Jesus

E. PAGE

IRA D. SANKEY

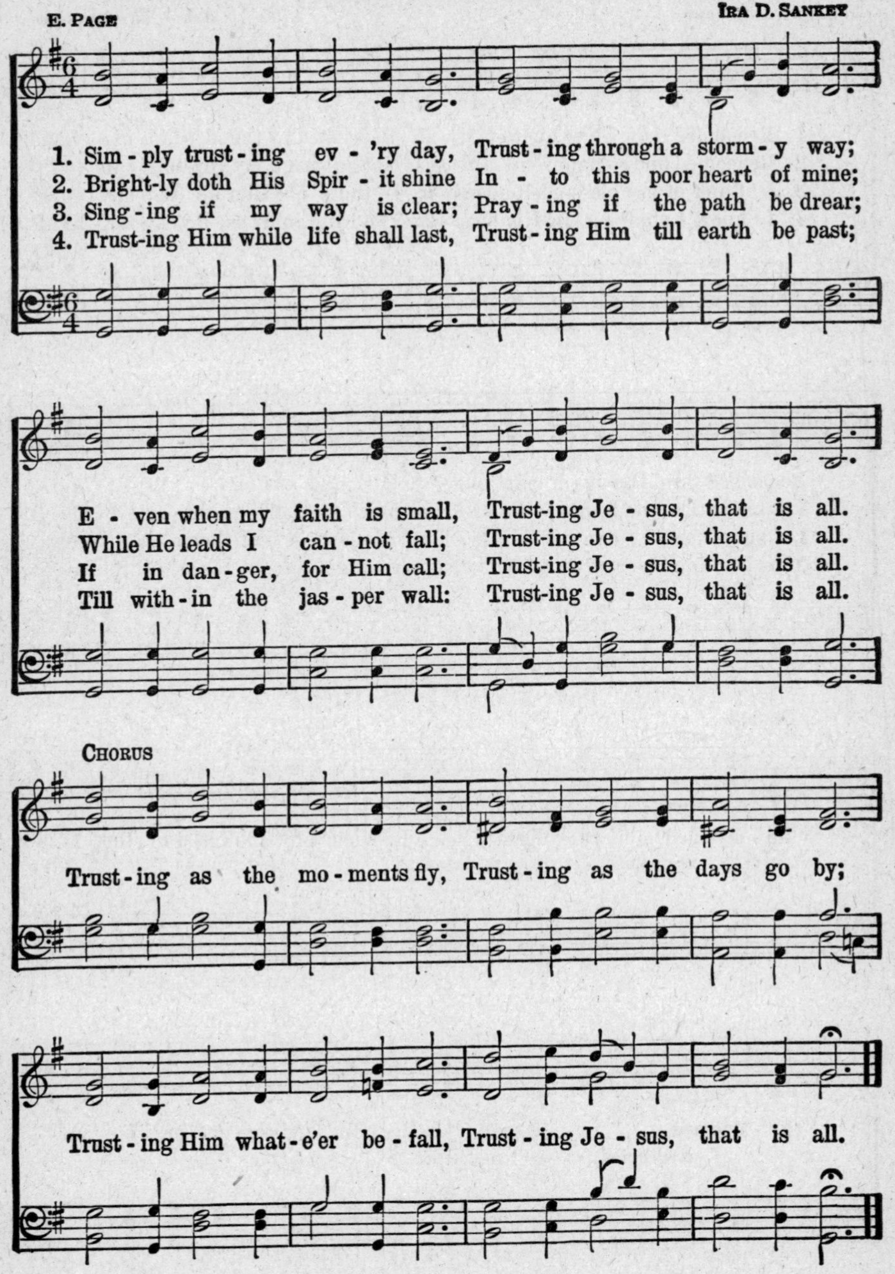
1. Sim - ply trust - ing ev - 'ry day, Trust - ing through a storm - y way;
2. Bright-ly doth His Spir - it shine In - to this poor heart of mine;
3. Sing - ing if my way is clear; Pray - ing if the path be drear;
4. Trust-ing Him while life shall last, Trust - ing Him till earth be past;
E - ven when my faith is small, Trust-ing Je - sus, that is all.
While He leads I can - not fall; Trust-ing Je - sus, that is all.
If in dan - ger, for Him call; Trust-ing Je - sus, that is all.
Till with - in the jas - per wall: Trust-ing Je - sus, that is all.
CHORUS
Trust - ing as the mo - ments fly, Trust - ing as the days go by;
Trust - ing Him what - e'er be - fall, Trust - ing Je - sus, that is all.

Softly and Tenderly

W. L. T. WILL L. THOMPSON

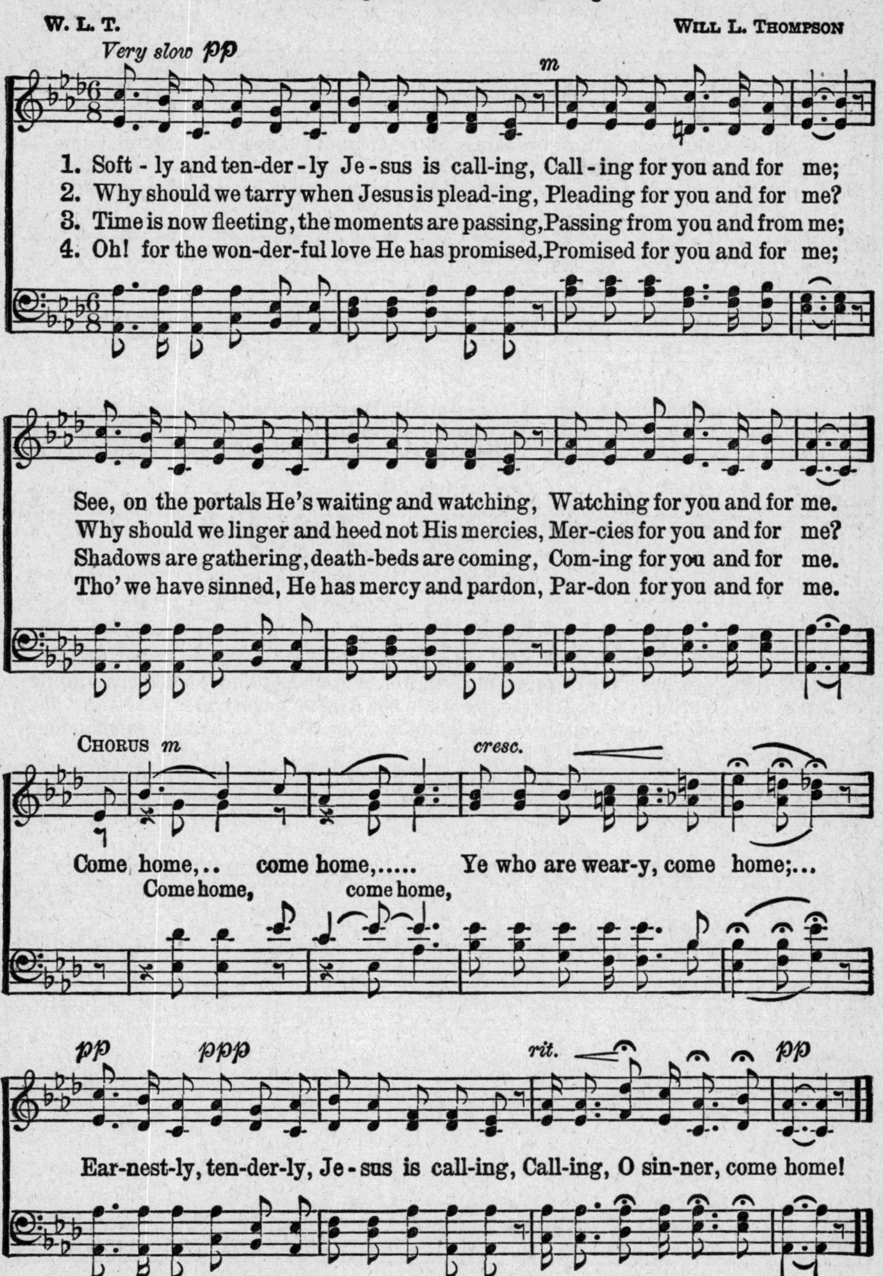
Very slow pp
m
1. Soft - ly and ten-der - ly Je - sus is call-ing, Call - ing for you and for me;
2. Why should we tarry when Jesus is plead-ing, Pleading for you and for me?
3. Time is now fleeting, the moments are passing, Passing from you and from me;
4. Oh! for the won-der-ful love He has promised, Promised for you and for me;
See, on the portals He's waiting and watching, Watching for you and for me.
Why should we linger and heed not His mercies, Mer-cies for you and for me?
Shadows are gathering, death-beds are coming, Com-ing for you and for me.
Tho' we have sinned, He has mercy and pardon, Par-don for you and for me.
CHORUS m
cresc.
Come home,.. come home,...... Ye who are wear-y, come home;...
Come home, come home,
pp ppp rit. pp
Ear-nest-ly, ten-der-ly, Je - sus is call-ing, Call-ing, O sin-ner, come home!

124 In His Keeping

Mrs. C. H. M.
Mrs. C. H. Morris
1. When the ear - ly morning breaking, Slumber from my eye-lids shaking, Comes the
2. Some-times dark clouds hang o'er me, Not one step I see be - fore me, Still, my
3. Gen - tle e - ven-tide is near-ing, Light from heaven dis-ap-pear-ing, Still the
bless-ed tho't with wak-ing, I am in His keep-ing. Day ad-vanc - es, la - bor
Sav - ior, I a - dore Thee, I am in His keep-ing. I can trust His hand to
bless-ed tho't so cheer-ing, I am in His keep-ing. Now night's curtains gather
bring-ing, Care, her mantle 'round me flinging, Yet midst all my soul keeps singing,
guide me, 'Neath His wings He'll safely hide me, And no harm can e'er be-tide me,
'round me, Yet its dan-gers have not found me, For His angel guards surround me,
Chorus
I am in His care. I am in my Father's keeping, I am in His ten-der
care; Wheth-er wak - ing, wheth-er sleep-ing, I am in His care.
rit.

Copyright, 1926, Renewal. Hope Publishing Co., owner

Launch Out 125

A. B. Simpson
R. Kelso Carter
1. The mer - cy of God is an o - cean di - vine, A bound-less and fath - om - less flood; Launch out in the deep, cut a - way the shore - line, And be lost in the full - ness of God.
2. But man - y, a - las! on - ly stand on the shore And gaze on the o - cean so wide; They nev - er have ven - tured its depths to ex - plore, Or to launch on the fath - om - less tide.
3. And oth - ers just ven - ture a - way from the land, And lin - ger so near to the shore, That the surf and the slime that beat o - ver the strand, Dash o'er them in floods ev - er - more.
4. Oh, let us launch out on this o - cean so broad, Where the floods of sal - va - tion e'er flow; Oh, let us be lost in the mer - cy of God, Till the depths of His full - ness we know.
Chorus
Launch out . . . in - to the deep,
Oh, launch out in the deep,
Oh, let the shore-line go,
Launch out, launch out in the o - cean di - vine, Out where the full tides flow.

126 I Belong to the King

IDA L. REED — MAURICE A. CLIFTON

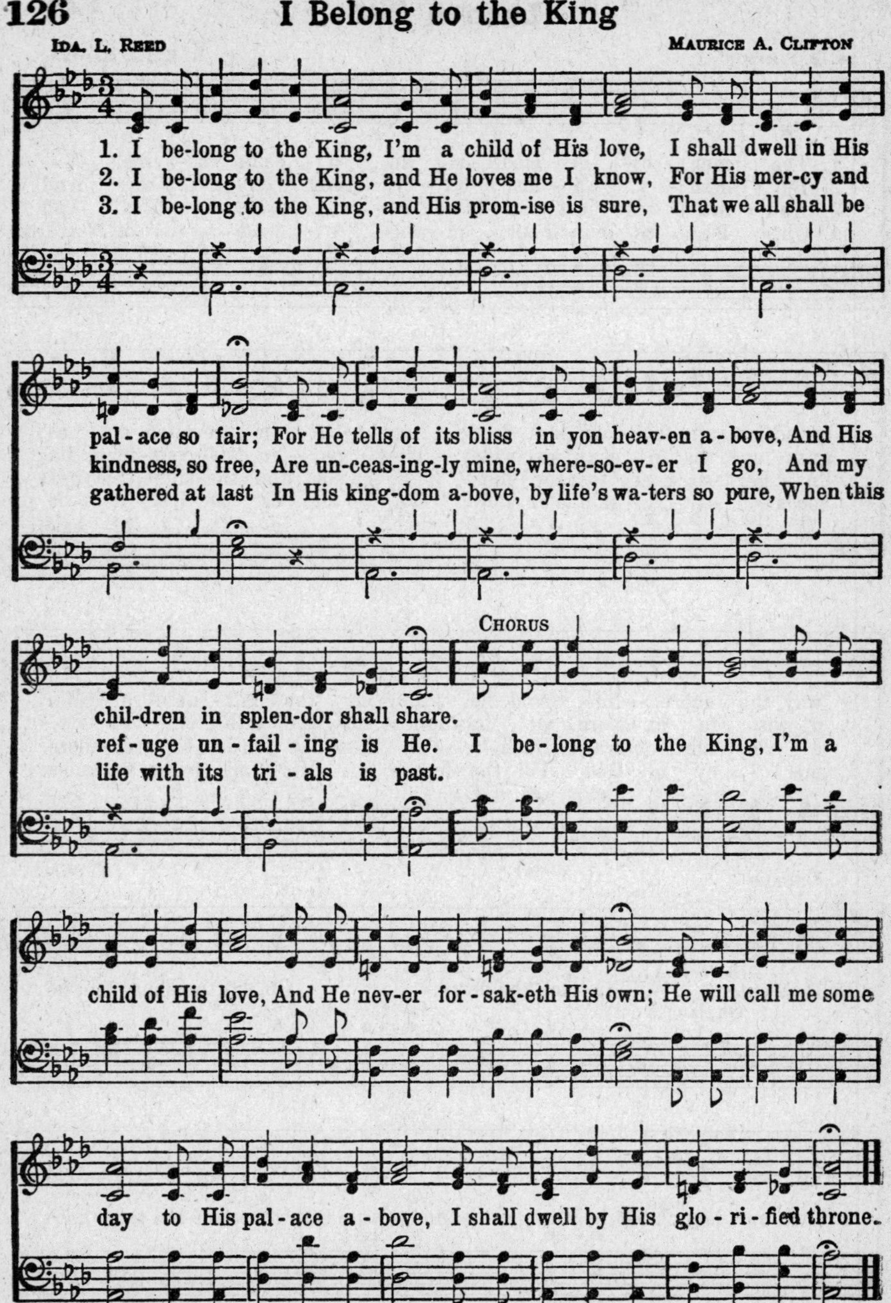
1. I be-long to the King, I'm a child of His love, I shall dwell in His
2. I be-long to the King, and He loves me I know, For His mer-cy and
3. I be-long to the King, and His prom-ise is sure, That we all shall be
pal-ace so fair; For He tells of its bliss in yon heav-en a-bove, And His
kindness, so free, Are un-ceas-ing-ly mine, where-so-ev-er I go, And my
gathered at last In His king-dom a-bove, by life's wa-ters so pure, When this
chil-dren in splen-dor shall share.
ref-uge un-fail-ing is He.
life with its tri-als is past.
CHORUS
I be-long to the King, I'm a
child of His love, And He nev-er for-sak-eth His own; He will call me some
day to His pal-ace a-bove, I shall dwell by His glo-ri-fied throne.

Carry Your Cross With a Smile

INA DULEY OGDON — CHAS. H. GABRIEL

1. Tho' your heart may be heav - y with sor - row and care, You may oth - ers to glad-ness be - guile, If a face like the light of the morning you wear, And car-ry your cross with a smile!
2. Let the well by the way-side that flows un - to all Strength im-part for each step of the mile; Let your faith the great prom-is - es oft - en re-call, And car-ry your cross with a smile!
3. For the work that you faith-ful - ly, will - ing - ly do, You shall reap a re-ward aft - er while; On - ly grace in your serv-ice can glo - ri - fy you, So car-ry your cross with a smile!
CHORUS
Car-ry your cross with a smile,... Car - ry your cross with a smile;... You may oth - ers from sad-ness to glad-ness be-guile, If you car - ry your cross with a smile!
Car - ry your cross with a smile, Car - ry your cross with a smile;

Copyright, 1916, by Homer A. Rodeheaver. International Copyright secured. Used by permission

128 Jesus Saves

PRISCILLA J. OWENS | WM. J. KIRKPATRICK

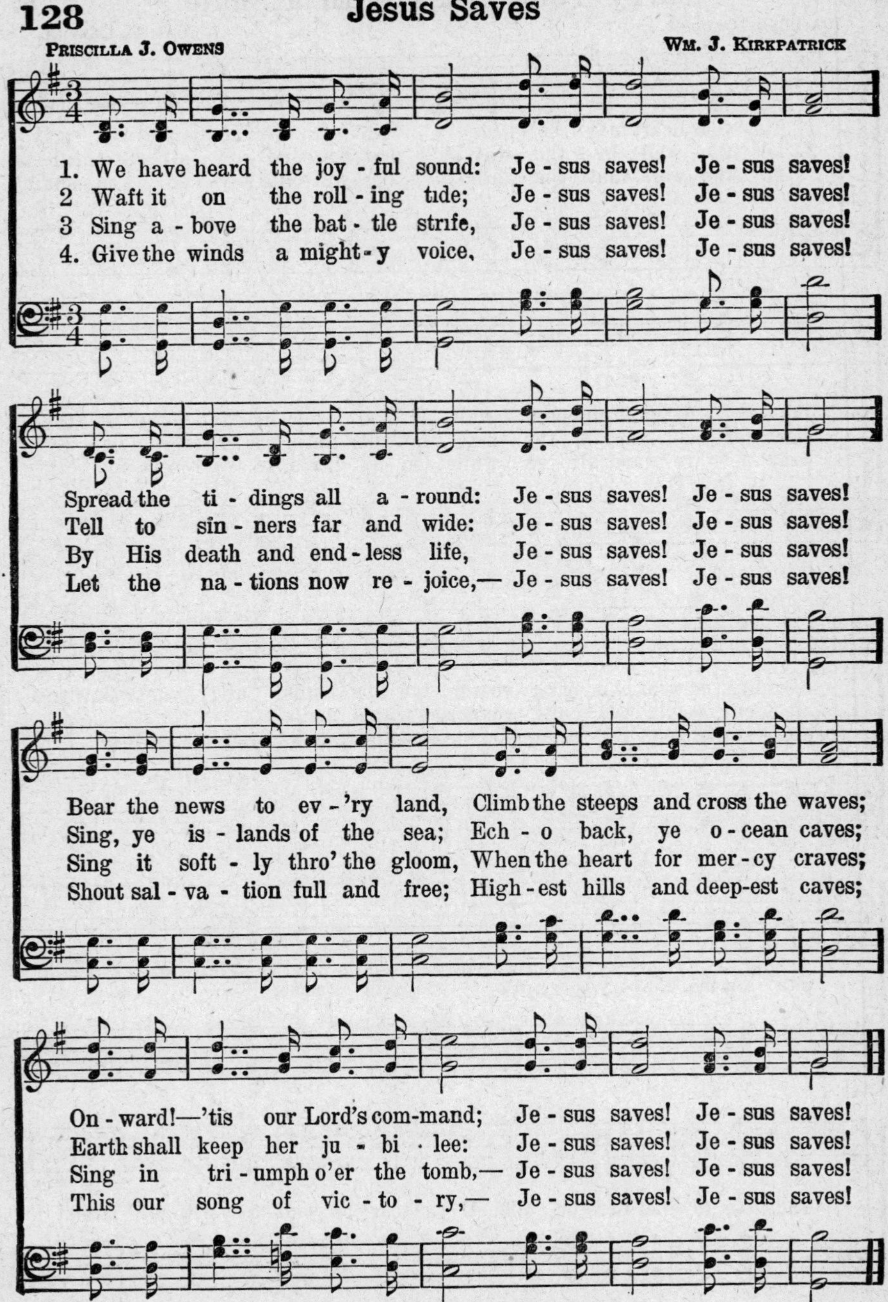
1. We have heard the joy - ful sound: Je - sus saves! Je - sus saves!
2 Waft it on the roll - ing tide; Je - sus saves! Je - sus saves!
3 Sing a - bove the bat - tle strife, Je - sus saves! Je - sus saves!
4. Give the winds a might - y voice, Je - sus saves! Je - sus saves!
Spread the ti - dings all a - round: Je - sus saves! Je - sus saves!
Tell to sin - ners far and wide: Je - sus saves! Je - sus saves!
By His death and end - less life, Je - sus saves! Je - sus saves!
Let the na - tions now re - joice,— Je - sus saves! Je - sus saves!
Bear the news to ev - 'ry land, Climb the steeps and cross the waves;
Sing, ye is - lands of the sea; Ech - o back, ye o - cean caves;
Sing it soft - ly thro' the gloom, When the heart for mer - cy craves;
Shout sal - va - tion full and free; High - est hills and deep-est caves;
On - ward!—'tis our Lord's com - mand; Je - sus saves! Je - sus saves!
Earth shall keep her ju - bi - lee: Je - sus saves! Je - sus saves!
Sing in tri - umph o'er the tomb,— Je - sus saves! Je - sus saves!
This our song of vic - to - ry,— Je - sus saves! Je - sus saves!

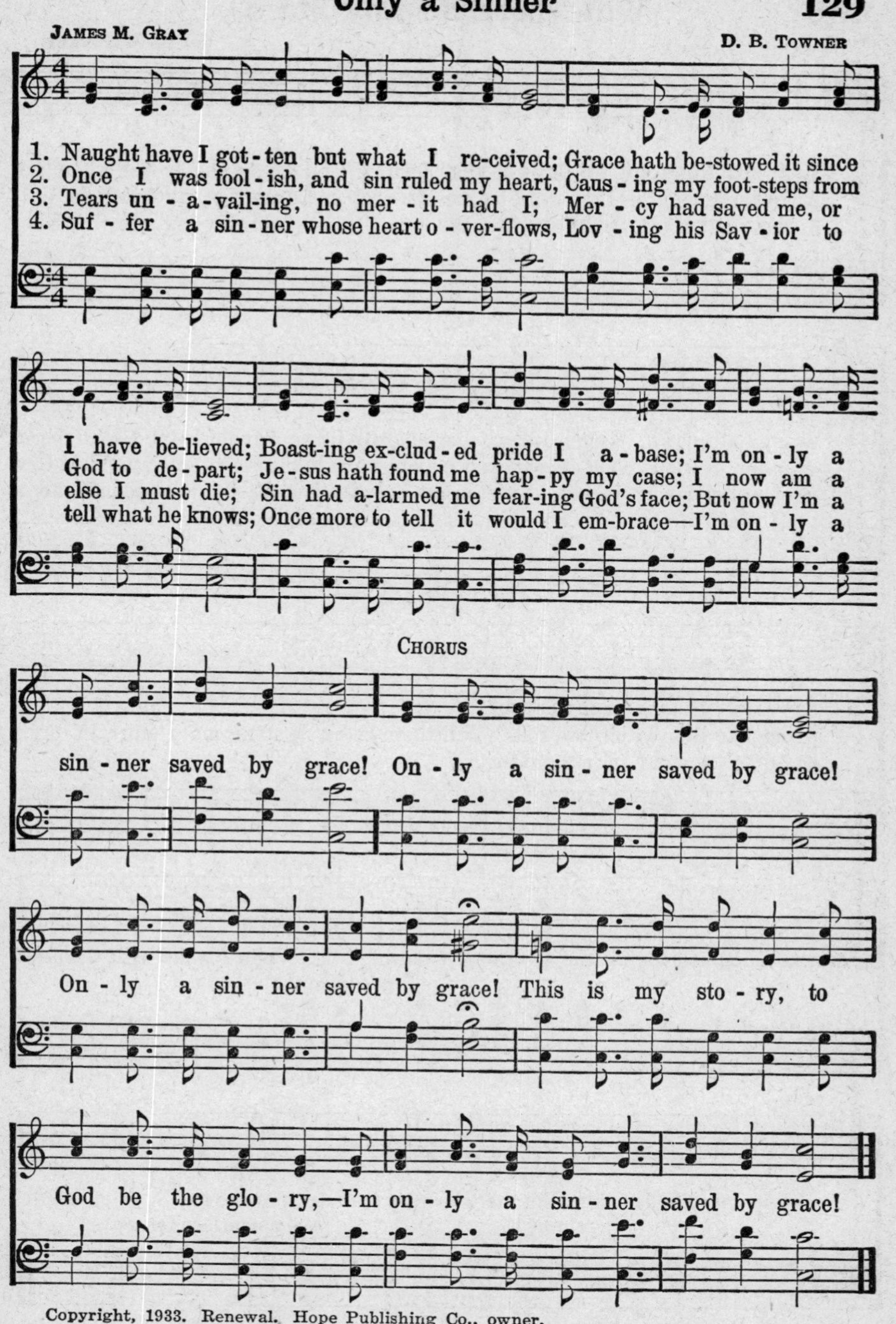
Only a Sinner
129
James M. Gray
D. B. Towner
1. Naught have I got-ten but what I re-ceived; Grace hath be-stowed it since
2. Once I was fool-ish, and sin ruled my heart, Caus-ing my foot-steps from
3. Tears un-a-vail-ing, no mer-it had I; Mer-cy had saved me, or
4. Suf-fer a sin-ner whose heart o-ver-flows, Lov-ing his Sav-ior to
I have be-lieved; Boast-ing ex-clud-ed pride I a-base; I'm on-ly a
God to de-part; Je-sus hath found me hap-py my case; I now am a
else I must die; Sin had a-larmed me fear-ing God's face; But now I'm a
tell what he knows; Once more to tell it would I em-brace—I'm on-ly a
Chorus
sin-ner saved by grace! On-ly a sin-ner saved by grace!
On-ly a sin-ner saved by grace! This is my sto-ry, to
God be the glo-ry,—I'm on-ly a sin-ner saved by grace!

Copyright, 1933. Renewal. Hope Publishing Co., owner.

130 Will There Be Any Stars?

E. E. Hewitt
Jno. R. Sweney
1. I am think-ing to-day of that beau-ti-ful land I shall reach when the
2. In the strength of the Lord let me la-bor and pray, Let me watch as a
3. Oh, what joy it will be when His face I be-hold, Liv-ing gems at His
sun go-eth down; When thro' wonderful grace by my Sav-ior I stand, Will there
win-ner of souls; That bright stars may be mine in the glo-ri-ous day, When His
feet to lay down; It would sweeten my bliss in the cit-y of gold, Should there
be an-y stars in my crown?
praise like the sea-bil-low rolls.
be an-y stars in my crown.
Chorus.
Will there be an-y stars, an-y stars in my
crown When at evening the sun go-eth down? . . . When I wake with the blest
go-eth down?
In the mansions of rest, Will there be an-y stars in my crown? . . A-men.
an-y stars in my crown?

Copyright, 1925. Renewal. Hope Publishing Company, owner.

Jesus Has Lifted Me

Avis B. Christiansen — Haldor Lillenas

1. Out of the depths to the glo - ry a - bove, I have been lift - ed in won - der - ful love; From ev - 'ry fet - ter my spir - it is free— For Je - sus has lift - ed me! . . . .
2. Out of the world in - to heav - en - ly rest, In - to the land of the ran-somed and blest; There in the glo - ry with Him I shall be— For Je - sus has lift - ed me! . . . .
3. Out of my - self in - to Him I a - dore, There to a - bide in His love ev - er - more; Thro' end - less a - ges His glo - ry to see— My Je - sus has lift - ed me! . . . .
lift - ed me!
CHORUS
Je - sus has lift - ed me! . . . Je - sus has lift - ed me! . . .
lift - ed me!
lift - ed me!
Out of the night in - to glo - ri - ous light, Yes, Je - sus has lift - ed me! . . .
lift - ed me!

Copyright, 1918, by Arthur W. McKee. Hope Publishing Co., owner

132 Saved!

OSWALD J. SMITH

ROGER M. HICKMAN

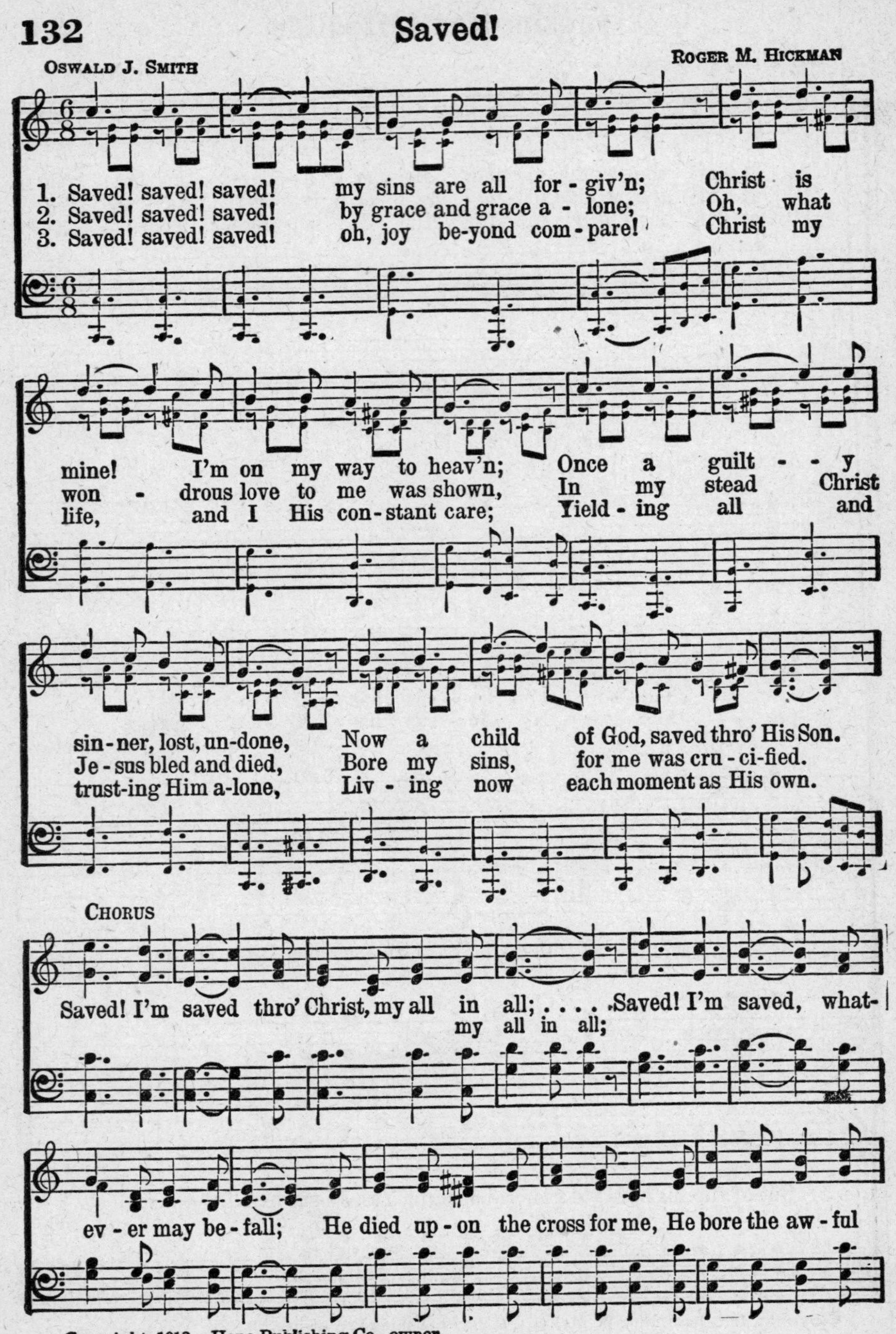
1. Saved! saved! saved! my sins are all for-giv'n; Christ is
2. Saved! saved! saved! by grace and grace a - lone; Oh, what
3. Saved! saved! saved! oh, joy be-yond com-pare! Christ my
mine! I'm on my way to heav'n; Once a guilt - - y
won - drous love to me was shown, In my stead Christ
life, and I His con-stant care; Yield - ing all and
sin-ner, lost, un-done, Now a child of God, saved thro' His Son.
Je - sus bled and died, Bore my sins, for me was cru - ci-fied.
trust-ing Him a-lone, Liv - ing now each moment as His own.
CHORUS
Saved! I'm saved thro' Christ, my all in all; . . . . Saved! I'm saved, what-
my all in all;
ev - er may be - fall; He died up - on the cross for me, He bore the aw - ful

Copyright, 1918. Hope Publishing Co., owner

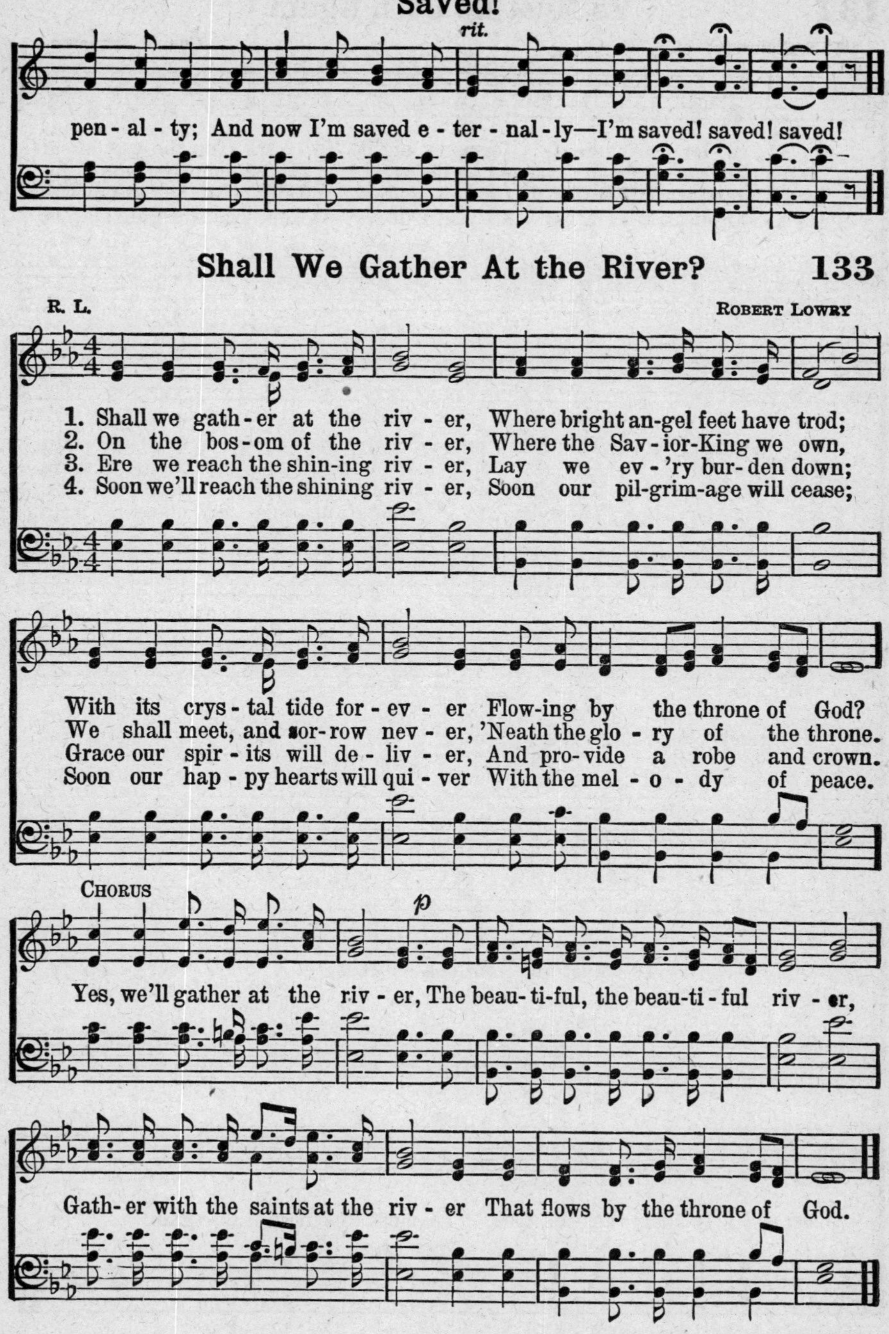
Saved!
rit.
pen - al - ty; And now I'm saved e - ter - nal - ly—I'm saved! saved! saved!
Shall We Gather At the River?
133
R. L.
Robert Lowry
1. Shall we gath - er at the riv - er, Where bright an - gel feet have trod;
2. On the bos - om of the riv - er, Where the Sav - ior-King we own,
3. Ere we reach the shin - ing riv - er, Lay we ev - 'ry bur - den down;
4. Soon we'll reach the shining riv - er, Soon our pil - grim - age will cease;
With its crys - tal tide for - ev - er Flow - ing by the throne of God?
We shall meet, and sor - row nev - er, 'Neath the glo - ry of the throne.
Grace our spir - its will de - liv - er, And pro - vide a robe and crown.
Soon our hap - py hearts will qui - ver With the mel - o - dy of peace.
Chorus
p
Yes, we'll gather at the riv - er, The beau - ti - ful, the beau - ti - ful riv - er,
Gath - er with the saints at the riv - er That flows by the throne of God.

Ye Must Be Born Again

W. T. Sleeper

Geo. C. Stebbins

1 A ru-ler once came to Je-sus by night, To ask Him the way of sal-va-tion and light; The Mas-ter made an-swer in words true and plain,
2. Ye children of men, at-tend to the word So sol-emn-ly ut-tered by Je-sus the Lord; And let not this mes-sage to you be in vain,
3. Oh, ye who would en-ter that glo-ri-ous rest, And sing with the ransomed the song of the blest; The life ev-er-last-ing if ye would ob-tain,
4. A dear one in heaven thy heart yearns to see, At the beautiful gate may be watching for thee; Then list to the note of this sol-emn re-frain,
"Ye must be born a-gain." . . a-gain.
Chorus
"Ye must be born a-gain, . . a-gain, Ye must be born a-gain; . . a-gain; I ver-i-ly, ver-i-ly say un-to thee, Ye must be born a-gain." . . . a-gain.

The Old Rugged Cross

Rev. G. B. Rev. Geo. Bennard

1. On a hill far a-way stood an old rug-ged cross, The em-blem of
2. Oh, that old rug-ged cross so de-spised by the world, Has a wondrous at-
3. In the old rug-ged cross, stained with blood so di-vine, A won-drous
4. To the old rug-ged cross I will ev-er be true, Its shame and re-
suf-f'ring and shame; And I love that old cross where the dear-est and best
trac-tion for me; For the dear Lamb of God left His glo-ry a-bove,
beau-ty I see; For 'twas on that old cross Je-sus suf-fered and died,
proach gladly bear; Then He'll call me some day to my home far a-way,
For a world of lost sin-ners was slain.
To bear it to dark Cal-va-ry.
To par-don and sanc-ti-fy me.
Where His glo-ry for-ev-er I'll share.
CHORUS
So I'll cher-ish the old rug-ged
cross, the
cross,.... Till my tro-phies at last I lay down; I will cling to the
old rugged cross,
old rug-ged cross,...... And ex-change it some day for a crown.
cross, the old rug-ged cross,

Copyright, 1913, by Geo. Bennard. Homer A. Rodeheaver, owner

136 I Am Praying for You

S. O'Maley Cluff | Ira D. Sankey

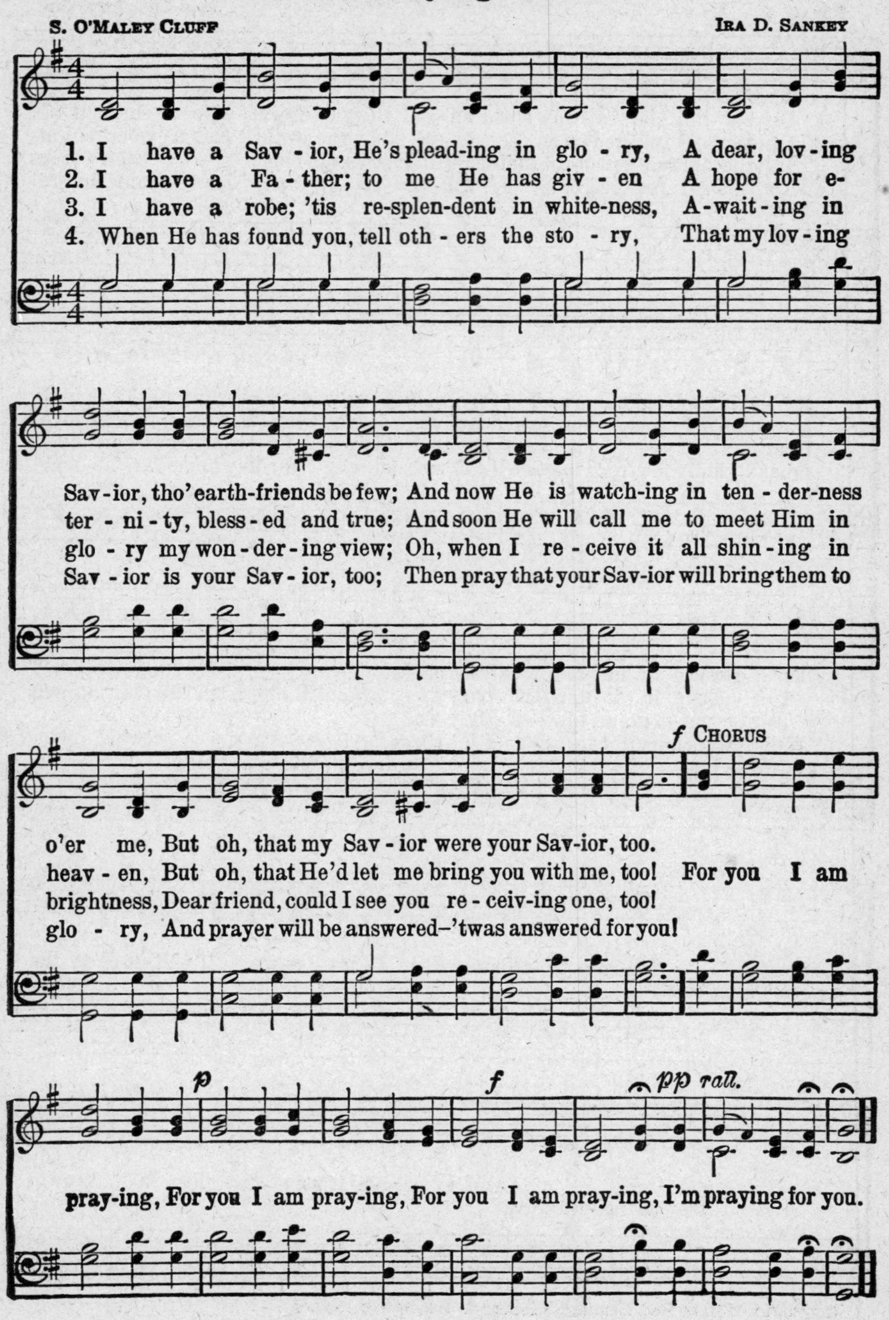

1. I have a Sav - ior, He's plead-ing in glo - ry, A dear, lov-ing Sav-ior, tho' earth-friends be few; And now He is watch-ing in ten - der-ness o'er me, But oh, that my Sav - ior were your Sav-ior, too.
2. I have a Fa - ther; to me He has giv - en A hope for e- ter - ni - ty, bless - ed and true; And soon He will call me to meet Him in heav - en, But oh, that He'd let me bring you with me, too!
3. I have a robe; 'tis re-splen-dent in white-ness, A-wait-ing in glo - ry my won-der-ing view; Oh, when I re - ceive it all shin-ing in brightness, Dear friend, could I see you re - ceiv-ing one, too!
4. When He has found you, tell oth - ers the sto - ry, That my lov-ing Sav - ior is your Sav - ior, too; Then pray that your Sav-ior will bring them to glo - ry, And prayer will be answered—'twas answered for you!
f CHORUS
For you I am pray-ing, For you I am pray-ing, For you I am pray-ing, I'm praying for you.
p
f
pp rall.

I Would Be Like Jesus

James Rowe — B. D. Ackley

1. Earth-ly pleas-ures vain-ly call me; I would be like Je-sus;
2. He has bro-ken ev-'ry fet-ter, I would be like Je-sus;
3. All the way from earth to Glo-ry, I would be like Je-sus;
4. That in Heav-en He may meet me, I would be like Je-sus;
would be like Je-sus;
Noth-ing world-ly shall en-thrall me; I would be like Je-sus.
That my soul may serve Him bet-ter, I would be like Je-sus.
Tell-ing o'er and o'er the sto-ry, I would be like Je-sus.
That His words "Well done" may greet me, I would be like Je-sus.
would be like Je-sus.
Chorus.
Be like Je-sus, this my song, In the home and in the throng;
Be like Je-sus, all day long! I would be like Je-sus. A-men.

Copyright, 1940. Renewal. The Rodeheaver Co., owner. Used by permission

138
One Day!
Rev. J. Wilbur Chapman, D.D.
Chas. H. Marsh
1. One day when heav - en was filled with His prais - es, One day when
2. One day they led Him up Cal - va - ry's moun-tain, One day they
3. One day they left Him a - lone in the gar - den, One day He
4. One day the grave could con - ceal Him no lon - ger, One day the
5. One day the trump - et will sound for His com - ing, One day the
sin was as black as could be,... Je - sus came forth to be
nailed Him to die on the tree;.. Suf - fer - ing an - guish, de-
rest - ed, from suf - fer - ing free;.. An - gels came down o'er His
stone rolled a - way from the door;. Then He a - rose, o - ver
skies with His glo - ries will shine; Won-der - ful day, my be-
born of a vir - gin—Dwelt amongst men, my ex - am - ple is He!...
spised and re - ject - ed: Bear - ing our sins, my Re - deem - er is He!...
tomb to keep vig - il; Hope of the hope - less, my Sav - ior is He!...
death He had con - quered; Now is as - cend - ed, my Lord ev - er - more!.
lov - ed ones bring - ing; Glo - ri - ous Sav - ior, this Je - sus is mine!.
Chorus
Liv - ing, He loved me; dy - ing, He saved me; Bur - ied, He
car - ried my sins far a - way;.. Ris - ing, He jus - ti - fied

Copyright, 1938. Renewal. The Rodeheaver Co., owner. Used by permission.

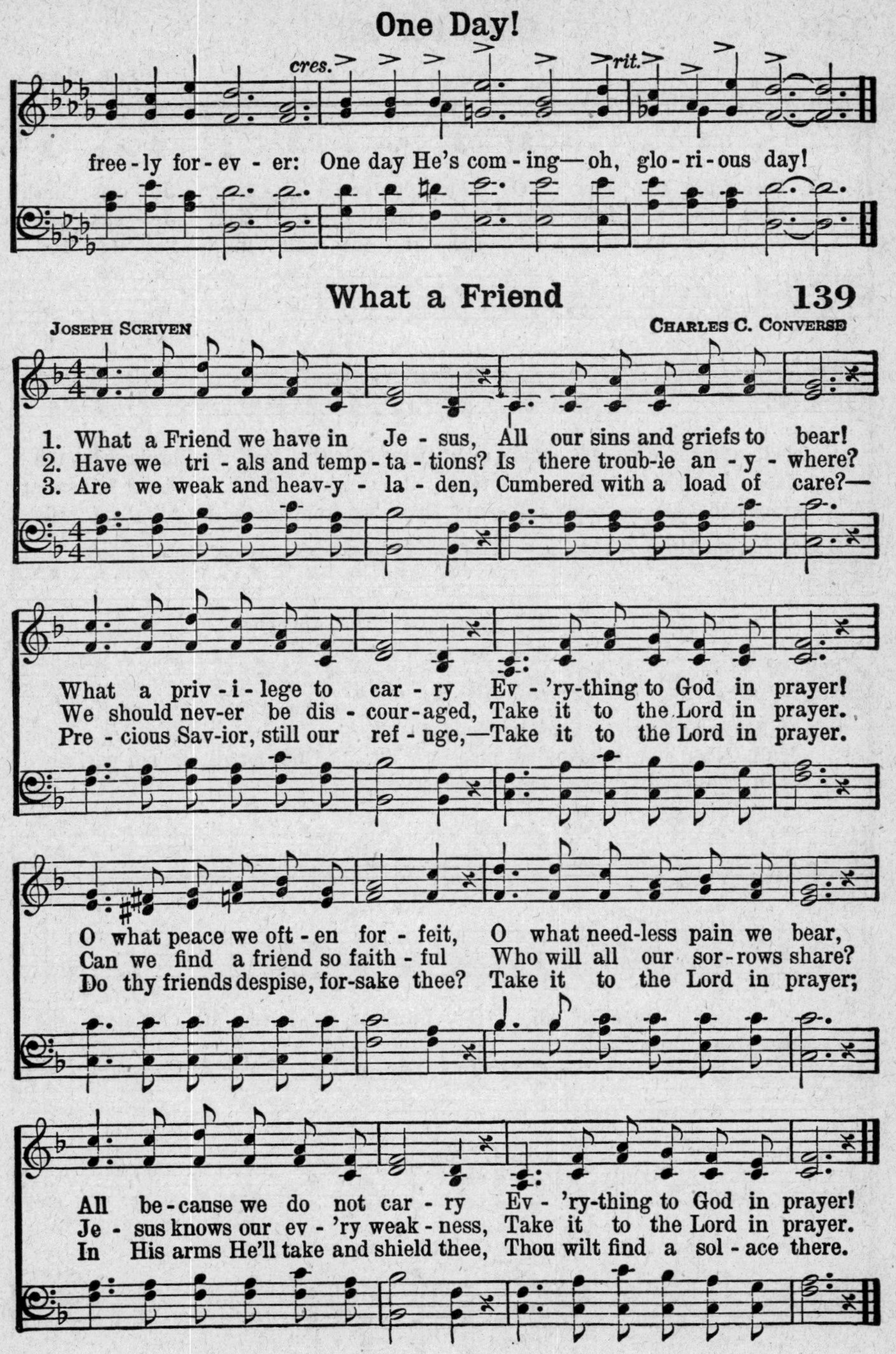
One Day!
cres.
rit.
free-ly for-ev-er: One day He's com-ing—oh, glo-ri-ous day!
What a Friend
139
Joseph Scriven
Charles C. Converse
1. What a Friend we have in Je-sus, All our sins and griefs to bear!
2. Have we tri-als and temp-ta-tions? Is there troub-le an-y-where?
3. Are we weak and heav-y-la-den, Cumbered with a load of care?—
What a priv-i-lege to car-ry Ev-'ry-thing to God in prayer!
We should nev-er be dis-cour-aged, Take it to the Lord in prayer.
Pre-cious Sav-ior, still our ref-uge,—Take it to the Lord in prayer.
O what peace we oft-en for-feit, O what need-less pain we bear,
Can we find a friend so faith-ful Who will all our sor-rows share?
Do thy friends despise, for-sake thee? Take it to the Lord in prayer;
All be-cause we do not car-ry Ev-'ry-thing to God in prayer!
Je-sus knows our ev-'ry weak-ness, Take it to the Lord in prayer.
In His arms He'll take and shield thee, Thou wilt find a sol-ace there.

Once For All

P. P. B. | P. P. BLISS

1. Free from the law, O hap-py con-di-tion, Je-sus hath bled, and there is re-mis-sion; Cursed by the law and bruised by the fall, Grace hath redeemed us once for all.
2. Now are we free—there's no con-dem-na-tion, Je-sus pro-vides a per-fect sal-va-tion; "Come un-to Me," O hear His sweet call, Come, and He saves us once for all.
3. "Chil-dren of God," O glo-ri-ous call-ing, Sure-ly His grace will keep us from fall-ing; Pass-ing from death to life at His call, Bless-ed sal-va-tion once for all.
CHORUS
Once for all, O sin-ner, re-ceive it, Once for all, O broth-er, be-lieve it; Cling to the Cross, the bur-den will fall, Christ hath re-deemed us once for all.

What Will You Do With Jesus? 141

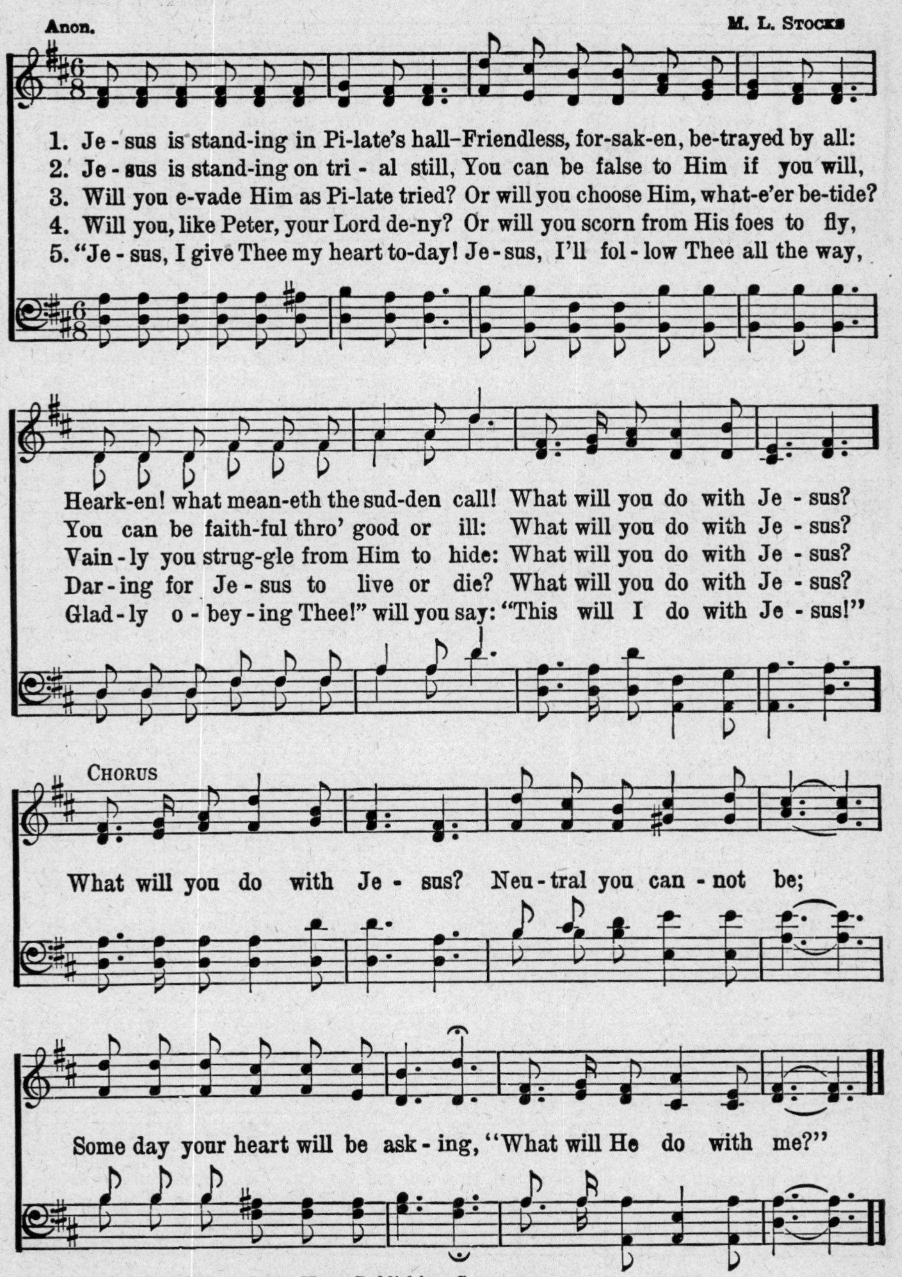
Anon.
M. L. Stocks
1. Je - sus is stand-ing in Pi-late's hall–Friendless, for-sak-en, be-trayed by all:
2. Je - sus is stand-ing on tri - al still, You can be false to Him if you will,
3. Will you e-vade Him as Pi-late tried? Or will you choose Him, what-e'er be-tide?
4. Will you, like Peter, your Lord de-ny? Or will you scorn from His foes to fly,
5. "Je - sus, I give Thee my heart to-day! Je - sus, I'll fol - low Thee all the way,
Heark-en! what mean-eth the sud-den call! What will you do with Je - sus?
You can be faith-ful thro' good or ill: What will you do with Je - sus?
Vain - ly you strug-gle from Him to hide: What will you do with Je - sus?
Dar - ing for Je - sus to live or die? What will you do with Je - sus?
Glad - ly o - bey - ing Thee!" will you say: "This will I do with Je - sus!"
Chorus
What will you do with Je - sus? Neu - tral you can - not be;
Some day your heart will be ask - ing, "What will He do with me?"

Copyright, 1933. Renewal. Hope Publishing Co., owner.

142 I Love to Tell the Story

Catherine Hankey — William G. Fischer

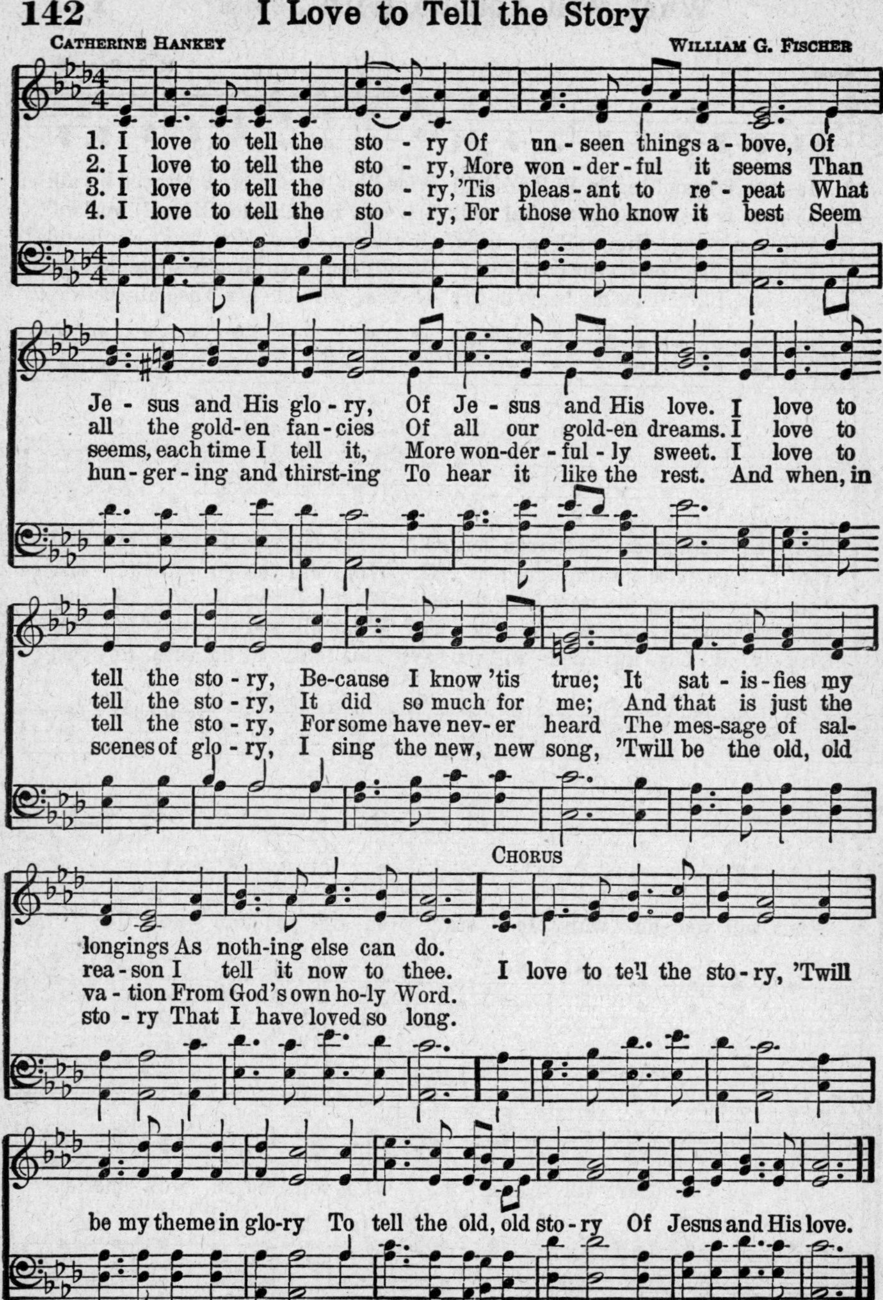
1. I love to tell the sto - ry Of un - seen things a - bove, Of
2. I love to tell the sto - ry, More won - der - ful it seems Than
3. I love to tell the sto - ry, 'Tis pleas - ant to re - peat What
4. I love to tell the sto - ry, For those who know it best Seem
Je - sus and His glo - ry, Of Je - sus and His love. I love to
all the gold - en fan - cies Of all our gold - en dreams. I love to
seems, each time I tell it, More won - der - ful - ly sweet. I love to
hun - ger - ing and thirst - ing To hear it like the rest. And when, in
tell the sto - ry, Be - cause I know 'tis true; It sat - is - fies my
tell the sto - ry, It did so much for me; And that is just the
tell the sto - ry, For some have nev - er heard The mes - sage of sal -
scenes of glo - ry, I sing the new, new song, 'Twill be the old, old
Chorus
longings As noth - ing else can do.
rea - son I tell it now to thee. I love to tell the sto - ry, 'Twill
va - tion From God's own ho - ly Word.
sto - ry That I have loved so long.
be my theme in glo - ry To tell the old, old sto - ry Of Jesus and His love.

True-Hearted, Whole-Hearted

FRANCES R. HAVERGAL — GEO. C. STEBBINS

1. True-hearted, whole-hearted, faith-ful and loy - al, King of our lives, by Thy grace we will be; Un-der the standard ex - alt - ed and roy - al, Strong in Thy strength we will bat-tle for Thee.
2. True-hearted, whole-hearted, full-est al - le-giance Yielding henceforth to our glo - ri - ous King; Val-iant en-deav-or and lov - ing o-be-dience, Free - ly and joy - ous - ly now would we bring.
3. True-hearted, whole-hearted, Sav - ior all - glo-rious! Take Thy great pow-er and reign there a - lone, O - ver our wills and af-fec-tions vic-to-rious, Free - ly sur-ren-dered and whol-ly Thine own.
CHORUS
Peal out the watch-word! si - lence it nev-er!
Song of our spir-its, re - joic - ing and free;
Peal out the watch-word! loy - al for - ev - er,
King of our lives, by Thy grace we will be.

Copyright, 1916, by Geo. C. Stebbins. Renewal. Hope Publishing Co., owner

144 What If It Were To-day?

Mrs. C. H. M. Mrs. C. H. Morris

1. Je - sus is com-ing to earth a-gain, What if it were to - day?
2. Sa-tan's do-min-ion will then be o'er, O that it were to - day!
3. Faith-ful and true would He find us here If He should come to - day?
Com-ing in pow-er and love to reign, What if it were to - day?
Sor - row and sigh-ing shall be no more, O that it were to - day!
Watching in glad-ness and not in fear, If He should come to - day?
Com-ing to claim His cho - sen Bride, All the re-deemed and pu - ri - fied,
Then shall the dead in Christ a - rise, Caught up to meet Him in the skies,
Signs of His com - ing mul - ti - ply, Morning light breaks in east-ern sky,
rit.
a tempo
O - ver this whole earth scat - tered wide, What if it were to - day?
When shall these glo - ries meet our eyes? What if it were to - day?
Watch, for the time is draw - ing nigh, What if it were to - day?
Chorus
Glo - ry, glo - ry! Joy to my heart 'twill bring;.. Glo - ry, glo - ry!
Joy to my heart 'twill bring;

Copyright, 1940, Renewal. Hope Publishing Co., owner.

What If It Were To-day?

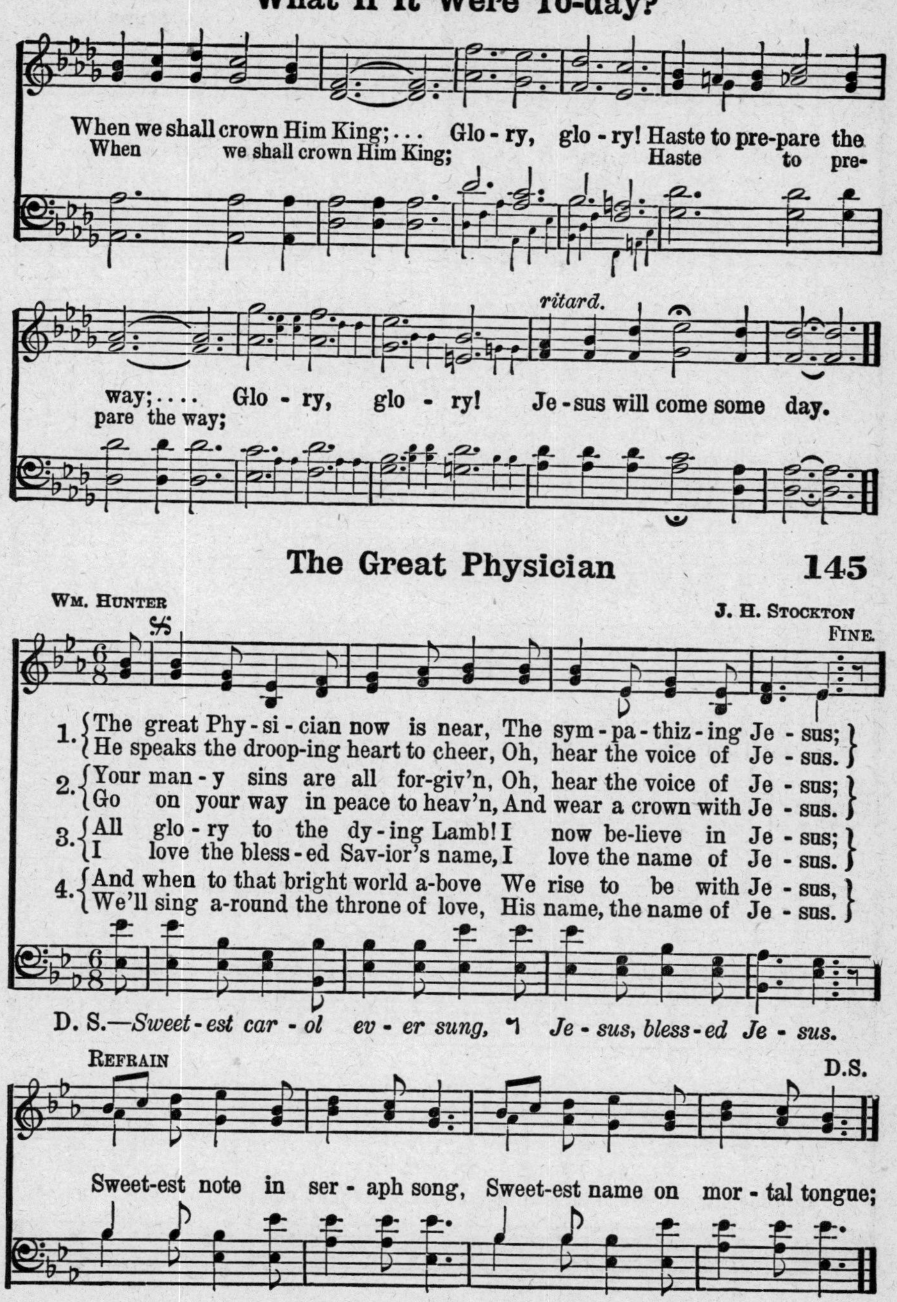
When we shall crown Him King; . . . Glo - ry, glo - ry! Haste to pre-pare the
When we shall crown Him King; Haste to pre-
way; . . . . Glo - ry, glo - ry! Je - sus will come some day.
pare the way;
ritard.
The Great Physician
145
Wm. Hunter
J. H. Stockton
Fine.
1. {The great Phy - si - cian now is near, The sym - pa - thiz - ing Je - sus;
He speaks the droop-ing heart to cheer, Oh, hear the voice of Je - sus.}
2. {Your man - y sins are all for-giv'n, Oh, hear the voice of Je - sus;
Go on your way in peace to heav'n, And wear a crown with Je - sus.}
3. {All glo - ry to the dy - ing Lamb! I now be-lieve in Je - sus;
I love the bless - ed Sav-ior's name, I love the name of Je - sus.}
4. {And when to that bright world a-bove We rise to be with Je - sus,
We'll sing a-round the throne of love, His name, the name of Je - sus.}
D. S.—Sweet - est car - ol ev - er sung, Je - sus, bless - ed Je - sus.
Refrain
D.S.
Sweet-est note in ser - aph song, Sweet-est name on mor - tal tongue;

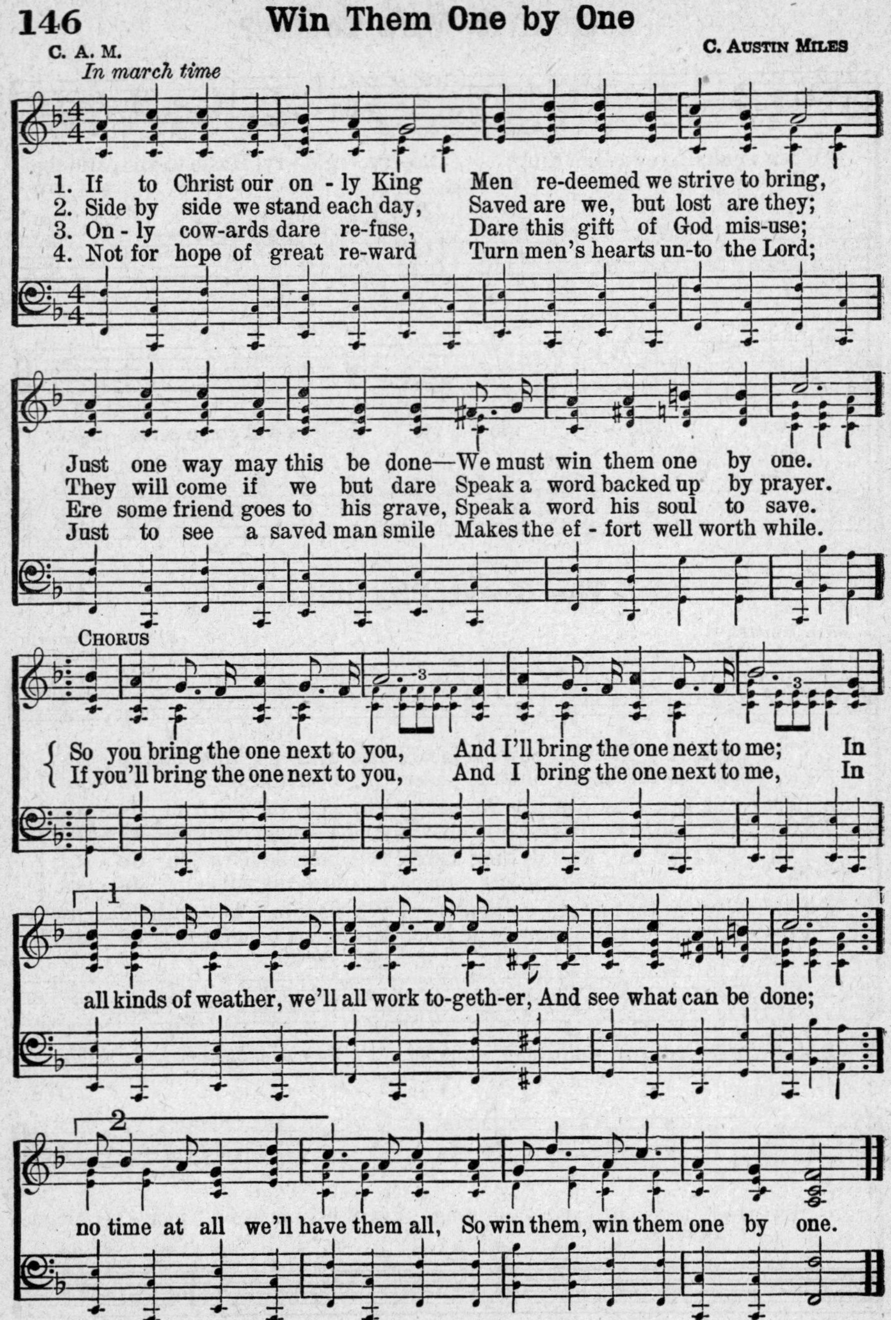
146
Win Them One by One
C. A. M.
C. Austin Miles
In march time
1. If to Christ our on - ly King Men re-deemed we strive to bring,
2. Side by side we stand each day, Saved are we, but lost are they;
3. On - ly cow-ards dare re-fuse, Dare this gift of God mis-use;
4. Not for hope of great re-ward Turn men's hearts un-to the Lord;
Just one way may this be done—We must win them one by one.
They will come if we but dare Speak a word backed up by prayer.
Ere some friend goes to his grave, Speak a word his soul to save.
Just to see a saved man smile Makes the ef - fort well worth while.
Chorus
So you bring the one next to you, And I'll bring the one next to me; In
If you'll bring the one next to you, And I bring the one next to me, In
1
all kinds of weather, we'll all work to-geth-er, And see what can be done;
2
no time at all we'll have them all, So win them, win them one by one.

Copyright, 1915. Rodeheaver Co., owner. Used by permission.

Saved By the Blood

S. J. HENDERSON — D. B. TOWNER

1. Saved by the blood of the Cru - ci - fied One! Now Ran - somed from
2. Saved by the blood of the Cru - ci - fied One! The an - gels re-
3. Saved by the blood of the Cru - ci - fied One! The Fa - ther He
4. Saved by the blood of the Cru - ci - fied One! All hail to the
sin and a new work be - gun, Sing praise to the Fa - ther and
joic - ing be-cause it is done; A child of the Fa - ther, joint-
spake, and His will it was done; Great price of my par - don, His
Fa - ther, all hail to the Son, All hail to the Spir - it, the
praise to the Son, Saved by the blood of the Cru - ci - fied One!
heir with the Son, Saved by the blood of the Cru - ci - fied One!
own pre-cious Son; Saved by the blood of the Cru - ci - fied One!
great Three in One! Saved by the blood of the Cru - ci - fied One!
CHORUS
Saved! . . saved! . . My sins are all pardoned my guilt is all gone!
Glo - ry, I'm saved! glo - ry, I'm saved!
Saved! . . saved! . . I am saved by the blood of the Cru-ci-fied One!
Glo - ry, I'm saved! glo - ry, I'm saved!

Copyright, 1931, Renewal. Hope Publishing Co., owner

148 We've a Story to Tell

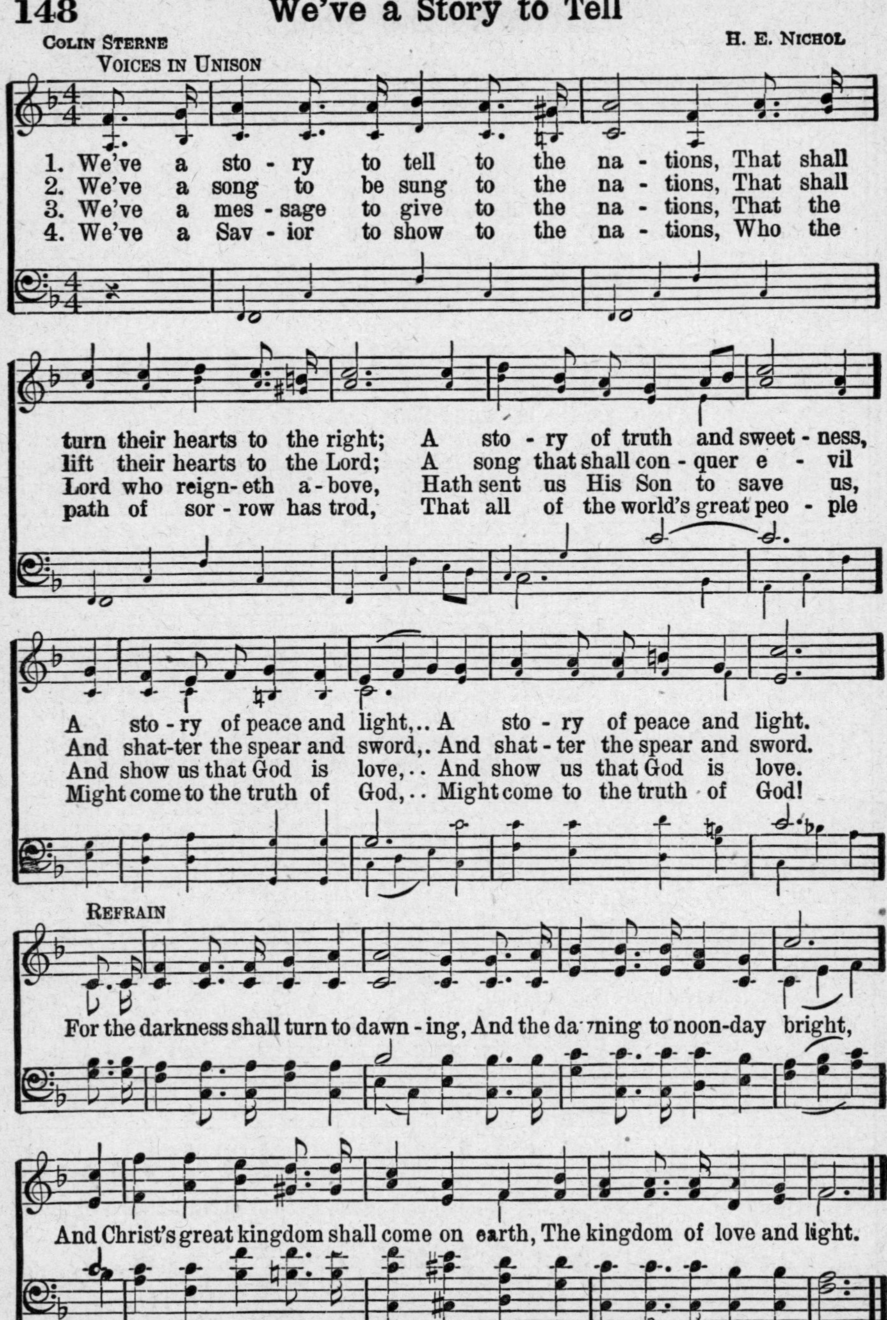
COLIN STERNE
H. E. NICHOL
VOICES IN UNISON
1. We've a sto - ry to tell to the na - tions, That shall turn their hearts to the right; A sto - ry of truth and sweet - ness, A sto - ry of peace and light,.. A sto - ry of peace and light.
2. We've a song to be sung to the na - tions, That shall lift their hearts to the Lord; A song that shall con - quer e - vil And shat-ter the spear and sword,. And shat - ter the spear and sword.
3. We've a mes - sage to give to the na - tions, That the Lord who reign-eth a - bove, Hath sent us His Son to save us, And show us that God is love,.. And show us that God is love.
4. We've a Sav - ior to show to the na - tions, Who the path of sor - row has trod, That all of the world's great peo - ple Might come to the truth of God,.. Might come to the truth of God!
REFRAIN
For the darkness shall turn to dawn - ing, And the dawning to noon-day bright,
And Christ's great kingdom shall come on earth, The kingdom of love and light.

Wonderful Peace

W. D. Cornell. Alt.
W. G. Cooper
1. Far a - way in the depths of my spir - it to - night Rolls a
2. What a treas - ure I have in this won - der - ful peace, Bur - ied
3. I am rest - ing to - night in this won - der - ful peace, Rest-ing
4. And me-thinks when I rise to that Cit - y of peace, Where the
5. Ah! soul, are you here with-out com - fort or rest, March-ing
mel - o - dy sweet-er than psalm; In ce - les - tial-like strains it un-
deep in the heart of my soul; So se - cure that no pow - er can
sweet-ly in Je - sus' con - trol; For I'm kept from all dan - ger by
Au - thor of peace I shall see, That one strain of the song which the
down the rough pathway of time? Make Je - sus your friend ere the
ceas - ing - ly falls O'er my soul like an in - fi - nite calm.
mine it a - way, While the years of e - ter - ni - ty roll.
night and by day, And His glo - ry is flood - ing my soul.
ran - somed will sing, In that heav - en - ly king - dom shall be:
shad - ows grow dark; Oh, ac - cept this sweet peace so sub - lime.
Chorus
Peace! peace! won-der-ful peace, Com-ing down from the Fa-ther a - bove; Sweep
o - ver my spir-it for - ev-er, I pray, In fath-om-less bil-lows of love.

Copyright, 1920, by W. G. Cooper. Renewal. Hope Publishing Co., owner

150 I'm Abiding in Canaan Land

Avis Burgeson — Haldor Lillenas

1. I'm a-bid-ing to-day in Ca-naan land, In the sun-light of God's love;
2. 'Tis a fore-taste of com-ing glo-ry yon-der In that Land beyond the sky,
3. Won't you enter the Land of peace and blessing, And its rapture with me share?
And the Savior's face ev-er shines before me As I jour-ney to my home a-bove.
Where in bliss un-told I shall ev-er wan-der In the bless-ed homeland by and by.
All your sin and guilt to the Lord confessing, You will have a blessed welcome there.
CHORUS
I'm a-bid-ing in Ca-naan Land! . . . . . I'm a-bid-ing in Ca-naan
in Ca-naan Land!
Land!
in Ca-naan Land!
1
Since He washed my sin a-way, It is glo-ry all the way,
I'm a-bid-ing in Ca-naan Land! . . .
Ca-naan Land!
2
All my sins have been for-giv'n,

Copyright, 1918. Hope Publishing Company, owner.

I'm Abiding in Canaan Land

And I'm on my way to heav'n, I'm a - bid - ing in Ca - naan Land!

Saved through Jesus' Blood
151
J. W. Van de Venter
J. W. Van de Venter
1. Some-time we'll stand be-fore the judgment bar, The quick, the ris - en dead;
2. I'll then re-ceive a bright and star-ry crown, As on - ly God can give;
3. Then we shall meet to nev - er part a - gain, Our toil will then be o'er;
The Lord will then make known the rec-ord there; Our names will all be read.
And when I've been with Him ten thousand years, I'll have no less to live.
We'll lay our bur-dens down at Je - sus' feet, And rest for ev - er-more.
Chorus
I'll be present when the roll is called, Pure and spotless thro' the
I'll be present, I'll be
I'll be pure
crim-son flood; I will answer when they call my name; Saved thro' Jesus' blood.
I will answer, I will

Copyright, 1927. Renewal by J. W. Van De Venter.
The Rodeheaver Company, owner. Used by permission

152 You May Have the Joy-bells
J. Edw. Ruark
Wm. J. Kirkpatrick
1. You may have the joy-bells ring-ing in your heart, And a peace that from you nev-er will de-part; Walk the straight and nar-row way, Live for Je-sus ev-'ry day, He will keep the joy-bells ringing in your heart.
2. Love of Je-sus in its full-ness you may know, And this love to those a-round you sweet-ly show; Words of kind-ness al-ways say, Deeds of mer-cy do each day, Then He'll keep the joy-bells ringing in your heart.
3. You will meet with tri-als as you jour-ney home; Grace suf-fi-cient He will give to o-ver-come; Tho' un-seen by mor-tal eye, He is with you ev-er nigh, And He'll keep the joy-bells ringing in your heart.
4. Let your life speak well of Je-sus ev-'ry day; Own His right to ev-'ry serv-ice you can pay; Sin-ners you can help to win If your life is pure and clean, And you keep the joy-bells ringing in your heart.
Fine
Chorus
D. S.—He will keep the joy-bells ring-ing in your heart.
Joy - - - bells ring-ing in your heart, Joy - - - - bells
Ring-ing in your heart, You may have the joy-bells
ringing in your heart; Take the Sav-ior here below With you ev'rywhere you go;
D.S.

Copyright, 1927, Renewal. Hope Publishing Co., owner

Moment By Moment

D. W. WHITTLE | MAY WHITTLE MOODY

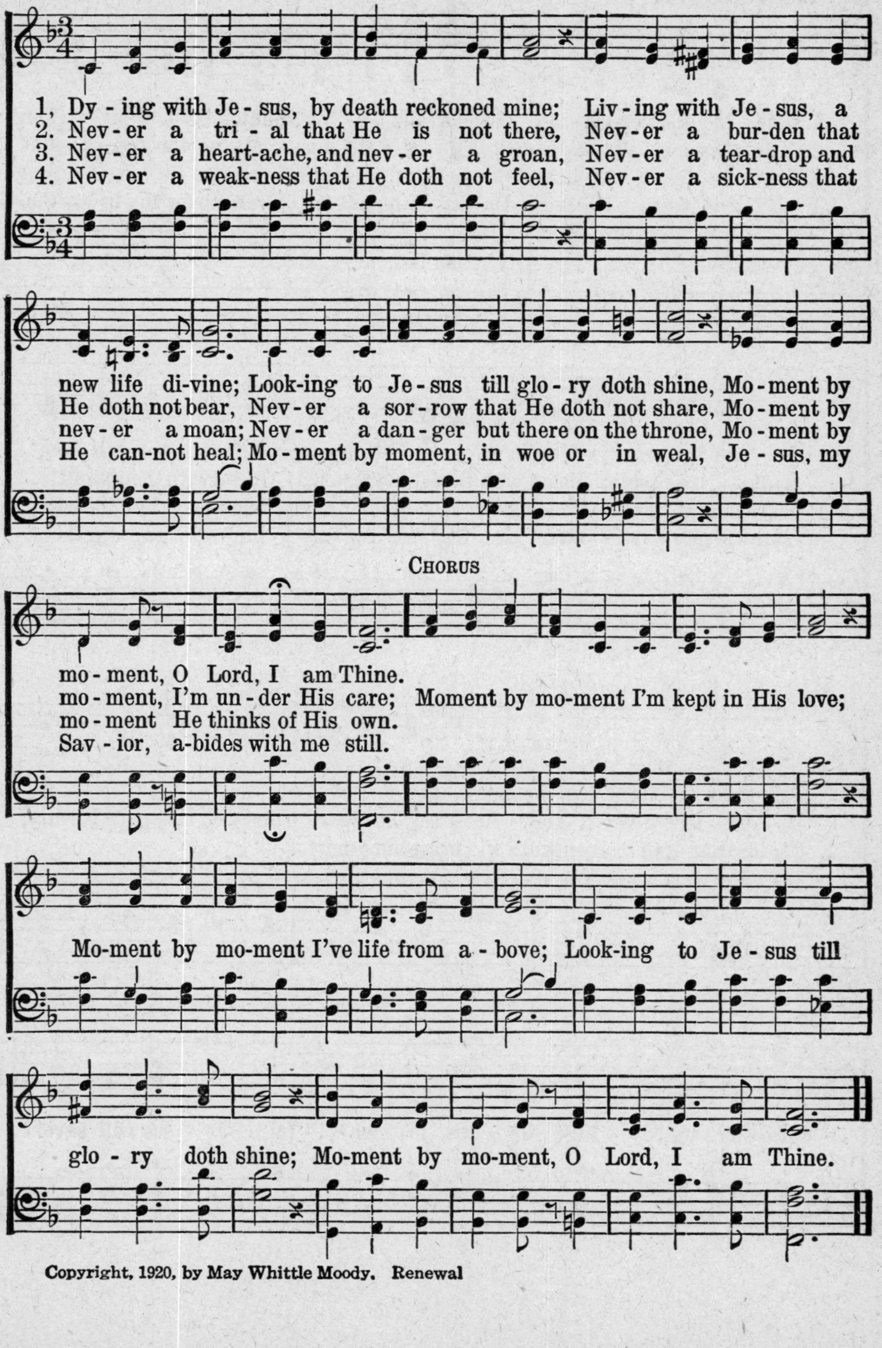

1, Dy - ing with Je - sus, by death reckoned mine; Liv - ing with Je - sus, a new life di-vine; Look-ing to Je - sus till glo - ry doth shine, Mo - ment by mo - ment, O Lord, I am Thine.

2. Nev - er a tri - al that He is not there, Nev - er a bur-den that He doth not bear, Nev - er a sor - row that He doth not share, Mo - ment by mo - ment, I'm un - der His care;

3. Nev - er a heart-ache, and nev - er a groan, Nev - er a tear-drop and nev - er a moan; Nev - er a dan - ger but there on the throne, Mo - ment by mo - ment He thinks of His own.

4. Nev - er a weak-ness that He doth not feel, Nev - er a sick-ness that He can-not heal; Mo - ment by moment, in woe or in weal, Je - sus, my Sav - ior, a-bides with me still.

CHORUS

Moment by mo-ment I'm kept in His love; Mo-ment by mo-ment I've life from a - bove; Look-ing to Je - sus till glo - ry doth shine; Mo-ment by mo-ment, O Lord, I am Thine.

Copyright, 1920, by May Whittle Moody. Renewal

154 Rescue the Perishing

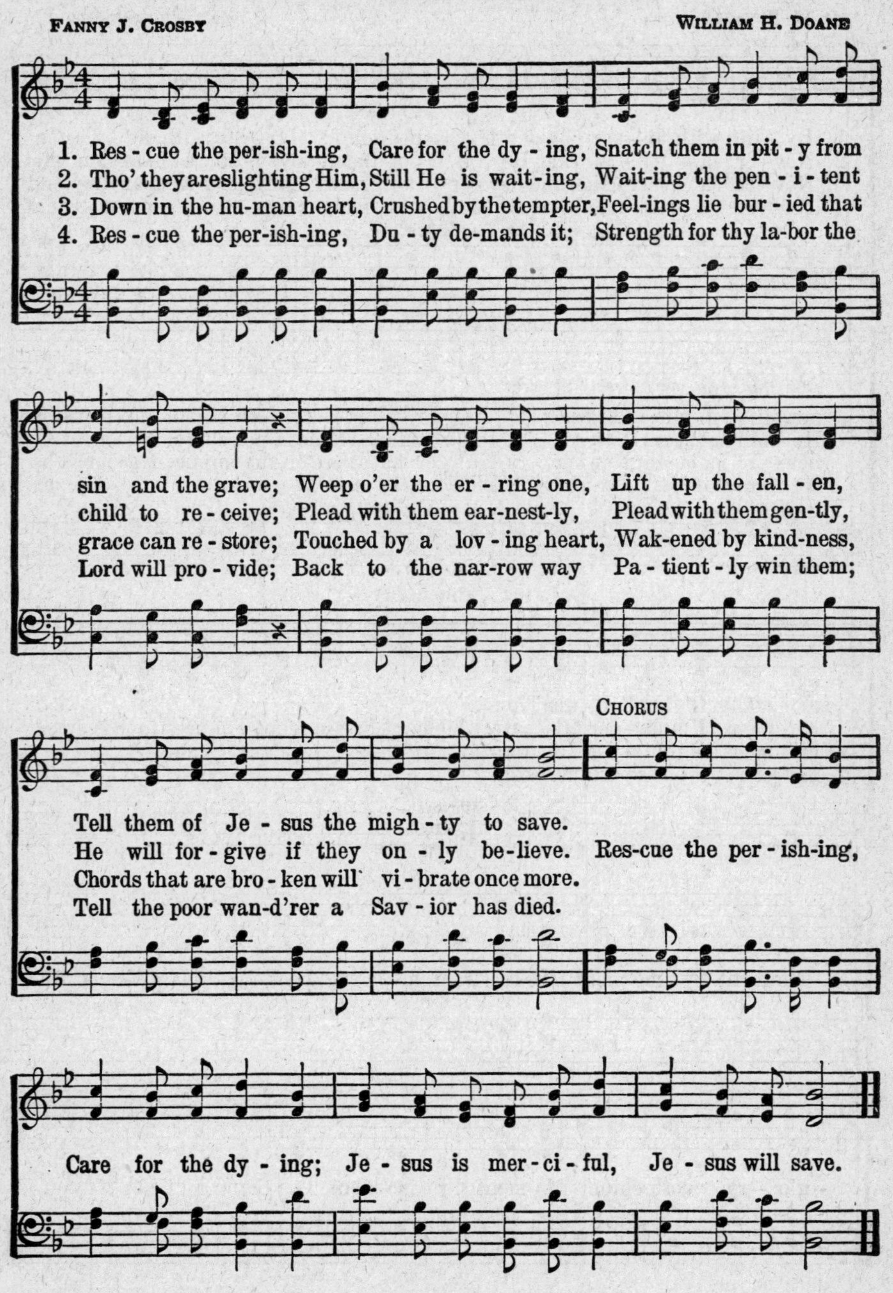
Fanny J. Crosby
William H. Doane
1. Res - cue the per-ish-ing, Care for the dy - ing, Snatch them in pit - y from
2. Tho' they are slighting Him, Still He is wait-ing, Wait-ing the pen - i - tent
3. Down in the hu-man heart, Crushed by the tempter, Feel-ings lie bur - ied that
4. Res - cue the per-ish-ing, Du - ty de-mands it; Strength for thy la-bor the
sin and the grave; Weep o'er the er - ring one, Lift up the fall - en,
child to re - ceive; Plead with them ear-nest-ly, Plead with them gen-tly,
grace can re - store; Touched by a lov - ing heart, Wak-ened by kind-ness,
Lord will pro - vide; Back to the nar-row way Pa - tient - ly win them;
Chorus
Tell them of Je - sus the migh - ty to save.
He will for - give if they on - ly be-lieve. Res-cue the per - ish-ing,
Chords that are bro - ken will vi - brate once more.
Tell the poor wan-d'rer a Sav - ior has died.
Care for the dy - ing; Je - sus is mer - ci - ful, Je - sus will save.

The Old-Time Fire

W. H. BATHURST (arr.)

D. B. TOWNER
Arr. by Fred Jacky

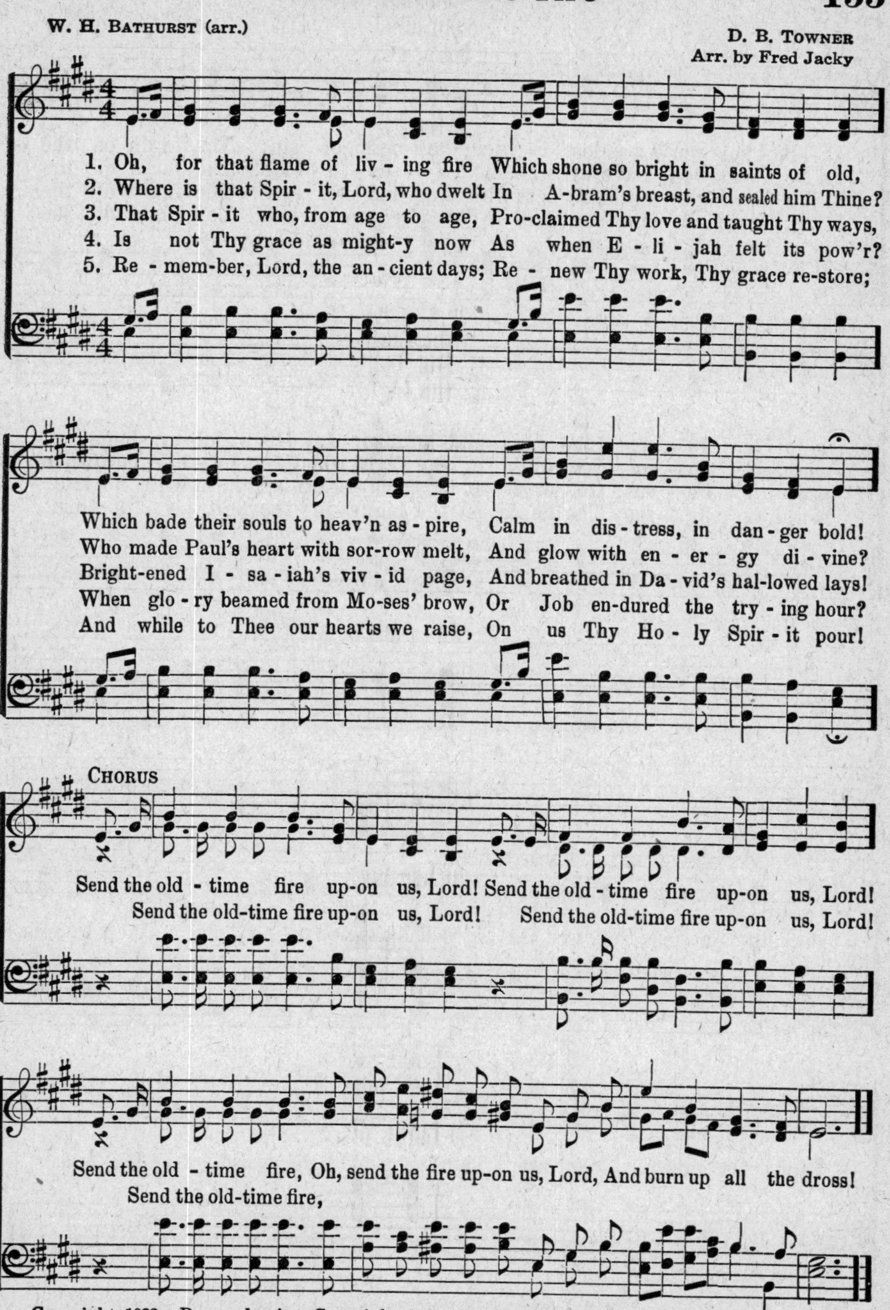
1. Oh, for that flame of liv - ing fire Which shone so bright in saints of old,
2. Where is that Spir - it, Lord, who dwelt In A-bram's breast, and sealed him Thine?
3. That Spir - it who, from age to age, Pro-claimed Thy love and taught Thy ways,
4. Is not Thy grace as might-y now As when E - li - jah felt its pow'r?
5. Re - mem-ber, Lord, the an - cient days; Re - new Thy work, Thy grace re-store;
Which bade their souls to heav'n as - pire, Calm in dis - tress, in dan - ger bold!
Who made Paul's heart with sor-row melt, And glow with en - er - gy di - vine?
Bright-ened I - sa - iah's viv - id page, And breathed in Da - vid's hal-lowed lays!
When glo - ry beamed from Mo-ses' brow, Or Job en-dured the try - ing hour?
And while to Thee our hearts we raise, On us Thy Ho - ly Spir - it pour!
CHORUS
Send the old - time fire up-on us, Lord! Send the old - time fire up-on us, Lord!
Send the old-time fire up-on us, Lord! Send the old-time fire up-on us, Lord!
Send the old - time fire, Oh, send the fire up-on us, Lord, And burn up all the dross!
Send the old-time fire,

Copyright, 1933. Renewal. Arr. Copyright, 1941. Hope Publishing Company, owner

156 The Light of the World is Jesus

P. P. B. | P. P. Bliss

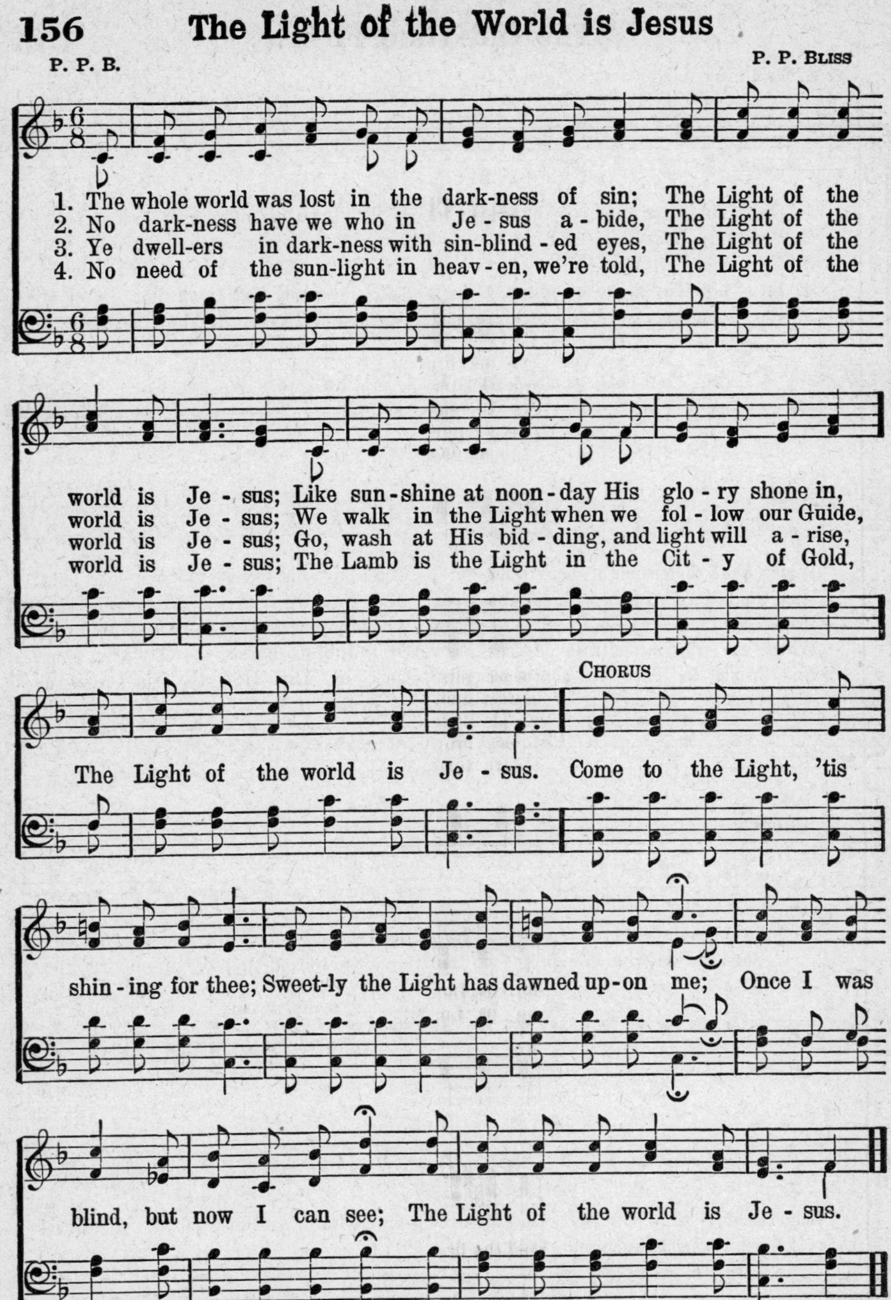
1. The whole world was lost in the dark-ness of sin; The Light of the
2. No dark-ness have we who in Je - sus a - bide, The Light of the
3. Ye dwell-ers in dark-ness with sin-blind - ed eyes, The Light of the
4. No need of the sun-light in heav - en, we're told, The Light of the
world is Je - sus; Like sun - shine at noon - day His glo - ry shone in,
world is Je - sus; We walk in the Light when we fol - low our Guide,
world is Je - sus; Go, wash at His bid - ding, and light will a - rise,
world is Je - sus; The Lamb is the Light in the Cit - y of Gold,
The Light of the world is Je - sus.
Chorus
Come to the Light, 'tis shin - ing for thee; Sweet-ly the Light has dawned up - on me; Once I was blind, but now I can see; The Light of the world is Je - sus.

The Old-Fashioned Way

Mrs. C. D. Martin — W. Stillman Martin

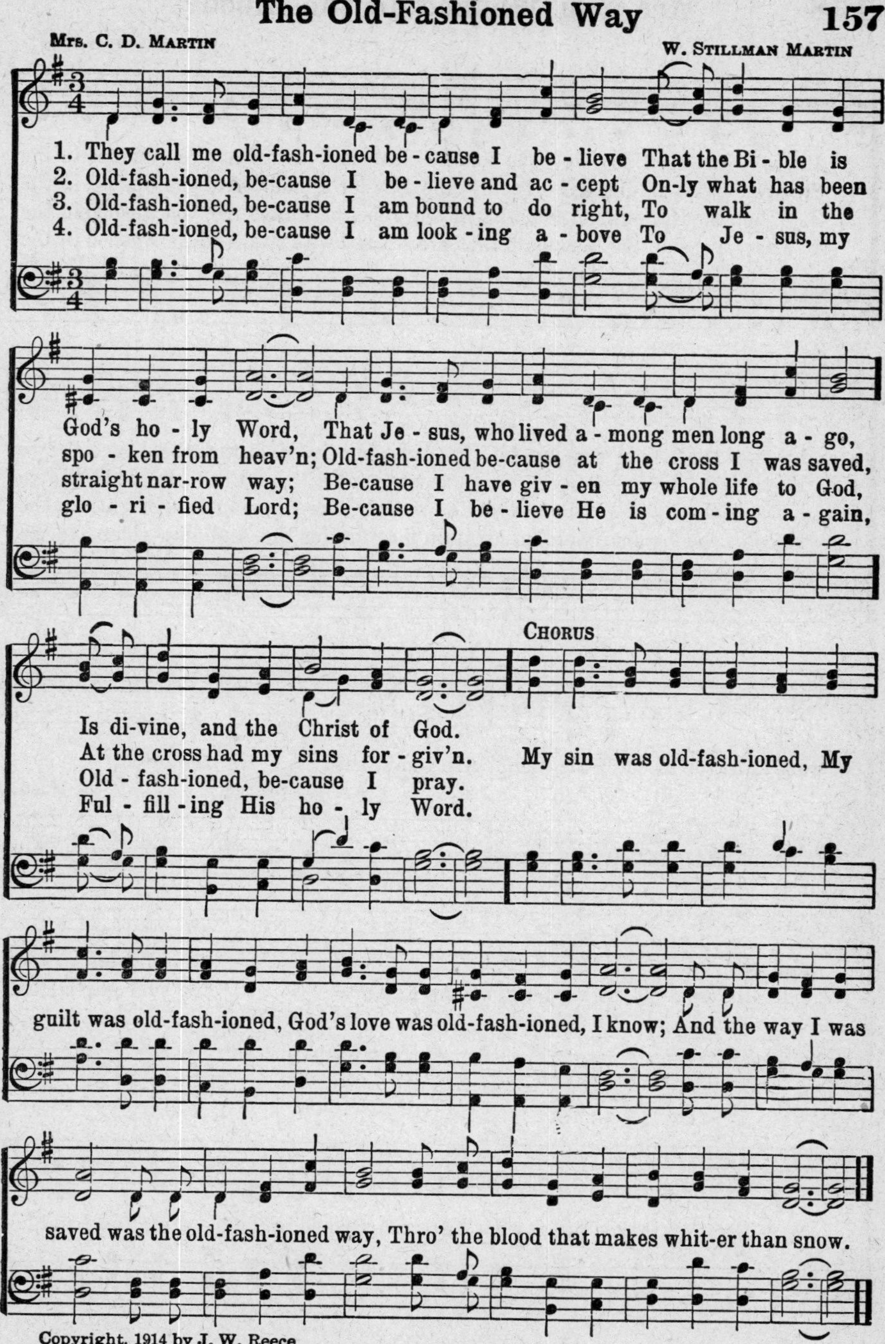
1. They call me old-fash-ioned be-cause I be-lieve That the Bi-ble is God's ho-ly Word, That Je-sus, who lived a-mong men long a-go, Is di-vine, and the Christ of God.
2. Old-fash-ioned, be-cause I be-lieve and ac-cept On-ly what has been spo-ken from heav'n; Old-fash-ioned be-cause at the cross I was saved, At the cross had my sins for-giv'n.
3. Old-fash-ioned, be-cause I am bound to do right, To walk in the straight nar-row way; Be-cause I have giv-en my whole life to God, Old-fash-ioned, be-cause I pray.
4. Old-fash-ioned, be-cause I am look-ing a-bove To Je-sus, my glo-ri-fied Lord; Be-cause I be-lieve He is com-ing a-gain, Ful-fill-ing His ho-ly Word.
Chorus
My sin was old-fash-ioned, My guilt was old-fash-ioned, God's love was old-fash-ioned, I know; And the way I was saved was the old-fash-ioned way, Thro' the blood that makes whit-er than snow.

Copyright, 1914 by J. W. Reece

158 Are You Washed In the Blood?

E. A. H. — Elisha A. Hoffman

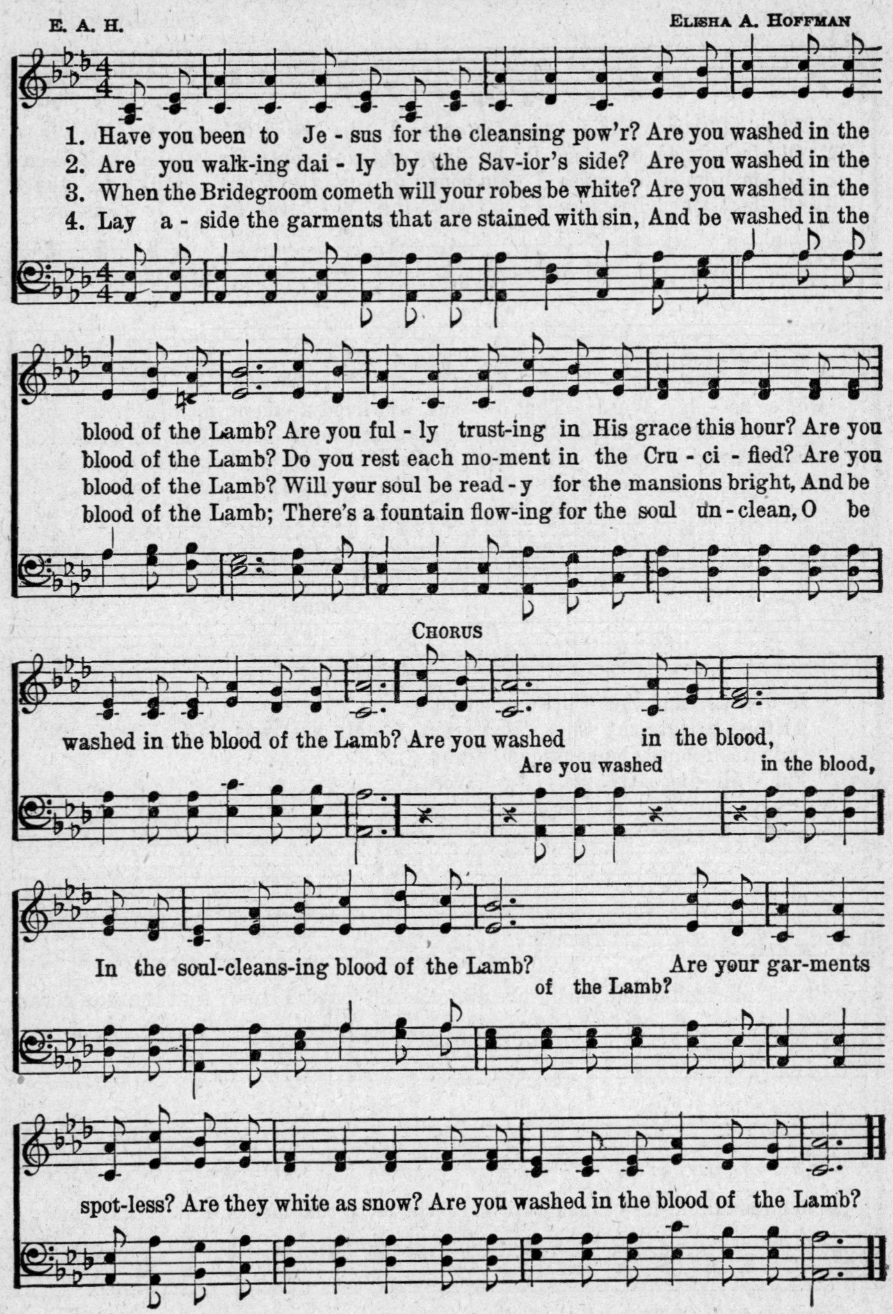
1. Have you been to Je - sus for the cleansing pow'r? Are you washed in the
2. Are you walk-ing dai - ly by the Sav-ior's side? Are you washed in the
3. When the Bridegroom cometh will your robes be white? Are you washed in the
4. Lay a - side the garments that are stained with sin, And be washed in the
blood of the Lamb? Are you ful - ly trust-ing in His grace this hour? Are you
blood of the Lamb? Do you rest each mo-ment in the Cru - ci - fied? Are you
blood of the Lamb? Will your soul be read - y for the mansions bright, And be
blood of the Lamb; There's a fountain flow-ing for the soul un - clean, O be
Chorus
washed in the blood of the Lamb? Are you washed in the blood,
Are you washed in the blood,
In the soul-cleans-ing blood of the Lamb? Are your gar-ments
of the Lamb?
spot-less? Are they white as snow? Are you washed in the blood of the Lamb?

Verily, Verily

G. M. J.
JAMES MCGRANAHAN
1. Oh, what a Sav - ior, that He died for me! From con - dem - na - tion He hath made me free; "He that be - liev - eth on the Son," saith He, "Hath ev - er - last - ing life."
2. All my in - iq - ui - ties on Him were laid, All my in - debt - ed - ness by Him was paid; All who be - lieve on Him, the Lord hath said, "Hath ev - er - last - ing life."
3. Though poor and need - y I can trust my Lord, Though weak and sin - ful I be - lieve His Word; Oh, glad mes - sage! ev - 'ry child of God "Hath ev - er - last - ing life."
4. Though all un - wor - thy, yet I will not doubt, For him that com - eth, He will not cast out; "He that be - liev - eth," oh, the good news shout, "Hath ev - er - last - ing life!"
CHORUS
"Ver - i - ly, ver - i - ly, I say un - to you," "Ver - i - ly, ver - i - ly," mes - sage ev - er new; "He that be - liev - eth on the Son," 'tis true, "Hath ev - er - last - ing life"

Copyright, 1920. Renewal. Hope Publishing Co., owner

160 Standing On the Promises

R. K. C. R. Kelso Carter

1. Stand-ing on the prom-is-es of Christ my King, Thro' e-ter-nal a-ges let His prais-es ring; Glo-ry in the high-est, I will shout and sing,
2. Stand-ing on the prom-is-es that can-not fail, When the howling storms of doubt and fear as-sail, By the liv-ing word of God I shall pre-vail,
3. Stand-ing on the prom-is-es of Christ the Lord, Bound to Him e-ter-nal-ly by love's strong cord, O-ver-com-ing dai-ly with the Spir-it's sword,
4. Stand-ing on the prom-is-es I can-not fall, Lis-t'ning ev-'ry mo-ment to the Spir-it's call, Rest-ing in my Sav-ior, as my all in all,
Stand-ing on the prom-is-es of God.
Chorus
Stand - - ing, stand - - ing,
Standing on the promises, standing on the promises,
Stand-ing on the prom-is-es of God my Sav-ior; Stand - - ing,
Stand-ing on the prom-is-es,
stand - - ing, I'm stand-ing on the prom-is-es of God.
stand-ing on the prom-is-es,

Stepping In the Light

E. E. Hewitt

Wm. J. Kirkpatrick

1. Try-ing to walk in the steps of the Sav-ior, Try-ing to fol-low our Sav-ior and King; Shap-ing our lives by His bless-ed ex-am-ple, Hap-py, how hap-py, the songs that we bring.
2. Press-ing more close-ly to Him who is lead-ing, When we are tempted to turn from the way; Trust-ing the arm that is strong to de-fend us, Hap-py, how hap-py, our prais-es each day.
3. Walk-ing in foot-steps of gen-tle for-bear-ance, Foot-steps of faith-ful-ness, mer-cy and love, Look-ing to Him for the grace free-ly prom-ised, Hap-py, how hap-py, our jour-ney a-bove.
4. Try-ing to walk in the steps of the Sav-ior, Up-ward, still upward we'll fol-low our Guide; When we shall see Him, "the King in His beau-ty," Hap-py, how hap-py, our place at His side.

CHORUS

How beau-ti-ful to walk in the steps of the Sav-ior, Stepping in the light, Step-ping in the light; How beau-ti-ful to walk in the steps of the Sav-ior, Led in paths of light.

Copyright, 1917, by Wm. J. Kirkpatrick. Renewal. Hope Publishing Company, owner

162 No Night There

JOHN R. CLEMENTS
H. P. DANKS
1. In the land of fade-less day Lies the "cit-y four-square,"
2. All the gates of pearl are made, In the "cit-y four-square,"
3. And the gates shall nev-er close To the "cit-y four-square,"
4. There they need no sun-shine bright, In that "cit-y four-square,"
It shall nev-er pass a-way, And there is "no night there."
All the streets with gold are laid, And there is "no night there."
There life's crys-tal riv-er flows, And there is "no night there."
For the Lamb is all the light, And there is "no night there."
CHORUS
mf
God shall "wipe a-way all tears;" There's no death, no pain, nor fears;
God shall "wipe a - way all tears;" There's no death, no pain, nor fears;
f
dim.
mf
And they count not time by years, For there is "no night there."
And they count not time by years, by years, For there is "no night..... there."

Copyright, 1927. Renewal. Hope Publishing Company, owner.

Jesus is All the World to Me

W. L. T.
Will L. Thompson
1. Je - sus is all the world to me, My life, my joy, my all;
2. Je - sus is all the world to me, My Friend in tri - als sore;
3. Je - sus is all the world to me, And true to Him I'll be;
4. Je - sus is all the world to me, I want no bet - ter friend;
He is my strength from day to day, With - out Him I would fall.
I go to Him for bless-ings, and He gives them o'er and o'er.
Oh, how could I this Friend de - ny, When He's so true to me?
I trust Him now, I'll trust Him when Life's fleet - ing days shall end.
When I am sad, to Him I go, No oth - er one can
He sends the sun - shine and the rain, He sends the har - vest's
Fol - low - ing Him I know I'm right, He watch - es o'er me
Beau - ti - ful life with such a Friend; Beau - ti - ful life that
f
pp
cheer me so; When I am sad He makes me glad, He's my Friend.
gold - en grain; Sun-shine and rain, har - vest of grain, He's my Friend.
day and night; Fol - low - ing Him, by day and night, He's my Friend.
has no end; E - ter - nal life, e - ter - nal joy, He's my Friend.

Copyright, 1932. Renewal. Hope Publishing Co., owner.

164 'Twas a Glad Day When Jesus Found Me

A. S. R.
Albert Simpson Reitz
1. I was lost in sin when Je - sus found me, But He res - cued me, all glo - ry to His name! And the cords of world - ly pleas - ure bound me, Till He saved me from sin and shame.
2. O the bells of heav - en now are ring - ing, For I hear their tones with - in my ran - somed soul; And my heart is filled with joy - ful sing - ing Since the Sav - ior hath made me whole.
3. O the joy when we shall meet in glo - ry, In the man - sions of my Father's home a - bove; And thro' end - less a - ges tell the sto - ry Of the Sav - ior's re - deem - ing love.
Chorus
'Twas a glad day when Je - sus found me, When His strong arms were thrown around me; When my sins He buried in the deep - est sea, And my soul He filled with joy and vic - to - ry; 'Twas a

Copyright, 1946, by A. S. Reitz. Renewal. Hope Publishing Co., owner

'Twas a Glad Day When Jesus Found Me
glad day, O hal-le - lu - jah! 'Twas a glad day He claimed His own; I will
shout a glad ho-san - na in glo-ry When I see Him up - on His throne.
Let the Lower Lights Be Burning
165
P. P. Bliss
P. P. Bliss
1. Bright-ly beams our Fa-ther's mer - cy From His light-house ev - er - more,
2, Dark the night of sin has set - tled, Loud the an - gry bil-lows roar;
3. Trim your fee - ble lamp, my broth-er, Some poor sail - or tem-pest - tossed,
Fine
But to us He gives the keep - ing Of the lights a - long the shore.
Ea - ger eyes are watching, long - ing, For the lights a - long the shore.
Try - ing now to make the har - bor, In the dark-ness may be lost.
D. S.–Some poor fainting, struggling sea - man You may res-cue, you may save.
Chorus
D. S.
Let the low - er lights be burn-ing! Send a gleam a - cross the wave!

166 Christ Returneth

H. L. Turner — James McGranahan

1. It may be at morn, when the day is a-wak-ing, When sunlight thro'
2. It may be at mid-day, it may be at twi-light, It may be, per-
3. While its hosts cry Hosanna, from heaven de-scend-ing, With glo-ri-fied
4. Oh, joy! oh, de-light! should we go with-out dy-ing, No sick-ness, no
dark-ness and shad-ow is break-ing, That Je-sus will come in the
chance, that the black-ness of mid-night Will burst in-to light in the
saints and the an-gels at-tend-ing, With grace on His brow, like a
sad-ness, no dread and no cry-ing, Caught up thro' the clouds with our
full-ness of glo-ry, To re-ceive from the world "His own."
blaze of His glo-ry, When Je-sus re-ceives "His own."
ha-lo of glo-ry, Will Je-sus re-ceive "His own."
Lord in-to glo-ry, When Je-sus re-ceives "His own."
Chorus
O Lord Je-sus, how long, how long Ere we shout the glad song, Christ re-
turn-eth! Hal-le-lu-jah! hal-le-lu-jah! A-men, Hal-le-lu-jah! A-men.
rit.

He is Able to Deliver Thee

W. A. O. W. A. OGDEN

1. 'Tis the grand-est theme thro' the a-ges rung; 'Tis the grandest theme for a mor-tal tongue; 'Tis the grandest theme that the world e'er sung, "Our God is a-ble to de-liv-er thee."
2. 'Tis the grand-est theme in the earth or main; 'Tis the grandest theme for a mor-tal strain; 'Tis the grandest theme, tell the world a-gain, "Our God is a-ble to de-liv-er thee."
3. 'Tis the grand-est theme, let the ti-dings roll, To the guilt-y heart, to the sin-ful soul; Look to God in faith, He will make thee whole, "Our God is a-ble to de-liv-er thee."
CHORUS.
He is a - - - - ble to de-liv-er thee,
a-ble, He is a-ble
He is a - - - - ble to de-liv-er thee; Tho' by sin op-prest,
a-ble, He is a-ble
Go to Him for rest; "Our God is a-ble to de-liv-er thee." A-MEN.

Copyright, 1915, by Mrs. W. A. Ogden. Renewal. Hope Publishing Co., owner.

168 Send the Light

Chas. H. Gabriel
Chas. H. Gabriel
1. There's a call comes ring-ing o'er the rest-less wave, "Send the light! . .
2. We have heard the Mac - e - do-nian call to - day, "Send the light! . .
3. Let us pray that grace may ev-'ry-where a - bound; Send the light! . .
4. Let us not grow wea-ry in the work of love, Send the light! . .
Send the light!
Send the light!" There are souls to res-cue, there are souls to save,
Send the light!" And a gold-en of-f'ring at the cross we lay,
Send the light! And a Christ-like spir - it ev - 'ry-where be found,
Send the light! Let us gath - er jew-els for a crown a - bove,
Send the light!
Refrain
Send the light! . . Send the light! . . Send the light! . . the
Send the light! Send the light! Send the light!
bless - ed gos - pel light; Let it shine . . . from shore to
the bless - ed gos - pel light; Let it shine
1
shore! . . . . . shine . . . for - ev - er - more. . . . .
from shore to shore! Let it shine for - ev - er-more.

Bringing In the Sheaves

KNOWLES SHAW GEORGE A. MINOR

1. Sow - ing in the morn - ing, sow-ing seeds of kind - ness, Sow-ing in the noon - tide and the dew - y eve; Wait - ing for the har - vest, and the time of reap-ing, We shall come re - joic - ing, bring-ing in the sheaves.
2. Sow - ing in the sun - shine, sow-ing in the shad - ows, Fear-ing nei - ther clouds nor win - ter's chill - ing breeze; By and by the har - vest, and the la - bor end - ed, We shall come re - joic - ing, bring-ing in the sheaves.
3. Go - ing forth with weep-ing, sow-ing for the Mas - ter, Tho' the loss sus - tained our spir - it oft - en grieves; When our weep - ing's o - ver, He will bid us wel-come, We shall come re - joic - ing, bring-ing in the sheaves.

CHORUS

Bring-ing in the sheaves, bring-ing in the sheaves, We shall come re-joic-ing, bring - ing in the sheaves;
Bring-ing in the sheaves, bring-ing in the sheaves, We shall come re-joic-ing, bring-ing in the sheaves.

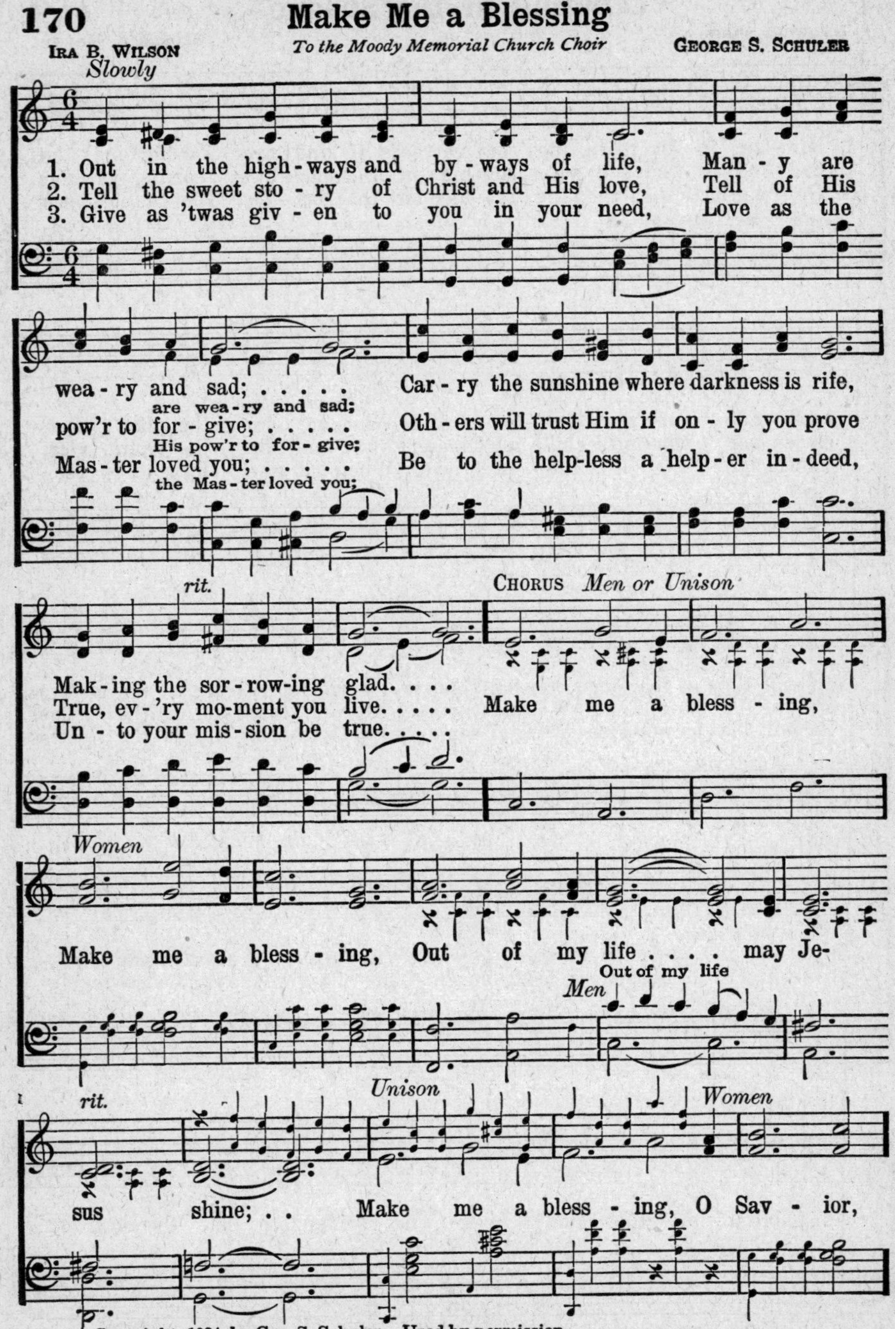
170
Make Me a Blessing
Ira B. Wilson
To the Moody Memorial Church Choir
George S. Schuler
Slowly
1. Out in the high-ways and by-ways of life, Man-y are wea-ry and sad; . . . . . Car-ry the sunshine where darkness is rife, Mak-ing the sor-row-ing glad. . . .
are wea-ry and sad;
2. Tell the sweet sto-ry of Christ and His love, Tell of His pow'r to for-give; . . . . . Oth-ers will trust Him if on-ly you prove True, ev-'ry mo-ment you live. . . . .
His pow'r to for-give;
3. Give as 'twas giv-en to you in your need, Love as the Mas-ter loved you; . . . . . Be to the help-less a help-er in-deed, Un-to your mis-sion be true. . . . .
the Mas-ter loved you;
rit.
CHORUS Men or Unison
Make me a bless-ing,
Women
Make me a bless-ing, Out of my life . . . . may Je-sus shine; . .
Men
Out of my life
rit.
Unison
Make me a bless-ing, O Sav-ior,
Women

Copyright, 1924, by Geo. S. Schuler. Used by permission

Make Me a Blessing

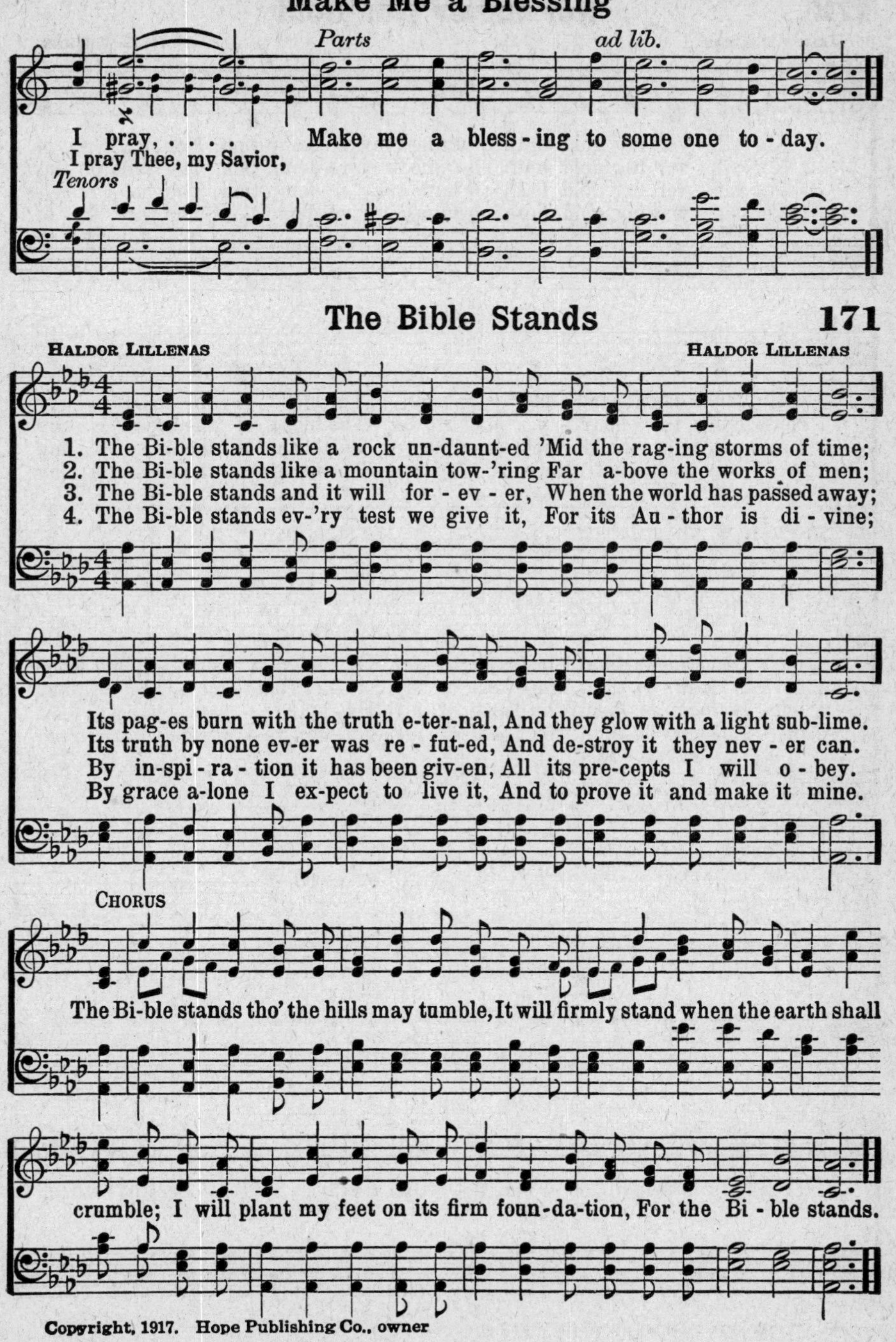

Parts
ad lib.
I pray, . . . Make me a bless-ing to some one to-day.
I pray Thee, my Savior,
Tenors

The Bible Stands
171
Haldor Lillenas
Haldor Lillenas
1. The Bi-ble stands like a rock un-daunt-ed 'Mid the rag-ing storms of time;
2. The Bi-ble stands like a mountain tow-'ring Far a-bove the works of men;
3. The Bi-ble stands and it will for-ev-er, When the world has passed away;
4. The Bi-ble stands ev-'ry test we give it, For its Au-thor is di-vine;
Its pag-es burn with the truth e-ter-nal, And they glow with a light sub-lime.
Its truth by none ev-er was re-fut-ed, And de-stroy it they nev-er can.
By in-spi-ra-tion it has been giv-en, All its pre-cepts I will o-bey.
By grace a-lone I ex-pect to live it, And to prove it and make it mine.
Chorus
The Bi-ble stands tho' the hills may tumble, It will firmly stand when the earth shall
crumble; I will plant my feet on its firm foun-da-tion, For the Bi-ble stands.

Copyright, 1917. Hope Publishing Co., owner

172 Nor Silver Nor Gold

James M. Gray — D. B. Towner

1. Nor sil - ver nor gold hath ob-tained my re-demp-tion, Nor rich - es of
2. Nor sil - ver nor gold hath ob-tained my re-demp-tion, The guilt on my
3. Nor sil - ver nor gold hath ob-tained my re-demp-tion, The ho - ly com-
4. Nor sil - ver nor gold hath ob-tained my re-demp-tion, The way in - to
earth could have saved my poor soul; The blood of the cross is my
con-science too heav - y had grown; The blood of the cross is my
mand-ment for - bade me draw near; The blood of the cross is my
heav - en could not thus be bought; The blood of the cross is my
on - ly foun - da-tion, The death of my Sav - ior now mak - eth me whole.
on - ly foun - da-tion, The death of my Sav - ior could on - ly a - tone.
on - ly foun - da-tion, The death of my Sav - ior re - mov - eth my fear.
on - ly foun - da-tion, The death of my Sav - ior re - demp-tion hath wrought
Chorus
I am re - deemed, ... but not with sil - ver;
I am re-deemed, I am re-deemed, but not with sil - ver;
I am bought, . but not with gold; Bought with a
I am bought, I am bought, but not with gold;

Copyright, 1928. Renewal. Hope Publishing Co., owner.

Nor Silver Nor Gold
price— . . . the blood of Je - sus, ... Pre-cious price of love un-told.
Bought with a price— the precious blood of Je-sus,
Full Surrender
173
Rebecca S. Pollard
Daniel B. Towner
1. Sav - ior, 'tis a full sur - ren-der, All I leave to fol - low Thee;
2. As I come in deep con - tri-tion, At this con - se - crat - ed hour,
3. No with-hold-ing—full con - fes-sion; Pleasures, rich-es, all must flee;
4. Oh, the joy of full sal - va-tion! Oh, the peace of love di - vine!
Thou my Lead-er and De-fend - er From this hour shalt ev - er be.
Hear, O Christ, my heart's pe-ti - tion, Let me feel the Spir - it's power!
Ho - ly Spir - it, take pos - ses-sion! I no more, but Thou in me.
Oh, the bliss of con - se - cra-tion! I am His, and He is mine.
Chorus
I sur-ren-der all! . . . . . . I sur-ren - der all! . . . . . .
I sur-ren-der all! I sur-ren-der all!
All I have I bring to Je - sus, I sur - ren - der all.

Copyright, 1929, Renewal. Hope Publishing Company, owner

174 O That Will Be Glory

C. H. G. CHAS. H. GABRIEL

1. When all my la-bors and tri-als are o'er, And I am safe on that beau-ti-ful shore, Just to be near the dear Lord I a-dore, Will thro' the a-ges be glo-ry for me. . . .
2. When, by the gift of His in-fi-nite grace, I am ac-cord-ed in Heav-en a place, Just to be there and to look on His face,
3. Friends will be there I have loved long a-go; Joy like a riv-er a-round me will flow; Yet, just a smile from my Sav-ior, I know,
rit.
CHORUS. Faster.
O that will be glo-ry for me, Glo-ry for me, glo-ry for me; When by His grace
O . . . . . . that will be glo-ry for me, Glo-ry for me, glo-ry for me;. . . . .
I shall look on His face, That will be glo-ry, be glo-ry for me. A-MEN.

Copyright, 1928. Renewal. Homer A. Rodeheaver, owner. Used by permission.

What Will it Be When We See Him? 175

Ada R. Habershon — D. B. Towner

1. If singing His praises is sweet to us here, What will it be when we see Him? And if to our hearts His own Word grows more dear, What will it be when we see Him?
2. How blest are the moments with Him which we spend, What will it be when we see Him? When perfect communion all tho't will transcend, What will it be when we see Him?
3. If we upon earth are amazed at His grace, What will it be when we see Him? If here, tho' but dimly, His beauty we trace, What will it be when we see Him?
4. Our heart burns within us when His voice is heard, What will it be when we see Him? And love to Himself in each bosom is stirred, What will it be when we see Him?
Chorus
What will it be when we see Him? What will it be when we see Him? We shall in an instant be wholly transformed, We'll know what He is when we see Him.

Copyright, 1916. Hope Publishing Co., owner

176 Whiter Than Snow

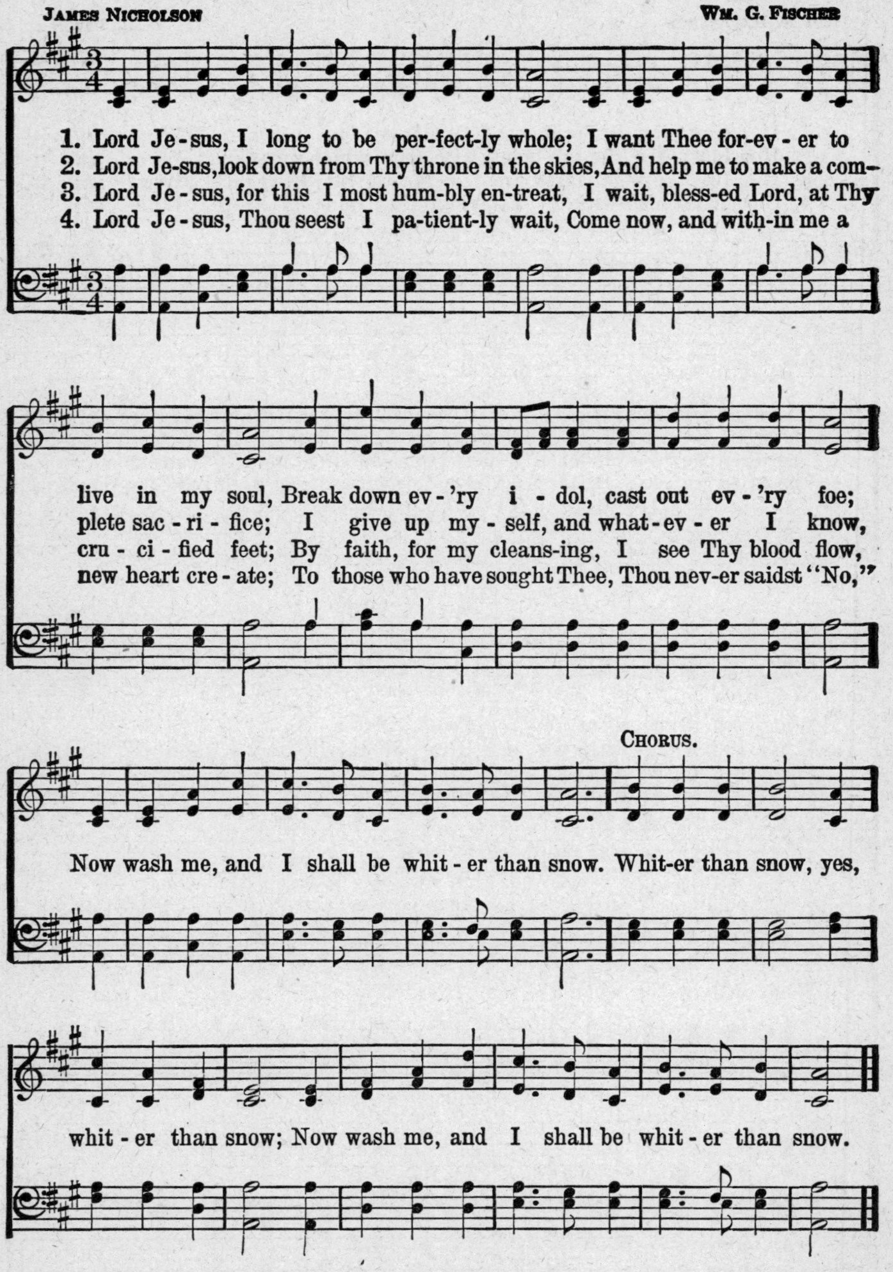
JAMES NICHOLSON
WM. G. FISCHER
1. Lord Je-sus, I long to be per-fect-ly whole; I want Thee for-ev-er to live in my soul, Break down ev-'ry i-dol, cast out ev-'ry foe;
2. Lord Je-sus, look down from Thy throne in the skies, And help me to make a com-plete sac-ri-fice; I give up my-self, and what-ev-er I know,
3. Lord Je-sus, for this I most hum-bly en-treat, I wait, bless-ed Lord, at Thy cru-ci-fied feet; By faith, for my cleans-ing, I see Thy blood flow,
4. Lord Je-sus, Thou seest I pa-tient-ly wait, Come now, and with-in me a new heart cre-ate; To those who have sought Thee, Thou nev-er saidst "No,"
Now wash me, and I shall be whit-er than snow.
CHORUS.
Whit-er than snow, yes, whit-er than snow; Now wash me, and I shall be whit-er than snow.

He Will Hold Me Fast

Ada R. Habershon

Robert Harkness

1. When I fear my faith will fail, Christ will hold me fast;
2. I could nev - er keep my hold, He will hold me fast;
3. I am pre - cious in His sight, He will hold me fast;
4. He'll not let my soul be lost, Christ will hold me fast;
rall.
When the tempt - er would pre - vail, He can hold me fast. . .
For my love is oft - en cold, He must hold me fast. . .
Those He saves are His de - light, He will hold me fast. . .
Bought by Him at such a cost, He will hold me fast. . .
Refrain a tempo
He will hold me fast, He will hold me fast;
hold me fast, hold me fast;
rall.
For my Savior loves me so, He will hold me fast.

Copyright, 1934. Renewal. Hope Publishing Co., owner.

178 Let Jesus Come Into Your Heart

C. H. M. Mrs. C. H. MORRIS

1. If you are tired of the load of your sin, Let Je - sus come in - to your heart; If you de - sire a new life to be - gin, Let Je - sus come in - to your heart.
2. If 'tis for pu - ri - ty now that you sigh, Let Je - sus come in - to your heart; Fountains for cleans-ing are flow - ing near by,
3. If there's a tem - pest your voice can - not still, Let Je - sus come in - to your heart; If there's a void this world nev - er can fill,
4. If you would join the glad songs of the blest, Let Je - sus come in - to your heart; If you would en - ter the man-sions of rest,
CHORUS
Just now, your doubt-ings give o'er; Just now, re - ject Him no more; Just now, throw o - pen the door; Let Je - sus come in - to your heart.

Copyright, 1926. Renewal. Hope Publishing Co., owner.

There is a Fountain 179

William Cowper | Lowell Mason

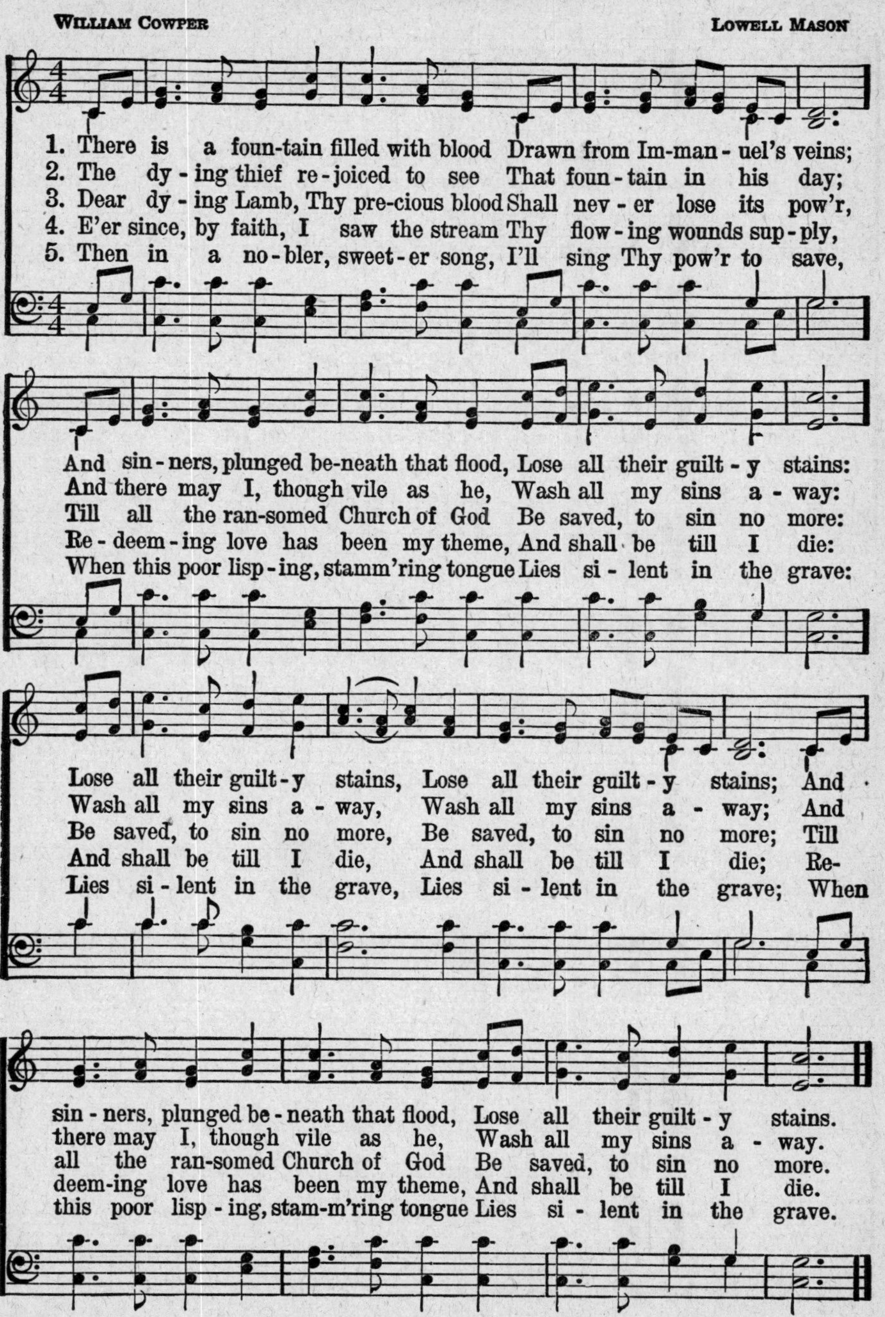
1. There is a foun-tain filled with blood Drawn from Im-man-uel's veins;
2. The dy-ing thief re-joiced to see That foun-tain in his day;
3. Dear dy-ing Lamb, Thy pre-cious blood Shall nev-er lose its pow'r,
4. E'er since, by faith, I saw the stream Thy flow-ing wounds sup-ply,
5. Then in a no-bler, sweet-er song, I'll sing Thy pow'r to save,
And sin-ners, plunged be-neath that flood, Lose all their guilt-y stains:
And there may I, though vile as he, Wash all my sins a-way:
Till all the ran-somed Church of God Be saved, to sin no more:
Re-deem-ing love has been my theme, And shall be till I die:
When this poor lisp-ing, stamm'ring tongue Lies si-lent in the grave:
Lose all their guilt-y stains, Lose all their guilt-y stains; And
Wash all my sins a-way, Wash all my sins a-way; And
Be saved, to sin no more, Be saved, to sin no more; Till
And shall be till I die, And shall be till I die; Re-
Lies si-lent in the grave, Lies si-lent in the grave; When
sin-ners, plunged be-neath that flood, Lose all their guilt-y stains.
there may I, though vile as he, Wash all my sins a-way.
all the ran-somed Church of God Be saved, to sin no more.
deem-ing love has been my theme, And shall be till I die.
this poor lisp-ing, stam-m'ring tongue Lies si-lent in the grave.

180 His Love Is All I Need

E. O. Excell E. O. Excell

1. The love of Je - sus, who can tell, Tho' he may know it, oh, so well?
2. The love of Je - sus, oh, what bliss, To hear Him whis-per, I am His!
3. The love of Je - sus, oh, how sweet, To hide in such a safe re - treat!
The love that ev - 'ry want sup-plies, The love that al-ways sat - is - fies;
Tho' I may fal - ter on the way, He will not let me go a - stray;
Tho' Sa - tan would my hopes de-stroy, My Sav - ior's love is still my joy;
rit.
Chorus
His love is all I need! So won-der - ful, His love to me!
More won - der-ful how could it be? My ev - 'ry sin on Him was laid;
My ev - 'ry debt by Him was paid; His love is all I need!
rit.

Copyright, 1936, Renewal. Hope Publishing Co., owner

O Zion, Haste

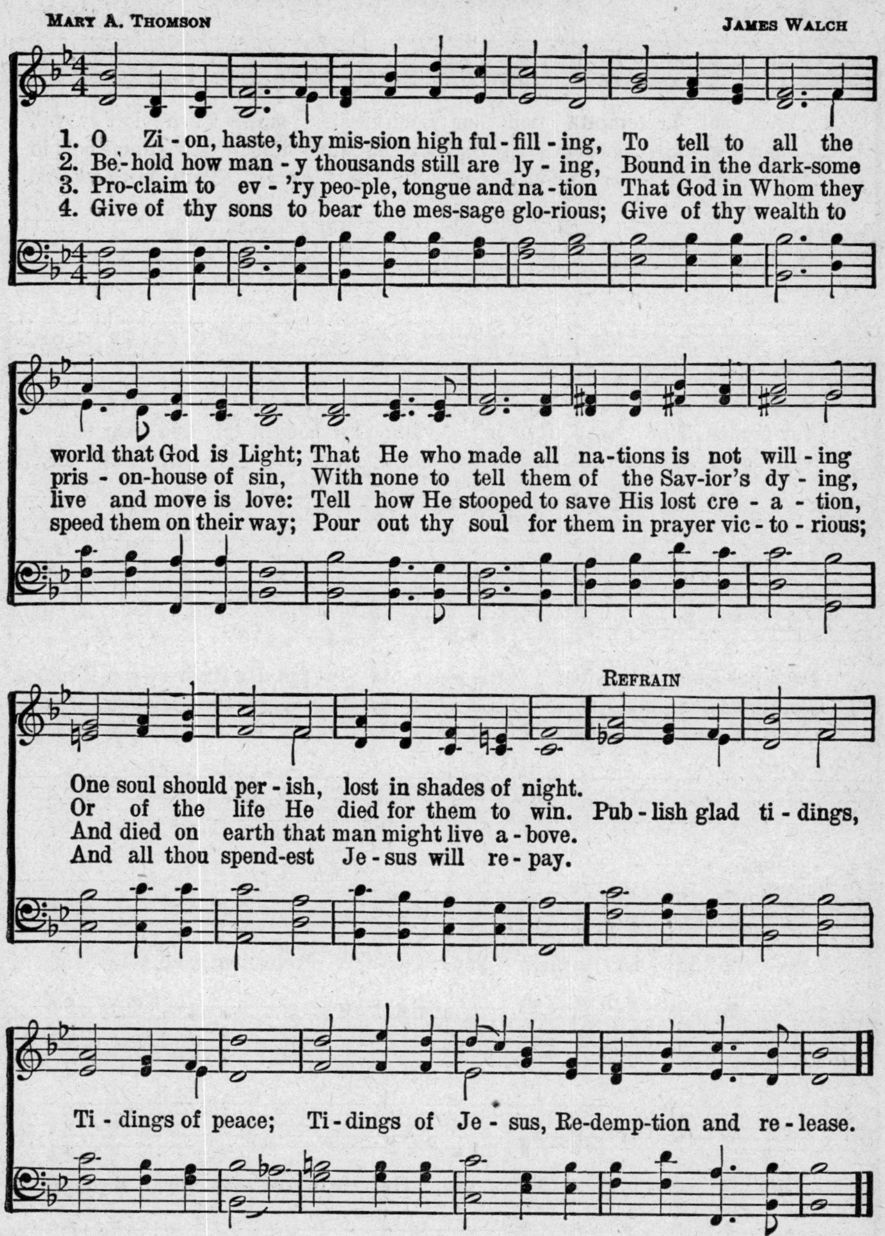
Mary A. Thomson
James Walch
1. O Zi - on, haste, thy mis-sion high ful - fill - ing, To tell to all the
2. Be-hold how man - y thousands still are ly - ing, Bound in the dark-some
3. Pro-claim to ev - 'ry peo-ple, tongue and na - tion That God in Whom they
4. Give of thy sons to bear the mes-sage glo-rious; Give of thy wealth to
world that God is Light; That He who made all na-tions is not will - ing
pris - on-house of sin, With none to tell them of the Sav-ior's dy - ing,
live and move is love: Tell how He stooped to save His lost cre - a - tion,
speed them on their way; Pour out thy soul for them in prayer vic - to - rious;
Refrain
One soul should per - ish, lost in shades of night.
Or of the life He died for them to win. Pub - lish glad ti - dings,
And died on earth that man might live a - bove.
And all thou spend-est Je - sus will re - pay.
Ti - dings of peace; Ti - dings of Je - sus, Re-demp-tion and re - lease.

182 Yield Not to Temptation

H. R. Palmer
H. R. Palmer
1. Yield not to temp-ta - tion, For yield-ing is sin, Each vic-t'ry will
2. Shun e - vil com-pan-ions, Bad lan-guage dis - dain, God's name hold in
3. To him that o'er-com-eth, God giv - eth a crown, Thro' faith we shall
help you Some oth - er to win; Fight man-ful - ly on - ward,
rev-erence, Nor take it in vain; Be thought-ful and ear - nest,
con - quer, Though of - ten cast down; He who is our Sav - ior,
Dark pas-sions sub - due, Look ev-er to Je-sus, He'll car-ry you through.
Kind-heart-ed and true, Look ev-er to Je - sus, He'll car-ry you through.
Our strength will re - new, Look ev-er to Je - sus, He'll car-ry you through.
Chorus
Ask the Sav - ior to help you, Com-fort, strengthen, and keep you,
He is will - ing to aid you, He will car - ry you through.

Is It the Crowning Day? 183

George Walker Whitcomb — Charles H. Marsh

1. Je - sus may come to - day, Glad day! Glad day! And I would see my Friend; Dan-gers and trou - bles would end If Je - sus should come to - day.
2. I may go home to - day, Glad day! Glad day! Seem-eth I hear their song; Hail to the ra - di - ant throng! If I should go home to - day.
3. Why should I anx-ious be? Glad day! Glad day! Lights ap - pear on the shore, Storms will af - fright nev - er - more, For He is "at hand" to - day.
4. Faithful I'll be to - day, Glad day! Glad day! And I will free - ly tell Why I should love Him so well, For He is my all to - day.
Chorus
Glad day! Glad day! Is it the crowning day? I'll live for to - day, nor anx - ious be, Je - sus, my Lord, I soon shall see; Glad day! Glad day! Is it the crown-ing day?
rit.

Copyright, 1938. Renewal. The Rodeheaver Co., owner. Used by permission.

184 I'll Stand By Until the Morning

W. W. D. JAMES MCGRANAHAN

1. Fierce and wild the storm is rag - ing Round a help - less bark,
2. Wea - ry, help-less, hope-less sea - men Faint - ing on the deck,
3. On a wild and storm - y o - cean, Sink - ing 'neath the wave,
4. Dar - ing death thy soul to res - cue, He in love has come,
On to doom 'tis swift - ly driv - ing, O'er the wa - ters dark!
With what joy they hail their Sav - ior, As He hails their wreck!
Souls that per - ish heed the mes - sage, Christ has come to save!
Leave the wreck and in Him trust - ing, Thou shalt reach thy home!
CHORUS
Joy, ... be-hold the Sav - ior, Joy, ... the message hear,
Joy, O joy, be - hold the Sav - ior, Joy, O joy, the mes-sage hear,
"I'll stand by un - til the morn-ing, I've come to save you, do not fear," Yes,

I'll Stand By Until the Morning

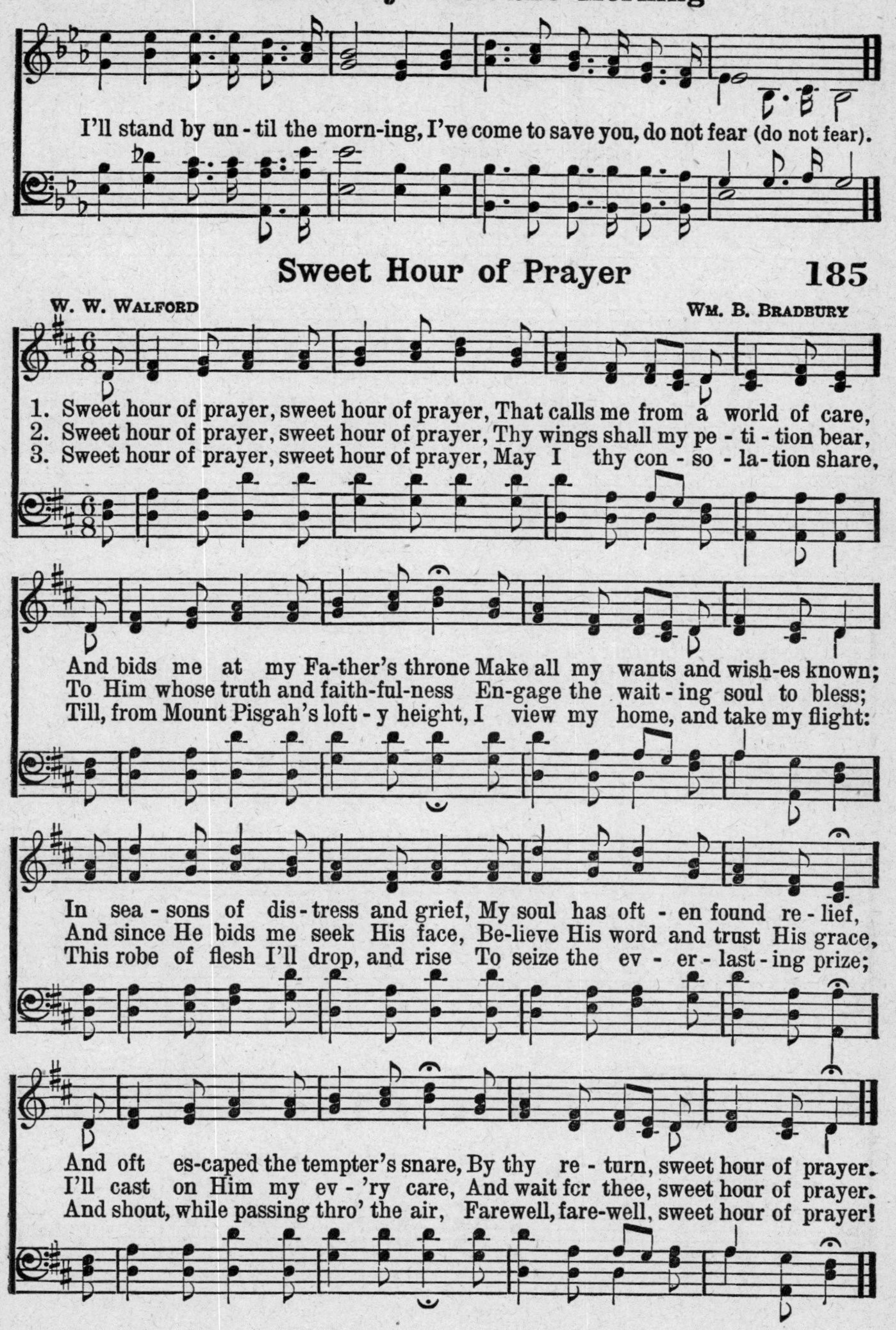
I'll stand by un - til the morn-ing, I've come to save you, do not fear (do not fear).
Sweet Hour of Prayer
185
W. W. Walford
Wm. B. Bradbury
1. Sweet hour of prayer, sweet hour of prayer, That calls me from a world of care,
2. Sweet hour of prayer, sweet hour of prayer, Thy wings shall my pe - ti - tion bear,
3. Sweet hour of prayer, sweet hour of prayer, May I thy con - so - la - tion share,
And bids me at my Fa-ther's throne Make all my wants and wish-es known;
To Him whose truth and faith-ful-ness En-gage the wait - ing soul to bless;
Till, from Mount Pisgah's loft - y height, I view my home, and take my flight:
In sea - sons of dis - tress and grief, My soul has oft - en found re - lief,
And since He bids me seek His face, Be-lieve His word and trust His grace,
This robe of flesh I'll drop, and rise To seize the ev - er - last - ing prize;
And oft es-caped the tempter's snare, By thy re - turn, sweet hour of prayer.
I'll cast on Him my ev - 'ry care, And wait fcr thee, sweet hour of prayer.
And shout, while passing thro' the air, Farewell, fare-well, sweet hour of prayer!

186 Jesus Is Calling

Fanny J. Crosby — Geo. C. Stebbins

1. Je - sus is ten - der - ly call - ing thee home—Call - ing to - day,
2. Je - sus is call - ing the wea - ry to rest— Call - ing to - day,
3. Je - sus is wait-ing; O come to Him now— Wait-ing to - day,
4. Je - sus is plead-ing; O list to His voice: Hear Him to - day,
call - ing to - day; Why from the sun - shine of love wilt thou roam
call - ing to - day; Bring Him thy bur - den and thou shalt be blest:
wait - ing to - day; Come with thy sins; at His feet low - ly bow;
hear Him to - day; They who be - lieve on His name shall re - joice;
Refrain
Far-ther and far-ther a - way?
He will not turn thee a - way. Call - - ing to - day, ...
Come, and no lon-ger de - lay.
Quick-ly a - rise and a - way. Call - ing, call - ing to - day, to - day,
Call - - ing to - day, ... Je - - - - sus is
Call - ing, call - ing to - day, to - day, Je - sus is ten - der - ly
call - - - ing, is ten - der - ly call - ing to - day.
call - ing to - day,

Love Lifted Me

James Rowe | Howard E. Smith

1. I was sink-ing deep in sin, Far from the peaceful shore, Ver-y deep-ly stained with-in, Sink-ing to rise no more; But the Mas-ter of the sea Heard my despairing cry, From the wa-ters lift-ed me, Now safe am I.
2. All my heart to Him I give, Ev-er to Him I'll cling, In His bless-ed pres-ence live, Ev-er His prais-es sing. Love so might-y and so true Mer-its my soul's best songs; Faith-ful, lov-ing serv-ice, too, To Him be-longs.
3. Souls in dan-ger, look a-bove, Je-sus com-plete-ly saves; He will lift you by His love Out of the an-gry waves. He's the Mas-ter of the sea, Bil-lows His will o-bey; He your Sav-ior wants to be—Be saved to-day.
Chorus
Love lift-ed me!.... Love lift-ed me!.... When noth-ing else could help, Love lift-ed me. Love lift-ed me.
e-ven me! e-ven me!

Copyright, 1939. Renewal. John T. Benson, Jr., owner. Nashville, Tenn. Used by permission.

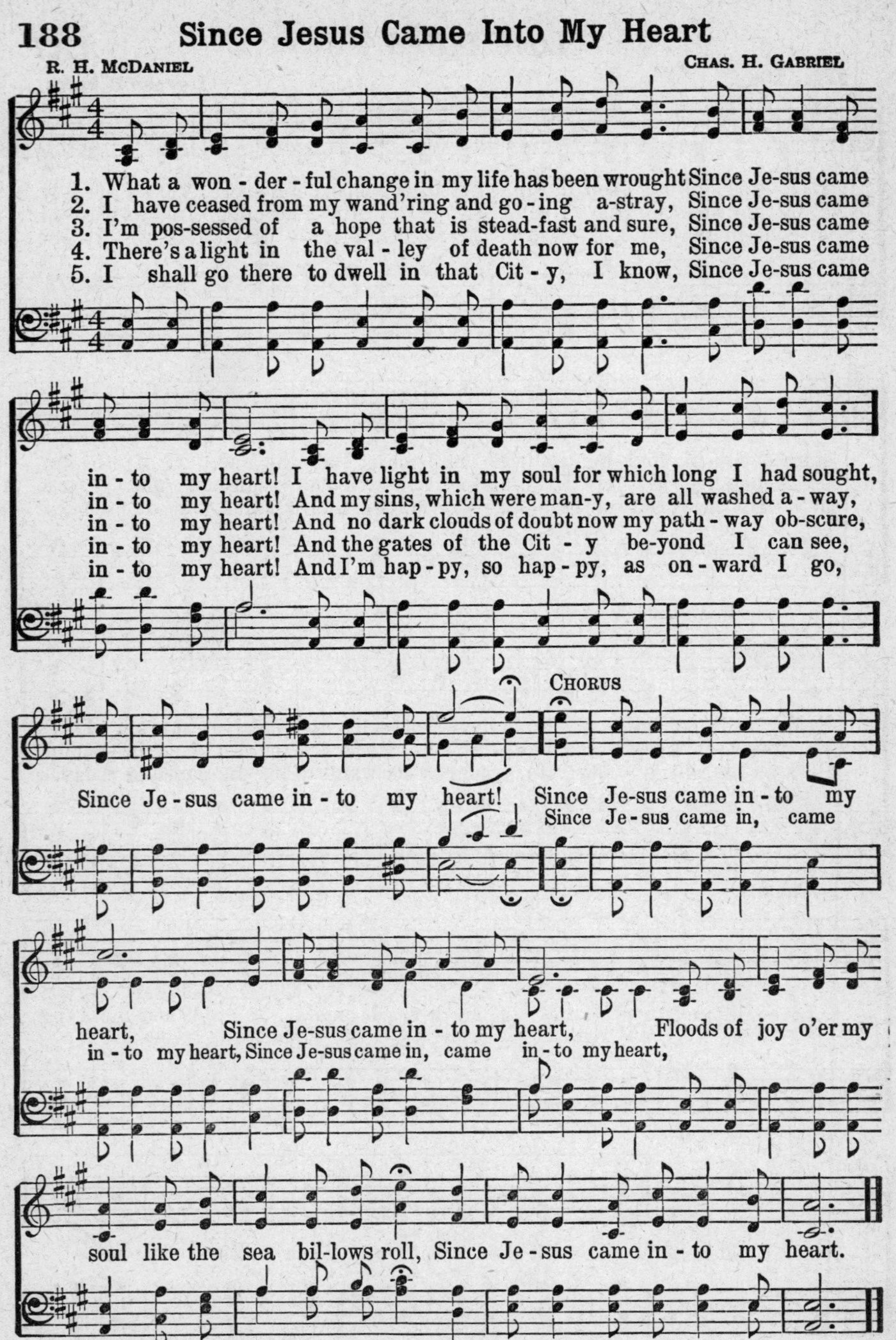
188 Since Jesus Came Into My Heart
R. H. McDaniel
Chas. H. Gabriel
1. What a won - der - ful change in my life has been wrought Since Je-sus came
2. I have ceased from my wand'ring and go - ing a-stray, Since Je-sus came
3. I'm pos-sessed of a hope that is stead-fast and sure, Since Je-sus came
4. There's a light in the val - ley of death now for me, Since Je-sus came
5. I shall go there to dwell in that Cit - y, I know, Since Je-sus came
in - to my heart! I have light in my soul for which long I had sought,
in - to my heart! And my sins, which were man-y, are all washed a - way,
in - to my heart! And no dark clouds of doubt now my path - way ob-scure,
in - to my heart! And the gates of the Cit - y be-yond I can see,
in - to my heart! And I'm hap - py, so hap - py, as on - ward I go,
Since Je - sus came in - to my heart!
Chorus
Since Je-sus came in - to my heart,
Since Je - sus came in, came in - to my heart,
Since Je-sus came in - to my heart,
Since Je-sus came in, came in - to my heart,
Floods of joy o'er my soul like the sea bil-lows roll, Since Je - sus came in - to my heart.

Copyright, 1914, by Chas. H. Gabriel. Homer A. Rodeheaver, owner. Used by permission.

Nailed to the Cross

Mrs. Frank A. Breck

Grant Colfax Tullar

1. There was One who was will-ing to die in my stead, That a soul so un-wor-thy might live; And the path to the cross He was will-ing to tread, All the sins of my life to for-give.
2. He is ten-der and lov-ing and pa-tient with me, While He cleans-es my heart of the dross; But "there's no con-dem-na-tion"—I know I am free, For my sins are all nailed to the cross.
3. I will cling to my Sav-ior and nev-er de-part—I will joy-ful-ly jour-ney each day. With a song on my lips and a song in my heart, That my sins have been tak-en a-way.
Refrain
They are nailed to the cross, They are nailed to the cross, O how much He was will-ing to bear! With what an-guish and loss Je-sus went to the cross! But He carried my sins with Him there.
pp
rit.

Copyright, 1927, by Grant C. Tullar. Renewal. Used by permission.

190 Far, Far On the Other Side

PAUL RADER
ARTHUR W. MCKEE
1. I've en - tered the land dear - ly bought by His blood, Passed o - ver
2. The gi - ants are con-quered the spies said were here, Je - sus is
3. The man - na is gone and the corn is my food, Dead to the
Jor - dan, sur - ren - dered to God; I've found His suf - fi - cien - cy
vic - tor, I need have no fear; Sum - mer in win - ter and
world and I'm liv - ing in God; I've ceased say - ing can't since I
here in this land, Glo - ry to Je - sus for - ev - er!
joy all the year, Glo - ry to Je - sus for - ev - er!
found that He could— Glo - ry to Je - sus for - ev - er!
CHORUS
Far, far on the oth - er side, I'm liv - ing a - cross the riv - er;
Burned are the bridges 'twixt me and the world, Glo-ry to Je - sus for - ev - er!

Copyright, 1918, by Arthur W. McKee. Hope Publishing Co., owner

Give of Your Best to the Master

H. B. G. Mrs. Charles Barnard

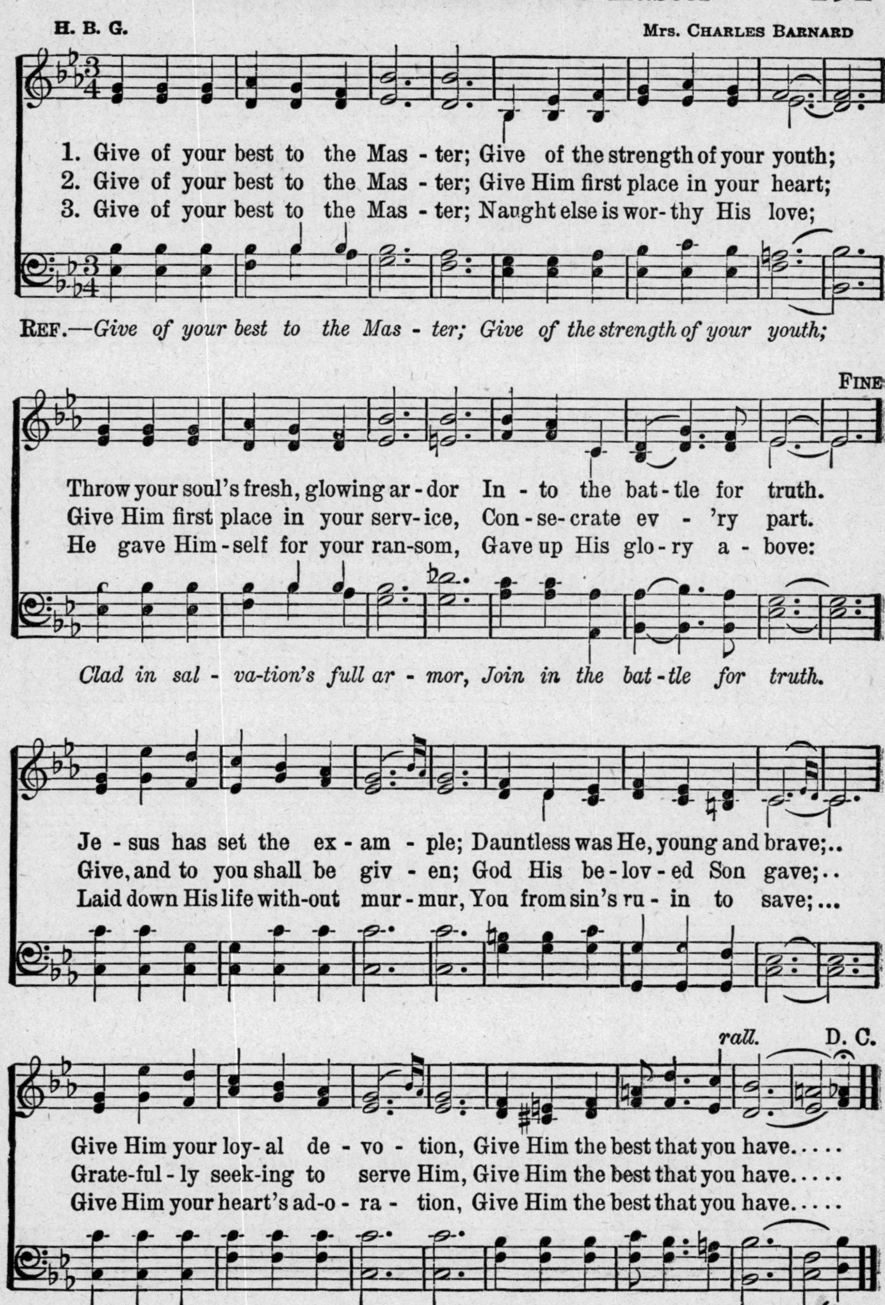
1. Give of your best to the Mas - ter; Give of the strength of your youth;
2. Give of your best to the Mas - ter; Give Him first place in your heart;
3. Give of your best to the Mas - ter; Naught else is wor-thy His love;
Ref.—Give of your best to the Mas - ter; Give of the strength of your youth;
Fine
Throw your soul's fresh, glowing ar - dor In - to the bat - tle for truth.
Give Him first place in your serv - ice, Con - se - crate ev - 'ry part.
He gave Him - self for your ran - som, Gave up His glo - ry a - bove:
Clad in sal - va-tion's full ar - mor, Join in the bat - tle for truth.
Je - sus has set the ex - am - ple; Dauntless was He, young and brave;..
Give, and to you shall be giv - en; God His be - lov - ed Son gave;..
Laid down His life with-out mur - mur, You from sin's ru - in to save;...
rall.
D. C.
Give Him your loy - al de - vo - tion, Give Him the best that you have.....
Grate-ful - ly seek-ing to serve Him, Give Him the best that you have.....
Give Him your heart's ad-o - ra - tion, Give Him the best that you have....

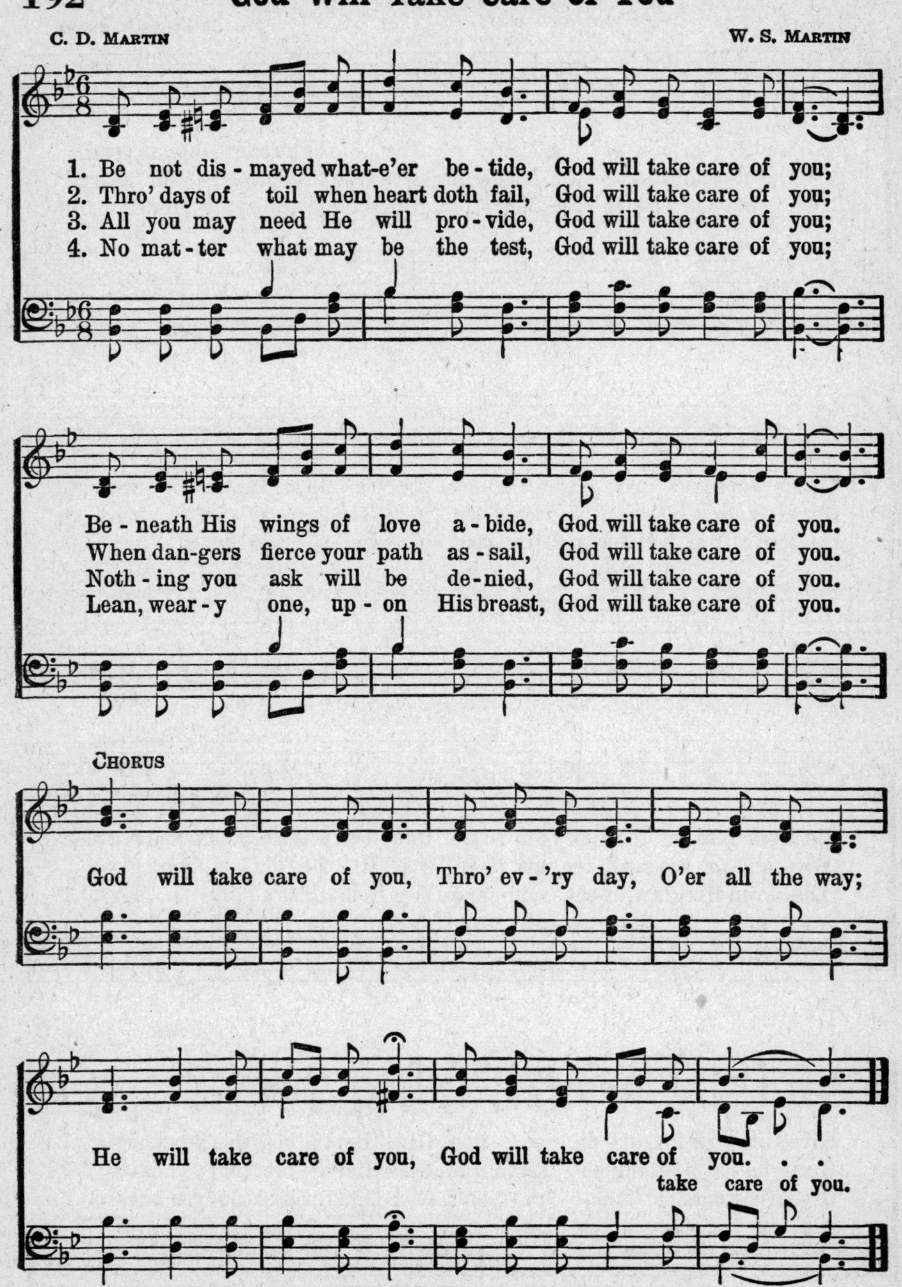
192
God Will Take Care of You
C. D. Martin
W. S. Martin
1. Be not dis - mayed what-e'er be - tide, God will take care of you;
2. Thro' days of toil when heart doth fail, God will take care of you;
3. All you may need He will pro - vide, God will take care of you;
4. No mat - ter what may be the test, God will take care of you;
Be - neath His wings of love a - bide, God will take care of you.
When dan-gers fierce your path as - sail, God will take care of you.
Noth - ing you ask will be de - nied, God will take care of you.
Lean, wear - y one, up - on His breast, God will take care of you.
Chorus
God will take care of you, Thro' ev - 'ry day, O'er all the way;
He will take care of you, God will take care of you. . .
take care of you.

Copyright, 1933. Renewal. Hope Publishing Co., owner.

I'll Be a Sunbeam 193

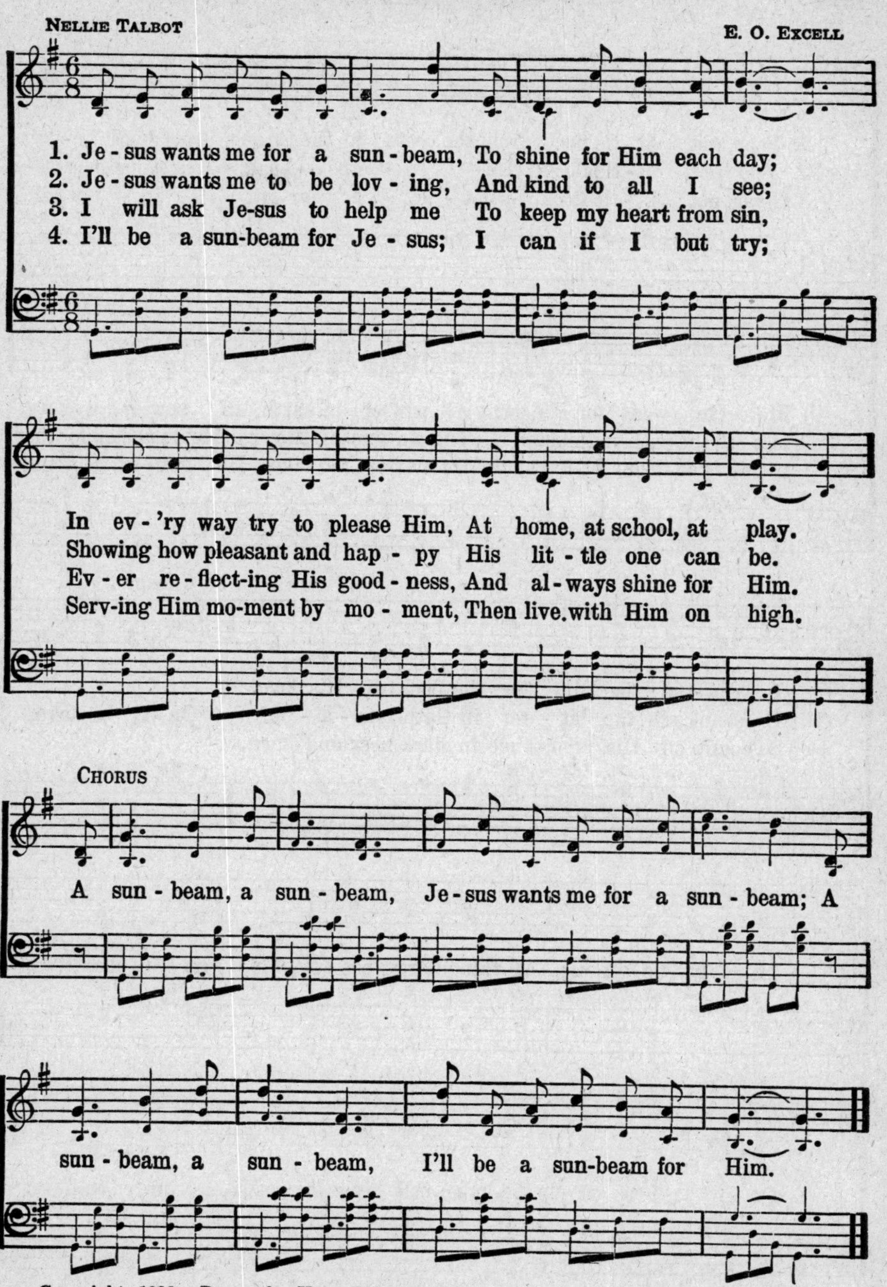
NELLIE TALBOT
E. O. EXCELL
1. Je - sus wants me for a sun - beam, To shine for Him each day;
2. Je - sus wants me to be lov - ing, And kind to all I see;
3. I will ask Je-sus to help me To keep my heart from sin,
4. I'll be a sun-beam for Je - sus; I can if I but try;
In ev - 'ry way try to please Him, At home, at school, at play.
Showing how pleasant and hap - py His lit - tle one can be.
Ev - er re - flect-ing His good - ness, And al - ways shine for Him.
Serv-ing Him mo-ment by mo - ment, Then live with Him on high.
CHORUS
A sun - beam, a sun - beam, Je - sus wants me for a sun - beam; A
sun - beam, a sun - beam, I'll be a sun-beam for Him.

Copyright, 1928. Renewal. Hope Publishing Co., owner.

194 Only Believe

P. R. PAUL RADER

1. Fear not, lit-tle flock, from the cross to the throne, From death in-to life He went for His own; All pow-er in earth, all pow-er a-bove, Is giv-en to Him for the flock of His love.

2. Fear not, lit-tle flock, He go-eth a-head, Your Shep-herd se-lect-eth the path you must tread; The wa-ters of Ma-rah He'll sweeten for thee, He drank all the bit-ter in Geth-sem-a-ne.

3. Fear not, lit-tle flock, what-ev-er your lot, He en-ters all rooms, "the doors be-ing shut;" He nev-er for-sakes, He nev-er is gone, So count on His pres-ence in dark-ness and dawn.

CHORUS

On-ly be-lieve, on-ly be-lieve; All things are pos-si-ble, on-ly be-lieve; On-ly be-lieve, on-ly be-lieve; All things are pos-si-ble, on-ly be-lieve.

Copyright, 1921, by Mrs. Paul Rader, owner. Used by permission.

My Sins Are Blotted Out, I Know! 195

M. D. MERRILL DUNLOP

1. What a won-drous mes - sage in God's Word! My sins are blot - ted
2. Once my heart was black but now, what joy, My sins are blot - ted
3. I shall stand some day be - fore my King, My sins all blot - ted
out, I know! If I trust in His re - deem - ing blood, My
out, I know! I have peace that noth - ing can de - stroy, My
out, I know! With the ran-somed host I then shall sing: "My
sins are blot-ted out, I know!
sins are blot-ted out, I know!
sins are blot-ted out, I know!"
CHORUS
My sins are blot-ted out, I know!
I know!
My sins are blot-ted out, I know! They are bur - ied in the
I know!
depths of the deep - est sea; My sins are blot-ted out, I know!
I know!

Copyright, 1927, by Merrill Dunlop. Used by permission

196 All the Way My Savior Leads Me

FANNY J. CROSBY — ROBERT LOWRY

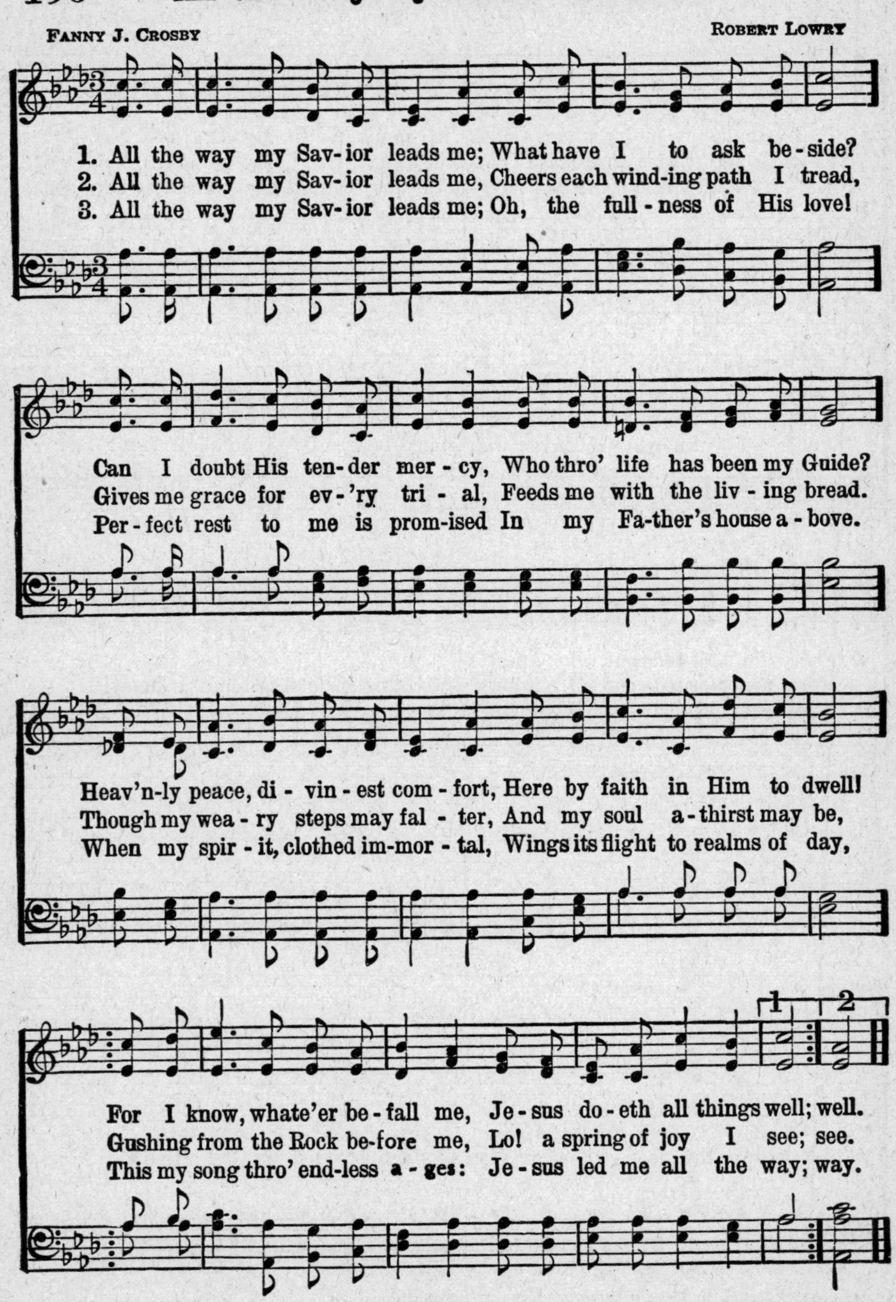
1. All the way my Sav-ior leads me; What have I to ask be-side?
2. All the way my Sav-ior leads me, Cheers each wind-ing path I tread,
3. All the way my Sav-ior leads me; Oh, the full-ness of His love!
Can I doubt His ten-der mer-cy, Who thro' life has been my Guide?
Gives me grace for ev-'ry tri-al, Feeds me with the liv-ing bread.
Per-fect rest to me is prom-ised In my Fa-ther's house a-bove.
Heav'n-ly peace, di-vin-est com-fort, Here by faith in Him to dwell!
Though my wea-ry steps may fal-ter, And my soul a-thirst may be,
When my spir-it, clothed im-mor-tal, Wings its flight to realms of day,
For I know, whate'er be-fall me, Je-sus do-eth all things well; well.
Gushing from the Rock be-fore me, Lo! a spring of joy I see; see.
This my song thro' end-less a-ges: Je-sus led me all the way; way.
1
2

Tell Me the Story of Jesus 197

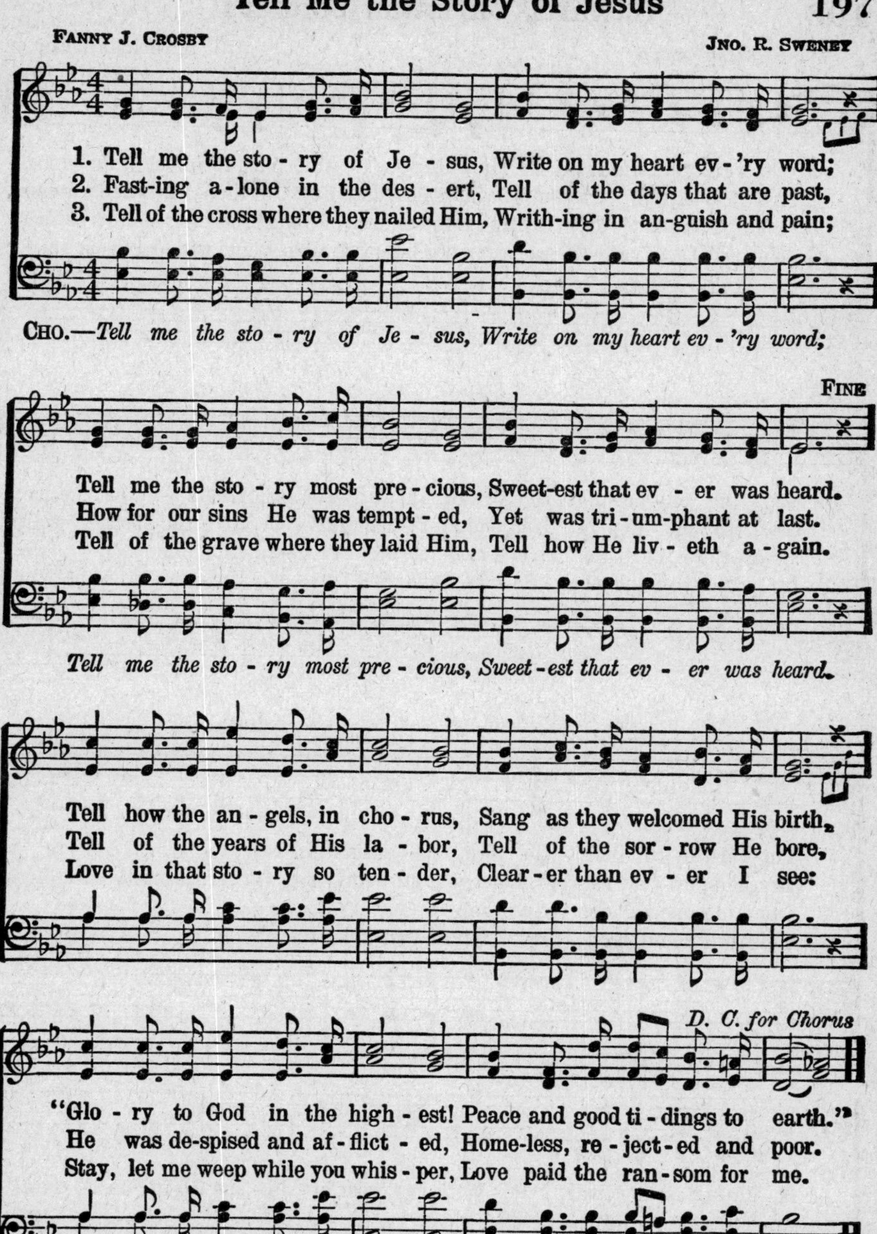

FANNY J. CROSBY
JNO. R. SWENEY
1. Tell me the sto - ry of Je - sus, Write on my heart ev - 'ry word;
2. Fast-ing a-lone in the des - ert, Tell of the days that are past,
3. Tell of the cross where they nailed Him, Writh-ing in an-guish and pain;
CHO.—Tell me the sto - ry of Je - sus, Write on my heart ev - 'ry word;
FINE
Tell me the sto - ry most pre - cious, Sweet-est that ev - er was heard.
How for our sins He was tempt - ed, Yet was tri - um-phant at last.
Tell of the grave where they laid Him, Tell how He liv - eth a - gain.
Tell me the sto - ry most pre - cious, Sweet - est that ev - er was heard.
Tell how the an - gels, in cho - rus, Sang as they welcomed His birth,
Tell of the years of His la - bor, Tell of the sor - row He bore,
Love in that sto - ry so ten - der, Clear - er than ev - er I see:
D. C. for Chorus
"Glo - ry to God in the high - est! Peace and good ti - dings to earth."
He was de-spised and af - flict - ed, Home-less, re - ject - ed and poor.
Stay, let me weep while you whis - per, Love paid the ran - som for me.

Copyright, 1907, by L. E. Sweney. Renewal. Homer A. Rodeheaver, owner
Copyright, 1917, by Homer A. Rodeheaver Used by permission

198 Onward, Christian Soldiers

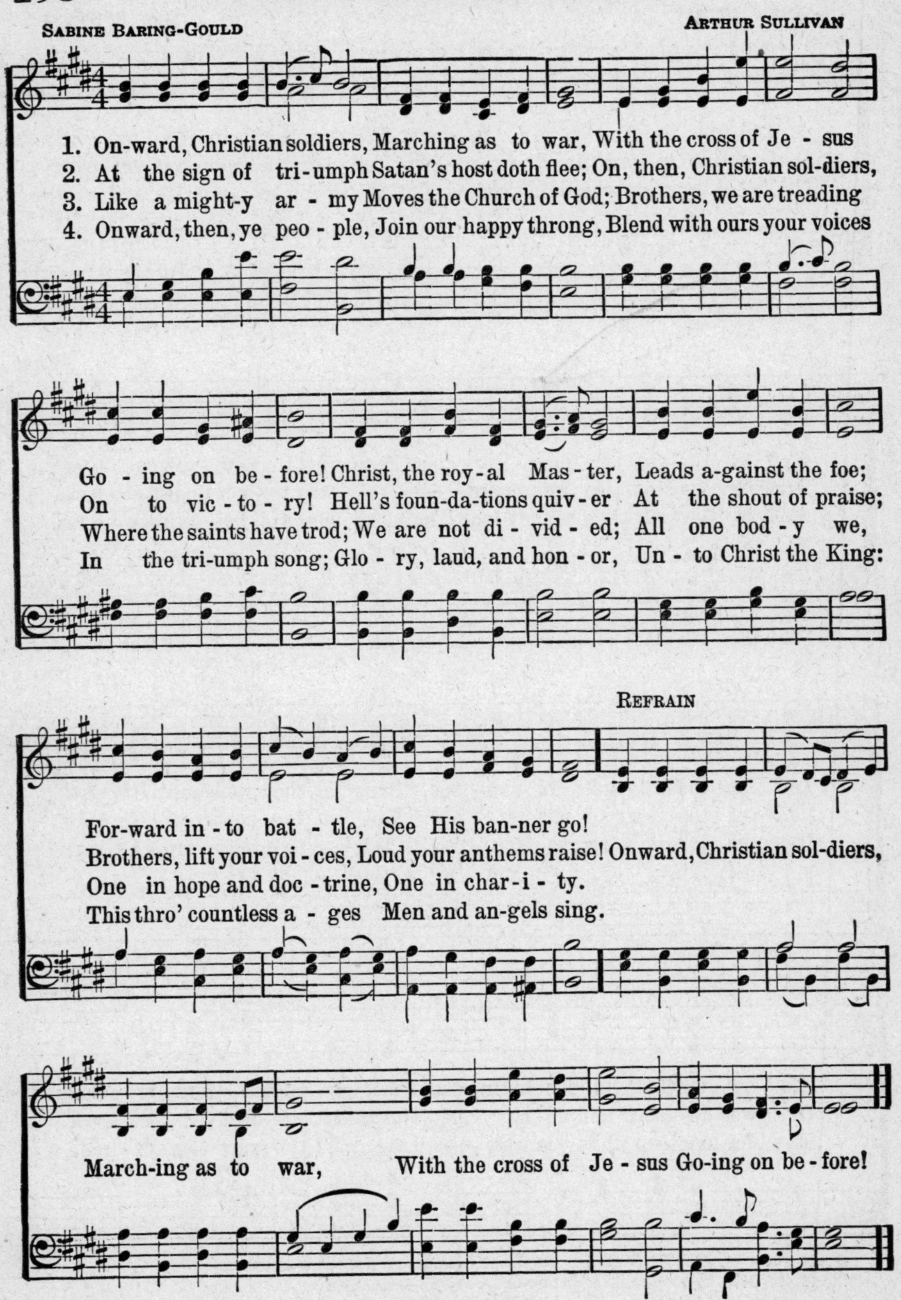
SABINE BARING-GOULD
ARTHUR SULLIVAN
1. On-ward, Christian soldiers, Marching as to war, With the cross of Je - sus
2. At the sign of tri-umph Satan's host doth flee; On, then, Christian sol-diers,
3. Like a might-y ar - my Moves the Church of God; Brothers, we are treading
4. Onward, then, ye peo - ple, Join our happy throng, Blend with ours your voices
Go - ing on be - fore! Christ, the roy-al Mas - ter, Leads a-gainst the foe;
On to vic - to - ry! Hell's foun-da-tions quiv - er At the shout of praise;
Where the saints have trod; We are not di - vid - ed; All one bod - y we,
In the tri-umph song; Glo - ry, laud, and hon - or, Un - to Christ the King:
REFRAIN
For-ward in - to bat - tle, See His ban-ner go!
Brothers, lift your voi - ces, Loud your anthems raise! Onward, Christian sol-diers,
One in hope and doc - trine, One in char - i - ty.
This thro' countless a - ges Men and an-gels sing.
March-ing as to war, With the cross of Je - sus Go-ing on be - fore!

Trust and Obey

J. H. SAMMIS

D. B. TOWNER

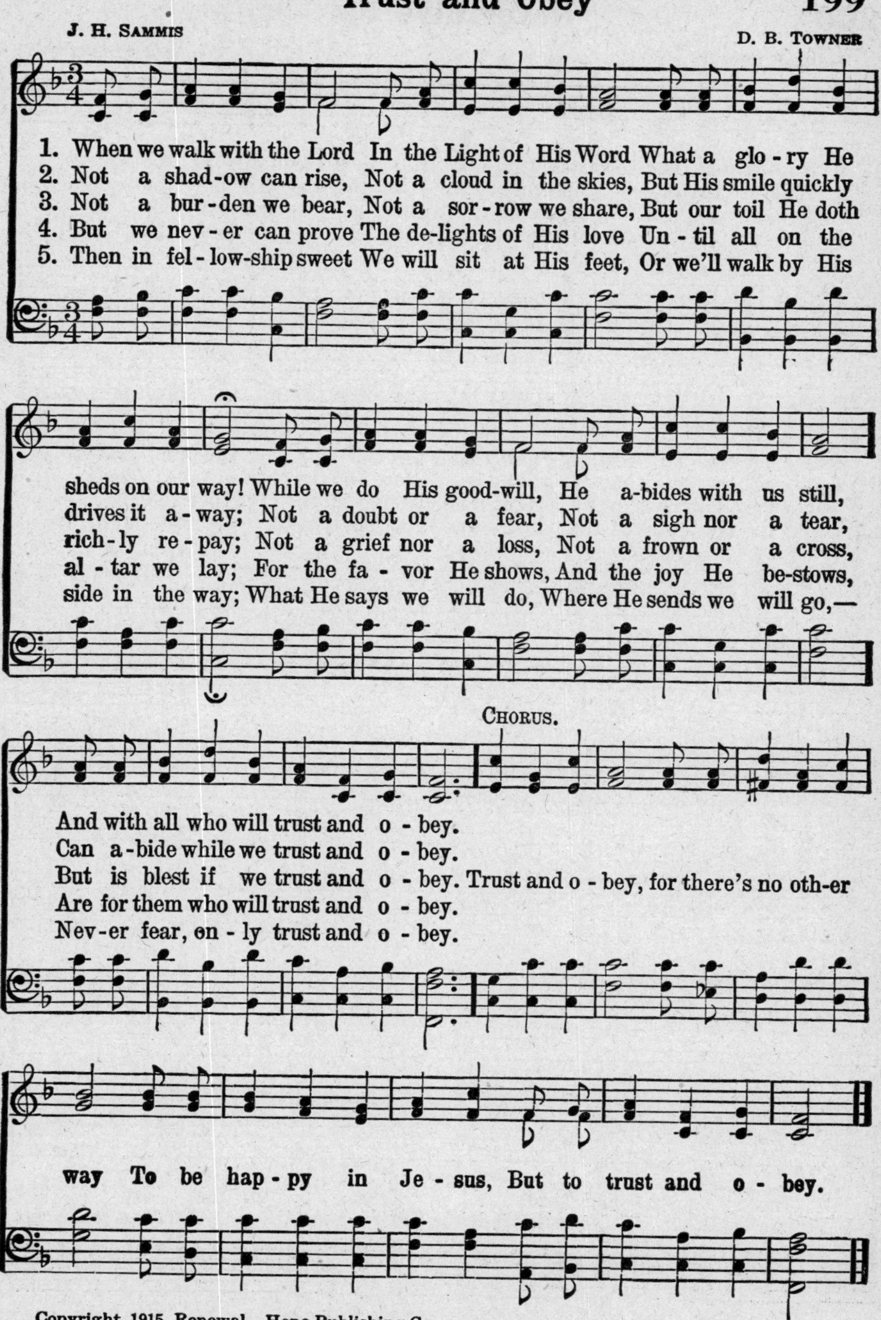
1. When we walk with the Lord In the Light of His Word What a glo - ry He
2. Not a shad-ow can rise, Not a cloud in the skies, But His smile quickly
3. Not a bur - den we bear, Not a sor - row we share, But our toil He doth
4. But we nev - er can prove The de-lights of His love Un - til all on the
5. Then in fel - low-ship sweet We will sit at His feet, Or we'll walk by His
sheds on our way! While we do His good-will, He a-bides with us still,
drives it a - way; Not a doubt or a fear, Not a sigh nor a tear,
rich-ly re - pay; Not a grief nor a loss, Not a frown or a cross,
al - tar we lay; For the fa - vor He shows, And the joy He be-stows,
side in the way; What He says we will do, Where He sends we will go,—
CHORUS.
And with all who will trust and o - bey.
Can a-bide while we trust and o - bey.
But is blest if we trust and o - bey. Trust and o - bey, for there's no oth-er
Are for them who will trust and o - bey.
Nev-er fear, on - ly trust and o - bey.
way To be hap - py in Je - sus, But to trust and o - bey.

Copyright, 1915, Renewal. Hope Publishing Co., owner

200 Never Give Up

Fanny J. Crosby — I. Allan Sankey

1. Nev-er be sad or de-spond-ing If thou hast faith to be-lieve;
2. What if thy bur-dens op-press thee; What tho' thy life may be drear;
3. Nev-er be sad or de-spond-ing, There is a mor-row for thee;
4. Nev-er be sad or de-spond-ing, Lean on the arm of thy Lord;
Grace, for the du-ties be-fore thee, Ask of thy God and re-ceive.
Look on the side that is bright-est, Pray, and thy path will be clear.
Soon thou shalt dwell in its bright-ness, There with the Lord thou shalt be.
Dwell in the depths of His mer-cy, Thou shalt re-ceive thy re-ward.
Chorus
Nev - - er give up, ... Nev - - er give up, ...
Nev-er give up, nev-er give up, Nev-er give up, nev-er give up,
Nev-er give up to thy sor-rows, Je-sus will bid them de-part;
Trust . . . . in the Lord, ... Trust . . . in the Lord, . . .
Trust in the Lord, trust in the Lord, Trust in the Lord, trust in the Lord,

Copyright, 1931. Renewal. Hope Publishing Co., owner.

Never Give Up
Sing when your tri - als are great - est, Trust in the Lord and take heart.
Look to the Lamb of God
201
H. G. Jackson
James M. Black
1. If you from sin are long-ing to be free, Look to the Lamb of God;
2. When Satan tempts, and doubts and fears assail, Look to the Lamb of God;
3. Are you a-wea - ry, does the way seem long? Look to the Lamb of God;
4. Fear not when shadows on your path-way fall, Look to the Lamb of God;
He, to re-deem you, died on Cal - va - ry, Look to the Lamb of God.
You in His strength shall o-ver all pre-vail, Look to the Lamb of God.
His love will cheer and fill your heart with song, Look to the Lamb of God.
In joy or sor - row Christ is all in all, Look to the Lamb of God.
Chorus
Look to the Lamb of God, Look to the Lamb of God,
the Lamb of God, the Lamb of God,
For He a - lone is a - ble to save you, Look to the Lamb of God.

202 **The Comforter Has Come**

F. Bottome — Wm. J. Kirkpatrick

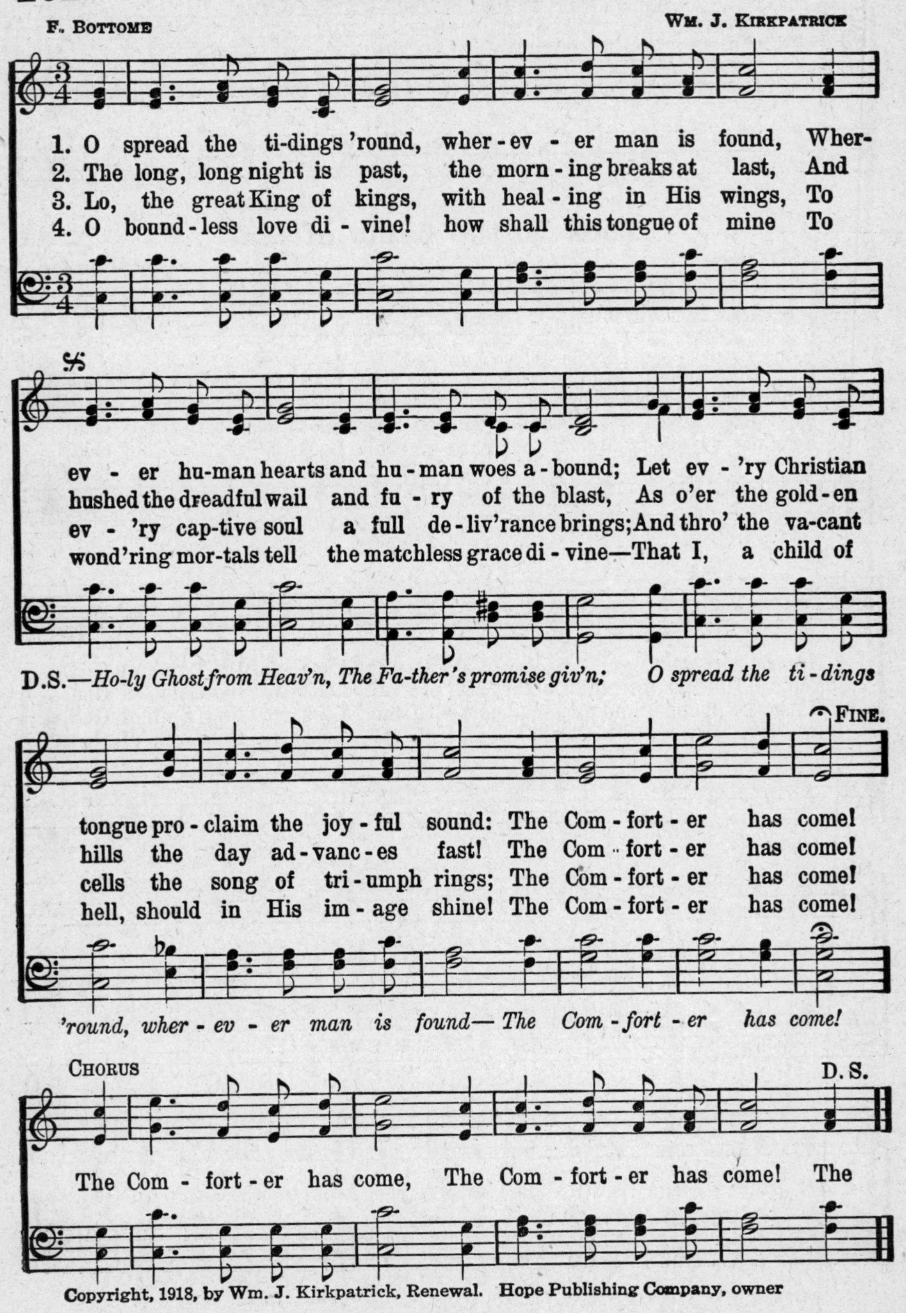

1. O spread the ti-dings 'round, wher-ev - er man is found, Wher-ev - er hu-man hearts and hu-man woes a-bound; Let ev - 'ry Christian tongue pro - claim the joy - ful sound: The Com - fort - er has come!
2. The long, long night is past, the morn - ing breaks at last, And hushed the dreadful wail and fu - ry of the blast, As o'er the gold - en hills the day ad - vanc - es fast! The Com - fort - er has come!
3. Lo, the great King of kings, with heal - ing in His wings, To ev - 'ry cap-tive soul a full de - liv'rance brings; And thro' the va-cant cells the song of tri - umph rings; The Com - fort - er has come!
4. O bound-less love di - vine! how shall this tongue of mine To wond'ring mor-tals tell the matchless grace di - vine—That I, a child of hell, should in His im - age shine! The Com - fort - er has come!
D.S.—Ho-ly Ghost from Heav'n, The Fa-ther's promise giv'n; O spread the ti - dings 'round, wher - ev - er man is found— The Com - fort - er has come!
Fine.
Chorus
The Com - fort - er has come, The Com - fort - er has come! The
D. S.

Copyright, 1918, by Wm. J. Kirkpatrick, Renewal. Hope Publishing Company, owner

Jesus, I Come

W. T. SLEEPER — GEO. C. STEBBINS

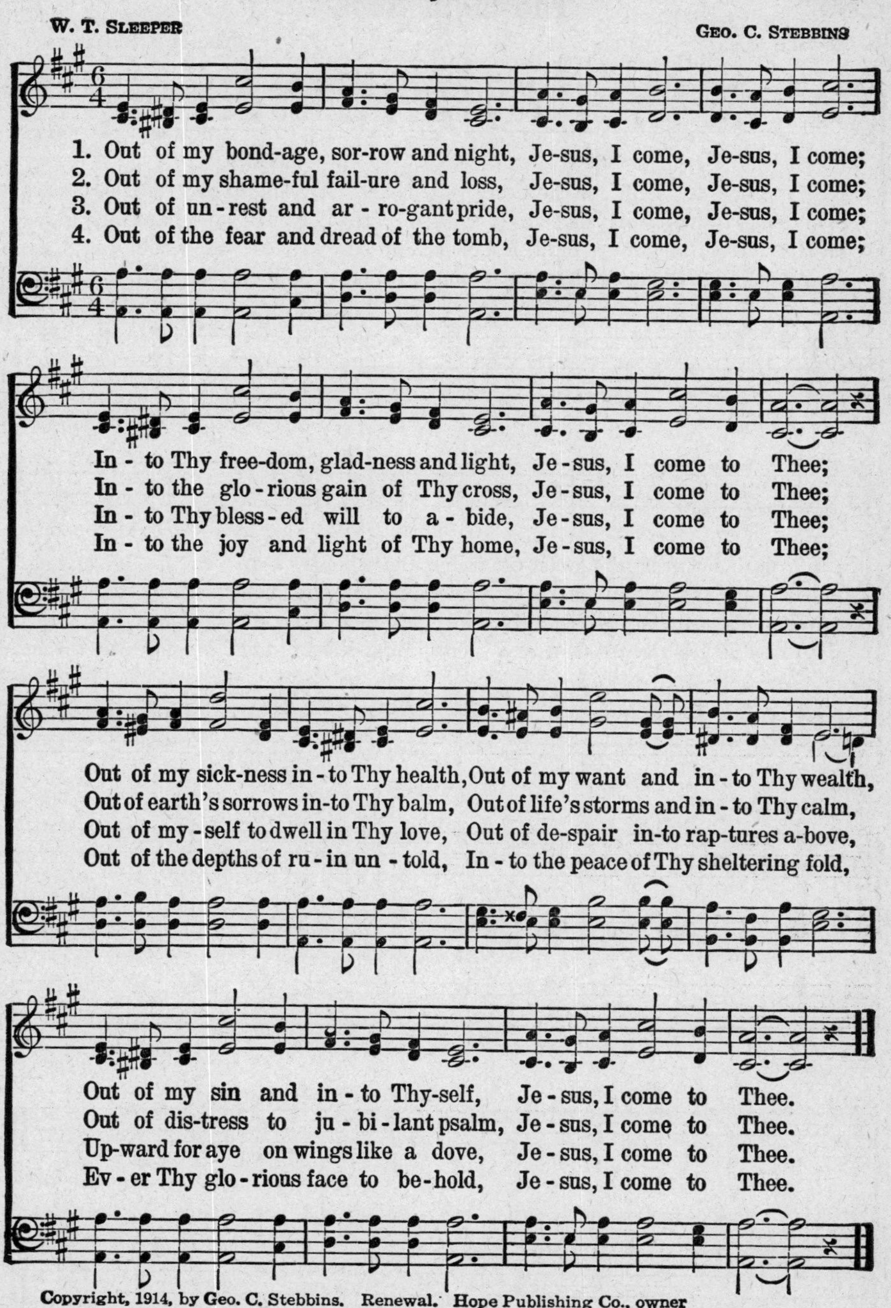
1. Out of my bond-age, sor-row and night, Je-sus, I come, Je-sus, I come;
2. Out of my shame-ful fail-ure and loss, Je-sus, I come, Je-sus, I come;
3. Out of un-rest and ar - ro-gant pride, Je-sus, I come, Je-sus, I come;
4. Out of the fear and dread of the tomb, Je-sus, I come, Je-sus, I come;
In - to Thy free-dom, glad-ness and light, Je - sus, I come to Thee;
In - to the glo - rious gain of Thy cross, Je - sus, I come to Thee;
In - to Thy bless - ed will to a - bide, Je - sus, I come to Thee;
In - to the joy and light of Thy home, Je - sus, I come to Thee;
Out of my sick-ness in - to Thy health, Out of my want and in - to Thy wealth,
Out of earth's sorrows in-to Thy balm, Out of life's storms and in - to Thy calm,
Out of my - self to dwell in Thy love, Out of de-spair in-to rap-tures a-bove,
Out of the depths of ru - in un - told, In - to the peace of Thy sheltering fold,
Out of my sin and in - to Thy-self, Je - sus, I come to Thee.
Out of dis-tress to ju - bi - lant psalm, Je - sus, I come to Thee.
Up-ward for aye on wings like a dove, Je - sus, I come to Thee.
Ev - er Thy glo - rious face to be-hold, Je - sus, I come to Thee.

Copyright, 1914, by Geo. C. Stebbins. Renewal. Hope Publishing Co., owner

204 The Solid Rock

EDWARD MOTE — WILLIAM B. BRADBURY

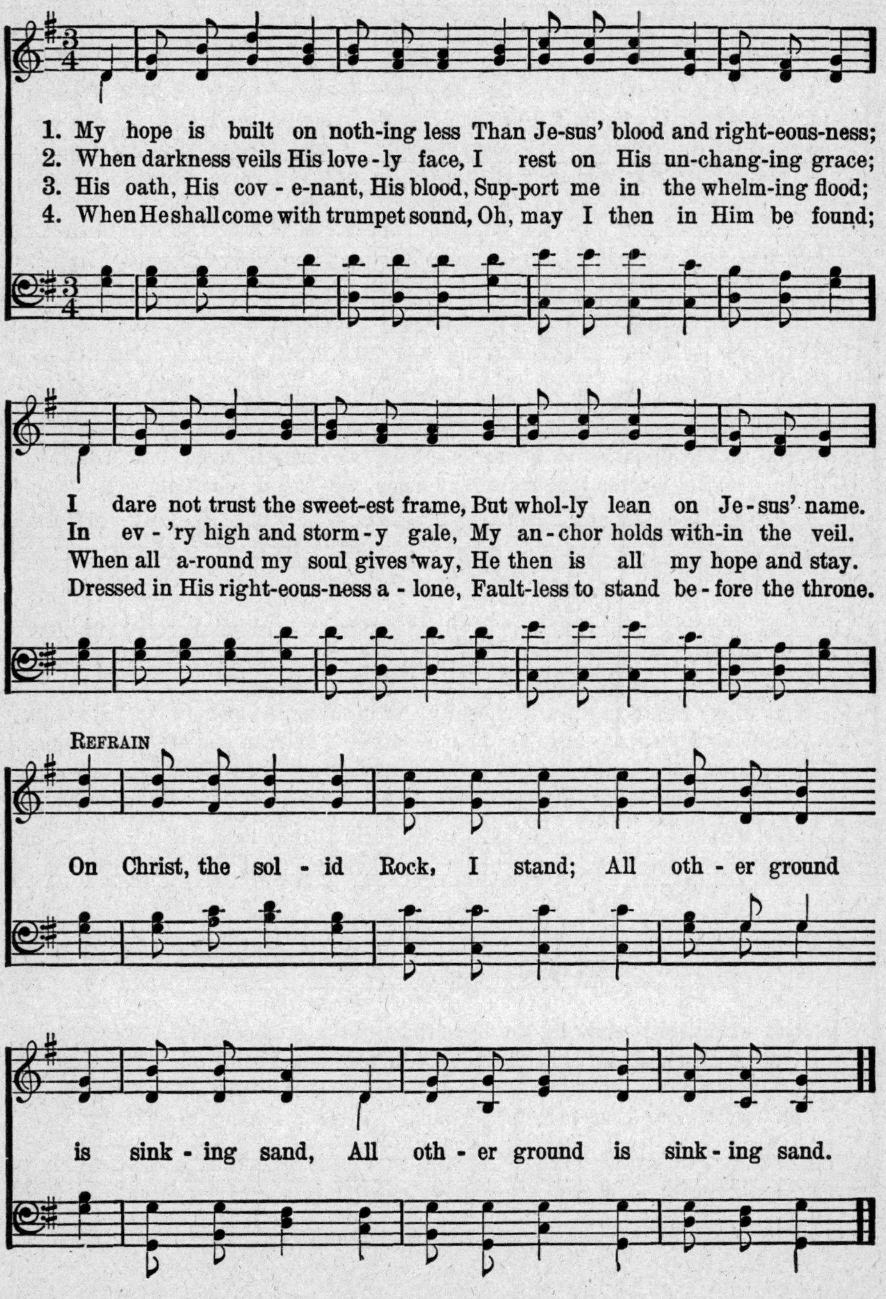

1. My hope is built on noth-ing less Than Je-sus' blood and right-eous-ness;
2. When darkness veils His love-ly face, I rest on His un-chang-ing grace;
3. His oath, His cov-e-nant, His blood, Sup-port me in the whelm-ing flood;
4. When He shall come with trumpet sound, Oh, may I then in Him be found;

I dare not trust the sweet-est frame, But whol-ly lean on Je-sus' name.
In ev-'ry high and storm-y gale, My an-chor holds with-in the veil.
When all a-round my soul gives way, He then is all my hope and stay.
Dressed in His right-eous-ness a-lone, Fault-less to stand be-fore the throne.

REFRAIN

On Christ, the sol-id Rock, I stand; All oth-er ground is sink-ing sand, All oth-er ground is sink-ing sand.

The Way of the Cross Leads Home

Jessie Brown Pounds — Chas. H. Gabriel

1. I must needs go home by the way of the cross, There's no oth - er way but this; I shall ne'er get sight of the Gates of Light, If the way of the cross I miss.
2. I must needs go on in the blood-sprinkled way, The path that the Sav - ior trod, If I ev - er climb to the heights sub-lime, Where the soul is at home with God.
3. Then I bid fare-well to the way of the world, To walk in it nev - er - more; For my Lord says "Come," and I seek my home, Where He waits at the o - pen door.
Chorus.
The way of the cross leads home, leads home, The way of the cross leads home; leads home; It is sweet to know, as I on-ward go, The way of the cross leads home. A - men.

Copyright, 1934. Renewal. Homer A. Rodeheaver, owner. Used by permission.

206 I Am Thine, O Lord

Fanny J. Crosby — W. H. Doane

1. I am Thine, O Lord, I have heard Thy voice, And it told Thy
2. Con-se-crate me now to Thy serv-ice, Lord, By the pow'r of
3. Oh, the pure de-light of a sin-gle hour That be-fore Thy
4. There are depths of love that I can-not know Till I cross the
love to me; But I long to rise in the arms of faith, And be
grace di-vine; Let my soul look up with a stead-fast hope, And my
throne I spend, When I kneel in prayer, and with Thee, my God, I com-
nar-row sea; There are heights of joy that I may not reach Till I
Refrain
clos-er drawn to Thee.
will be lost in Thine.
mune as friend with friend!
rest in peace with Thee.
Draw me near - er, near-er, bless-ed
near-er, near-er,
Lord, To the cross where Thou hast died; Draw me near-er, near-er,
near-er, bless-ed Lord, To Thy pre-cious, bleed-ing side.

He Hideth My Soul

FANNY J. CROSBY

WM. J. KIRKPATRICK

Allegretto
1. A won-der-ful Sav-ior is Je-sus my Lord, A won-der-ful Sav-ior to me, He hid-eth my soul in the cleft of the rock, Where riv-ers of pleas-ure I see.
2. A won-der-ful Sav-ior is Je-sus my Lord, He tak-eth my bur-den a-way, He hold-eth me up, and I shall not be moved, He giv-eth me strength as my day.
3. With num-ber-less bless-ings each mo-ment He crowns, And filled with His full-ness di-vine, I sing in my rap-ture, oh, glo-ry to God For such a Re-deem-er as mine!
4. When clothed in His brightness, transport-ed I rise To meet Him in clouds of the sky, His per-fect sal-va-tion, His won-der-ful love, I'll shout with the mil-lions on high.
CHORUS
He hid-eth my soul in the cleft of the rock That shadows a dry, thirst-y land; He hid-eth my life in the depths of His love, And cov-ers me there with His hand, And cov-ers me there with His hand.

Copyright, 1918, by Wm. J. Kirkpatrick. Renewal. Hope Publishing Co., owner

208 There Shall Be Showers of Blessing

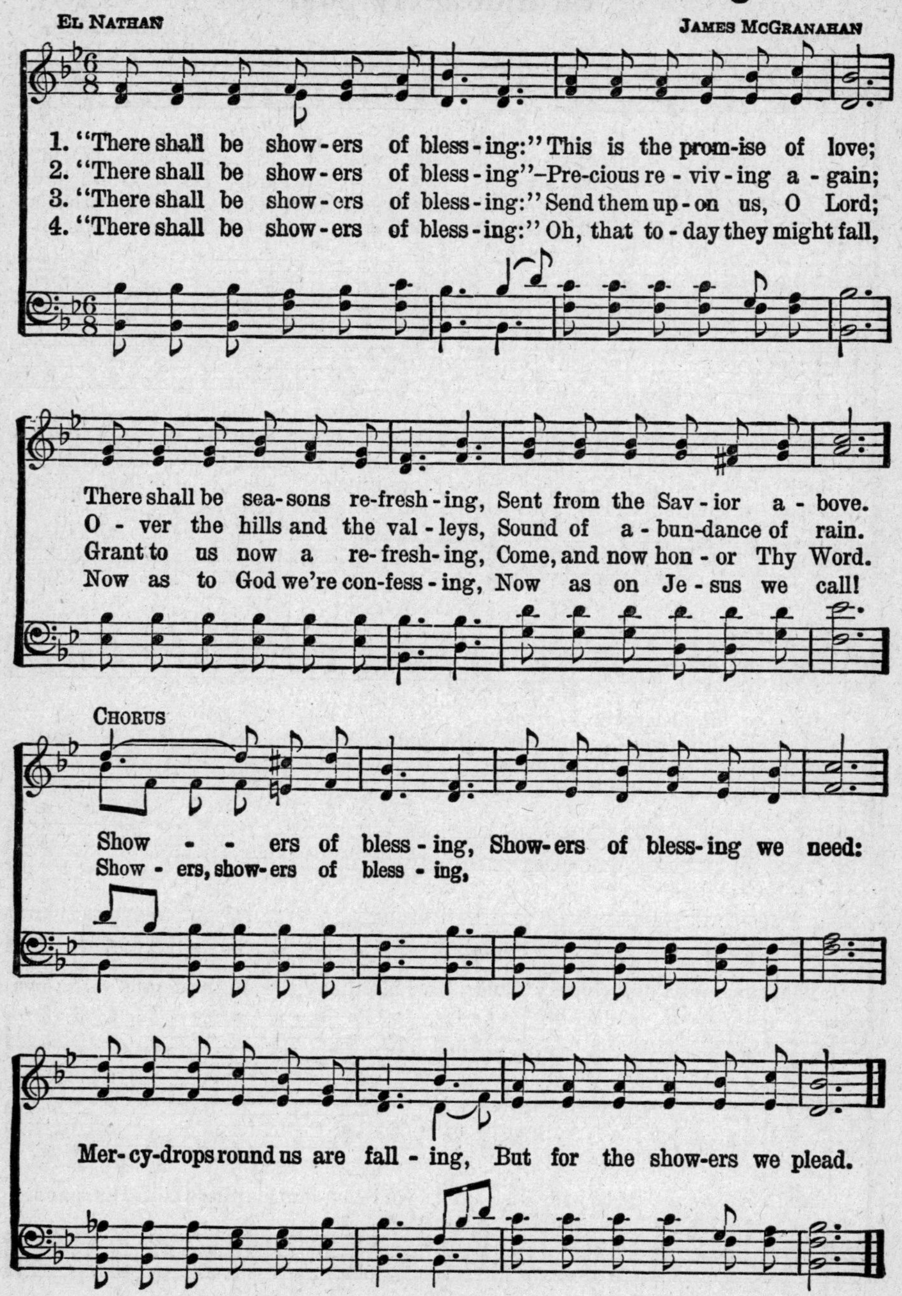

El Nathan
James McGranahan
1. "There shall be show-ers of bless-ing:" This is the prom-ise of love;
2. "There shall be show-ers of bless-ing"–Pre-cious re-viv-ing a-gain;
3. "There shall be show-ers of bless-ing:" Send them up-on us, O Lord;
4. "There shall be show-ers of bless-ing:" Oh, that to-day they might fall,
There shall be sea-sons re-fresh-ing, Sent from the Sav-ior a-bove.
O-ver the hills and the val-leys, Sound of a-bun-dance of rain.
Grant to us now a re-fresh-ing, Come, and now hon-or Thy Word.
Now as to God we're con-fess-ing, Now as on Je-sus we call!
Chorus
Show - - ers of bless-ing, Show-ers of bless-ing we need:
Show-ers, show-ers of bless-ing,
Mer-cy-drops round us are fall-ing, But for the show-ers we plead.

It Is Well With My Soul 209

H. G. Spafford
P. P. Bliss
1. When peace, like a river, attendeth my way, When sorrows like sea-billows roll; Whatever my lot, Thou hast taught me to say, It is well, it is well with my soul.
2. Though Satan should buffet, tho' trials should come, Let this blest assurance control, That Christ has regarded my helpless estate, And hath shed His own blood for my soul.
3. My sin—oh, the bliss of this glorious tho't—My sin—not in part, but the whole, Is nailed to the cross and I bear it no more, Praise the Lord, praise the Lord, O my soul!
4. And, Lord, haste the day when the faith shall be sight, The clouds be rolled back as a scroll, The trump shall resound and the Lord shall descend, "Even so"—it is well with my soul.
Chorus
It is well . . . . . with my soul, ... It is well, it is well with my soul.
It is well with my soul,

210 Blessed Assurance

FANNY J. CROSBY
MRS. J. F. KNAPP
1. Bless-ed as-sur-ance, Je-sus is mine! Oh, what a fore-taste of glo-ry di-vine! Heir of sal-va-tion, pur-chase of God, Born of His Spir-it, washed in His blood.
2. Per-fect sub-mis-sion, per-fect de-light, Vi-sions of rap-ture now burst on my sight; An-gels de-scend-ing, bring from a-bove Ech-oes of mer-cy, whis-pers of love.
3. Per-fect sub-mis-sion, all is at rest, I in my Sav-ior am hap-py and blest; Watching and wait-ing, look-ing a-bove, Filled with His goodness, lost in His love.
CHORUS
This is my sto-ry, this is my song, Prais-ing my Sav-ior all the day long; This is my sto-ry, this is my song, Prais-ing my Sav-ior all the day long.

Grace, Enough For Me

E. O. E. E. O. Excell

1. In looking thro' my tears one day, I saw Mount Calvary;
2. While standing there, my trembling heart, Once full of agony,
3. When I beheld my ev'ry sin Nailed to the cruel tree,
4. When I am safe within the veil, My portion there will be,
Beneath the cross there flowed a stream Of grace, enough for me.
Could scarce believe the sight I saw Of grace, enough for me.
I felt a flood go thro' my soul Of grace, enough for me.
To sing thro' all the years to come Of grace, enough for me.
Chorus.
Grace is flowing from Calvary, . . .
enough for me. Grace is flowing from Calvary for me,
Grace as fathomless as the sea, . . Grace for time and eternity, ...
Grace as fathomless as the rolling sea, Grace for time and eternity, His abundant grace I see,
Grace . . . enough for me.
enough for me.

Copyright, 1933. Renewal. Hope Publishing Co., owner.

212 Near to the Heart of God

CLELAND B. McAFEE — CLELAND B. McAFEE

1. There is a place of qui - et rest, Near to the heart of God,
2. There is a place of com-fort sweet, Near to the heart of God,
3. There is a place of full re-lease, Near to the heart of God,

A place where sin can - not mo - lest, Near to the heart of God.
A place where we our Sav - ior meet, Near to the heart of God.
A place where all is joy and peace, Near to the heart of God.

REFRAIN

O Je - sus, blest Re - deem - er, Sent from the heart of God,
Hold us, who wait be - fore Thee, Near to the heart of God.

Copyright. 1931, Renewal. The Lorenz Pub. Co., owner. Used by permission

213 There's a Wideness in God's Mercy

FREDERICK W. FABER — LIZZIE S. TOURJÉE

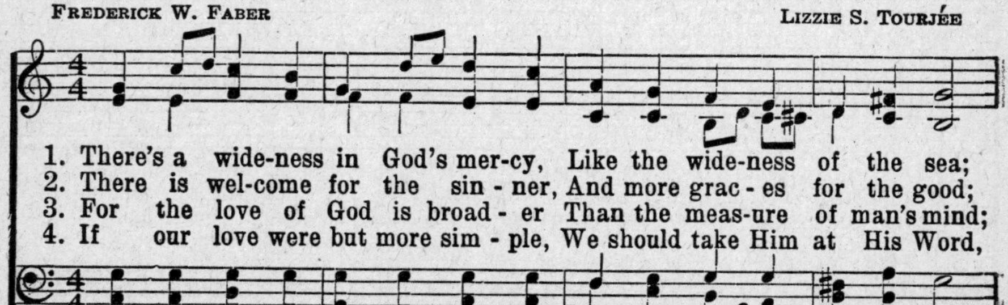
1. There's a wide-ness in God's mer-cy, Like the wide-ness of the sea;
2. There is wel-come for the sin - ner, And more grac - es for the good;
3. For the love of God is broad - er Than the meas-ure of man's mind;
4. If our love were but more sim - ple, We should take Him at His Word,

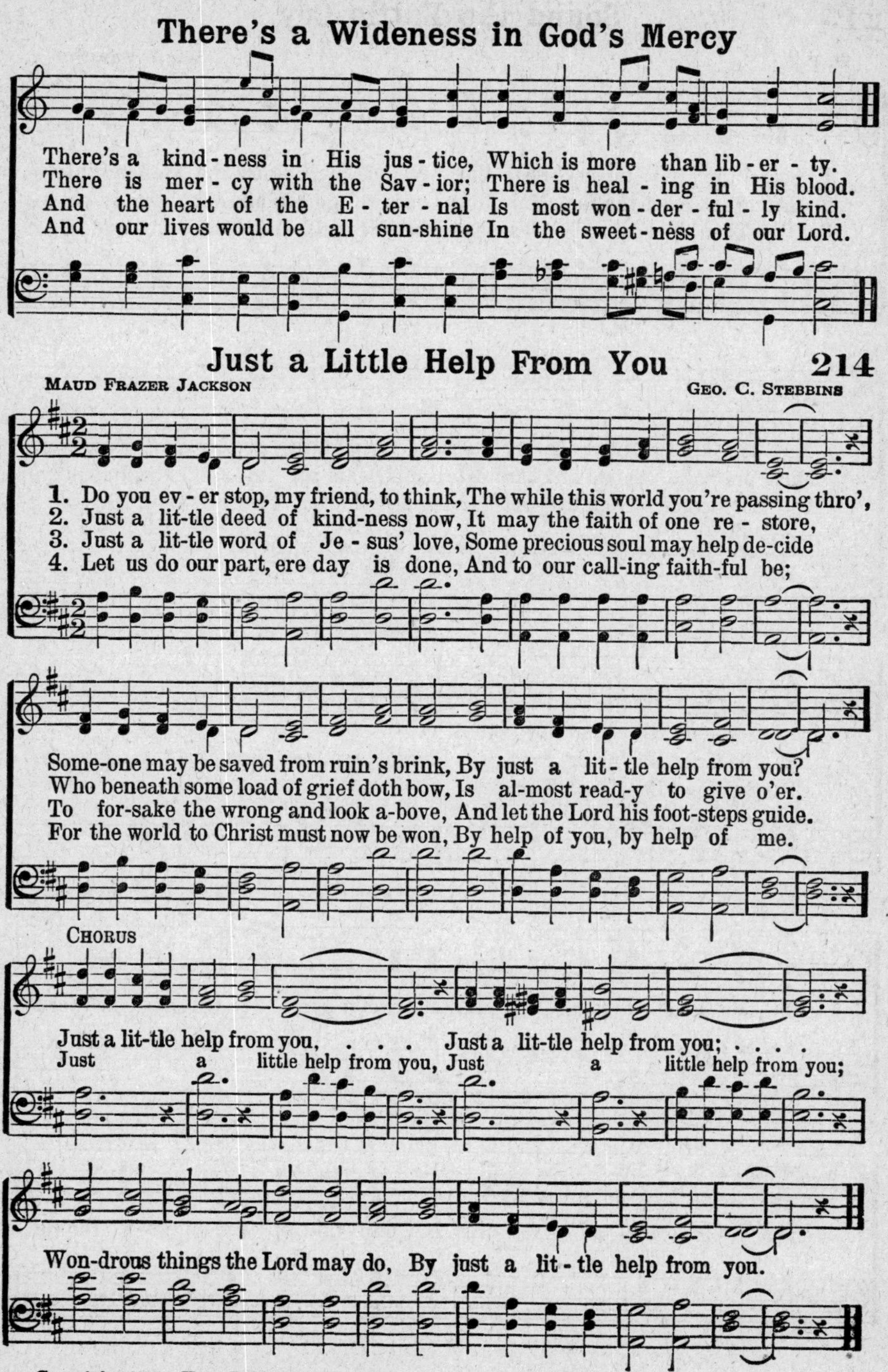
There's a Wideness in God's Mercy
There's a kind-ness in His jus-tice, Which is more than lib-er-ty.
There is mer-cy with the Sav-ior; There is heal-ing in His blood.
And the heart of the E-ter-nal Is most won-der-ful-ly kind.
And our lives would be all sun-shine In the sweet-ness of our Lord.
Just a Little Help From You
214
Maud Frazer Jackson
Geo. C. Stebbins
1. Do you ev-er stop, my friend, to think, The while this world you're passing thro',
2. Just a lit-tle deed of kind-ness now, It may the faith of one re-store,
3. Just a lit-tle word of Je-sus' love, Some precious soul may help de-cide
4. Let us do our part, ere day is done, And to our call-ing faith-ful be;
Some-one may be saved from ruin's brink, By just a lit-tle help from you?
Who beneath some load of grief doth bow, Is al-most read-y to give o'er.
To for-sake the wrong and look a-bove, And let the Lord his foot-steps guide.
For the world to Christ must now be won, By help of you, by help of me.
Chorus
Just a lit-tle help from you, . . . Just a lit-tle help from you; . . . .
Just a little help from you, Just a little help from you;
Won-drous things the Lord may do, By just a lit-tle help from you.

Copyright, 1915. Hope Publishing Co., owner

215 Sound the Battle Cry

W. F. S. — Wm. F. Sherwin

1. Sound the bat-tle cry! See, the foe is nigh; Raise the standard high For the Lord; Gird your ar-mor on, Stand firm, ev-'ry one; Rest your cause up-on His ho-ly word.
2. Strong to meet the foe, Marching on we go, While our cause we know, Must pre-vail; Shield and banner bright, Gleam-ing in the light; Bat-tling for the right We ne'er can fail.
3. O! Thou God of all, Hear us when we call, Help us one and all By Thy grace; When the bat-tle's done, And the vic-t'ry's won, May we wear the crown Be-fore Thy face.
Chorus ff
Rouse, then, sol-diers, ral-ly round the ban-ner, Read-y, stead-y, pass the word a-long; On-ward, for-ward, shout a-loud Ho-san-na! Christ is Cap-tain of the might-y throng.

Loyalty to Christ

DR. E. T. CASSEL
FLORA H. CASSEL
1. From o-ver hill and plain There comes the signal strain, 'Tis loy-al-ty, loy-al-ty,
2. O hear, ye brave, the sound That moves the earth around, 'Tis loy-al-ty, loy-al-ty,
3. Come, join our loy-al throng, We'll rout the giant wrong, 'Tis loy-al-ty, loy-al-ty,
4. The strength of youth we lay At Je-sus' feet to-day, 'Tis loy-al-ty, loy-al-ty,
loy-al-ty to Christ; Its mu-sic rolls a-long, The hills take up the song,
loy-al-ty to Christ; A-rise to dare and do, Ring out the watch-word true,
loy-al-ty to Christ; Where Satan's banners float We'll send the bu-gle note,
loy-al-ty to Christ; His gos-pel we'll pro-claim Thro'-out the world's domain,
CHORUS.
Of loy-al-ty, loy-al-ty, Yes, loy-al-ty to Christ. "On to vic-to-ry! On to
vic-to-ry!" Cries our great Commander; "On!" . . . We'll move at His command,
great Commander; "On!"
We'll soon possess the land, Thro' loyalty, loyalty, Yes, loy-al-ty to Christ. A-MEN.

Copyright, 1921. Renewal. In "Triumphant Songs." Hope Publishing Co., owner.

217 Christ Receiveth Sinful Men

Arr. from NEUMASTER, 1671
JAMES MCGRANAHAN
1. Sin - ners Je - sus will re - ceive; Sound this word of grace to all
2. Come, and He will give you rest; Trust Him, for His word is plain;
3. Now my heart con-demns me not, Pure be - fore the law I stand;
4. Christ re - ceiv - eth sin - ful men, E - ven me with all my sin;
Who the heav'n - ly path-way leave, All who lin - ger, all who fall.
He will take the sin - ful - est; Christ re - ceiv - eth sin - ful men.
He who cleansed me from all spot, Sat - is - fied its last de-mand.
Purged from ev - 'ry spot and stain, Heav'n with Him I en - ter in.
REFRAIN
Sing it o'er. . . . . . . and o'er a - gain; . . . . . . Christ re-
Sing it o'er a-gain, Sing it o'er a-gain; Christ re-
ceiv - - - eth sin-ful men; . . . . . Make the mes - - - sage
ceiv-eth sin - ful men, Christ re-ceiv - eth sin - ful men; Make the message plain,
clear and plain: . . . . . . Christ re - ceiv - eth sin - ful men.
Make the mes-sage plain:

Since I Have Been Redeemed

E. O. E.
E. O. Excell
1. I have a song I love to sing, Since I have been re - deemed,
2. I have a Christ that sat - is - fies, Since I have been re - deemed,
3. I have a wit - ness bright and clear, Since I have been re - deemed,
4. I have a home pre-pared for me, Since I have been re - deemed,
Of my Re - deem-er, Sav - ior, King, Since I have been re - deemed.
To do His will my high - est prize, Since I have been re - deemed.
Dis - pel - ling ev - 'ry doubt and fear, Since I have been re - deemed.
Where I shall dwell e - ter - nal - ly, Since I have been re - deemed.
Chorus.
Since I . . . . . have been re-deemed, Since I have been re-
Since I have been redeemed, Since I have been redeemed,
deemed, I will glo - ry in His name; Since I . . . . . have been re-
Since I have been redeemed, Since
deemed, I will glo - ry in my Sav - ior's name.
I have been re-deemed,

219 Open My Eyes, That I May See

C. H. S. CHAS. H. SCOTT

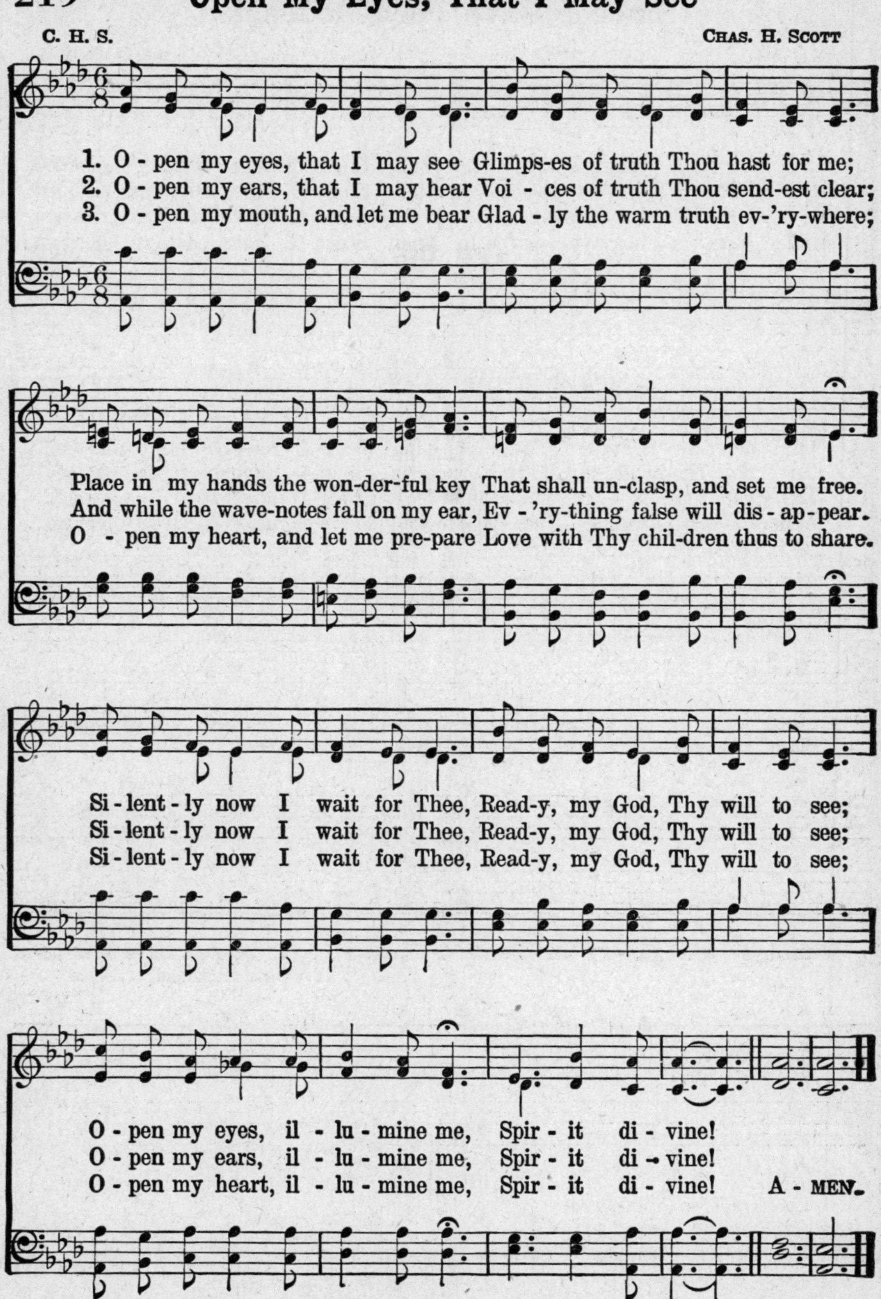
1. O - pen my eyes, that I may see Glimps-es of truth Thou hast for me;
2. O - pen my ears, that I may hear Voi - ces of truth Thou send-est clear;
3. O - pen my mouth, and let me bear Glad - ly the warm truth ev-'ry-where;
Place in my hands the won-der-ful key That shall un-clasp, and set me free.
And while the wave-notes fall on my ear, Ev - 'ry-thing false will dis - ap-pear.
O - pen my heart, and let me pre-pare Love with Thy chil-dren thus to share.
Si-lent-ly now I wait for Thee, Read-y, my God, Thy will to see;
Si-lent-ly now I wait for Thee, Read-y, my God, Thy will to see;
Si-lent-ly now I wait for Thee, Read-y, my God, Thy will to see;
O - pen my eyes, il - lu - mine me, Spir - it di - vine!
O - pen my ears, il - lu - mine me, Spir - it di - vine!
O - pen my heart, il - lu - mine me, Spir - it di - vine! A - MEN.

Copyright, 1923. Renewal by H. F. Sayles. F. E. Hathaway, owner. Used by permission.

No, Not One! 220

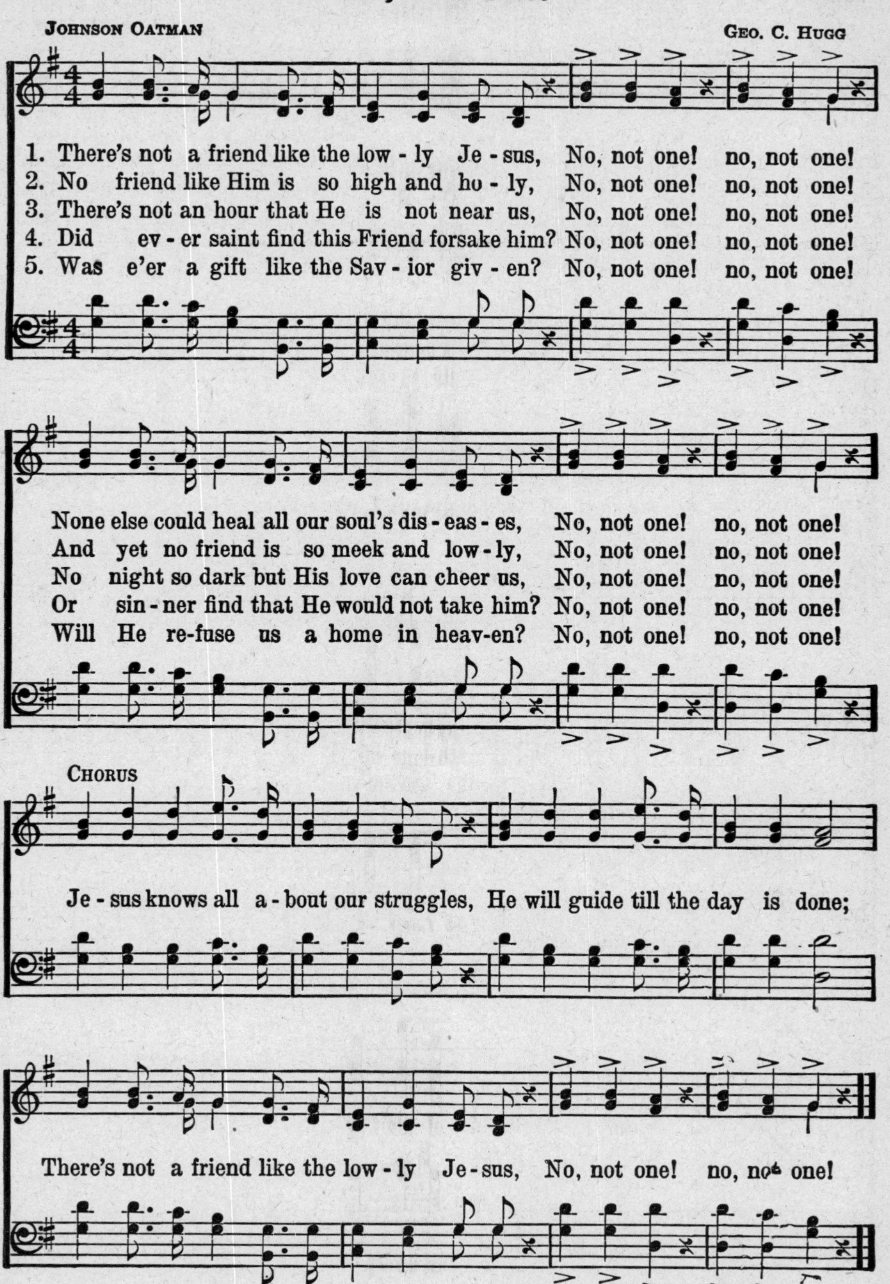

JOHNSON OATMAN
GEO. C. HUGG
1. There's not a friend like the low - ly Je - sus, No, not one! no, not one!
2. No friend like Him is so high and ho - ly, No, not one! no, not one!
3. There's not an hour that He is not near us, No, not one! no, not one!
4. Did ev - er saint find this Friend forsake him? No, not one! no, not one!
5. Was e'er a gift like the Sav - ior giv - en? No, not one! no, not one!
None else could heal all our soul's dis - eas - es, No, not one! no, not one!
And yet no friend is so meek and low - ly, No, not one! no, not one!
No night so dark but His love can cheer us, No, not one! no, not one!
Or sin - ner find that He would not take him? No, not one! no, not one!
Will He re-fuse us a home in heav-en? No, not one! no, not one!
CHORUS
Je - sus knows all a - bout our struggles, He will guide till the day is done;
There's not a friend like the low - ly Je - sus, No, not one! no, not one!

221 Go and Tell the Story

W. A. O. W. A. OGDEN
Descant (small notes) by Fred Jacky

1. Go and tell the sto - ry to thy friends to-day, How the Lord of glo - ry
2. Go and tell the sto - ry, of His pow'r to save, Of the sin - ful "Le-gion"
3. Go and tell the sto - ry, how He reigns a-bove, Win - ning men to glo - ry
Sing Descant only on D.S.
met thee on thy way; How He cleansed thy spir - it from the stain of sin,
sunk be-neath the wave; Tell of His com-pas - sion, of His love so true,
thro' His dy - ing love; How He waits to crown them kings for - ev - er-more,
D.S.—And the soul that hears it, and in faith be - lieves,
Descant Ah!......................
FINE.
CHORUS
Driv-ing out the foes who reigned thy heart with-in.
Of the won-drous things the Lord hath done for you. Go and tell the sto - ry,
In the home a - wait - ing, on the oth - er shore.
Straightway he the cleans-ing from the Lord re-ceives.
Sing
Ah!.......................
Sing
D. S.
tell it far and wide, How the Lord of glo - ry for the sin - ner died;

Arr. Copyright, 1941. Hope Publishing Company, owner

Wear a Crown

222

Harriette Waters — A. E. Lind

1. Bu - gle calls are ring-ing out, "For-ward" is the bat-tle shout, See where floats the conqu'ring sign, On-ward to the war di - vine!
2. Sound the charge against the foe, Lay the hosts of er - ror low; In His name, vic-to-rious King, Let the song of tri-umph ring!
3. Fight the fight of faith and love, Look-ing un - to Him a - bove; Loy - al sol - diers, do and dare, Your Commander's joy to share.
CHORUS Adapted and Arr.
And when the bat-tle's o-ver We shall wear a crown, We shall wear a crown, We shall wear a crown! And when the bat-tle's o-ver We shall wear a crown In the new Je-ru - sa-lem!
FINE
D.S.–when the battle's o-ver We shall wear a crown In the new Je - ru - sa - lem!
Wear a crown, Wear a crown, wear a crown, Wear a crown, A-way o - ver Jor - dan! And
D. S.

223
Leave It There
C. Albert Tindley
Arr. by Chas. A. Tindley, Jr.
Moderato
1. If the world from you with-hold of its sil - ver and its gold, And you
2. If your bod - y suf - fers pain and your health you can't re-gain, And your
3. When your en - e - mies as - sail and your heart be - gins to fail, Don't for-
4. When your youthful days are gone and old age is steal-ing on, And your
have to get a-long with mea-ger fare, Just re-mem-ber, in His word, how He
soul is al-most sink-ing in de - spair, Je - sus knows the pain you feel, He can
get that God in heav-en answers prayer; He will make a way for you and will
bod - y bends beneath the weight of care; He will nev - er leave you then, He'll go
feeds the lit - tle bird; Take your bur - den to the Lord and leave it there.
save and He can heal; Take your bur - den to the Lord and leave it there.
lead you safe - ly thro'; Take your bur - den to the Lord and leave it there.
with you to the end; Take your bur - den to the Lord and leave it there.
Chorus
Leave it there, . . . leave it there, ... Take your bur-den to the
Leave it there, leave it there,
Lord and leave it there; . . . . If you trust and nev - er doubt, He will
leave it there;

Copyright, 1916, by C. A. Tindley. Hope Publishing Co., owner

Leave It There

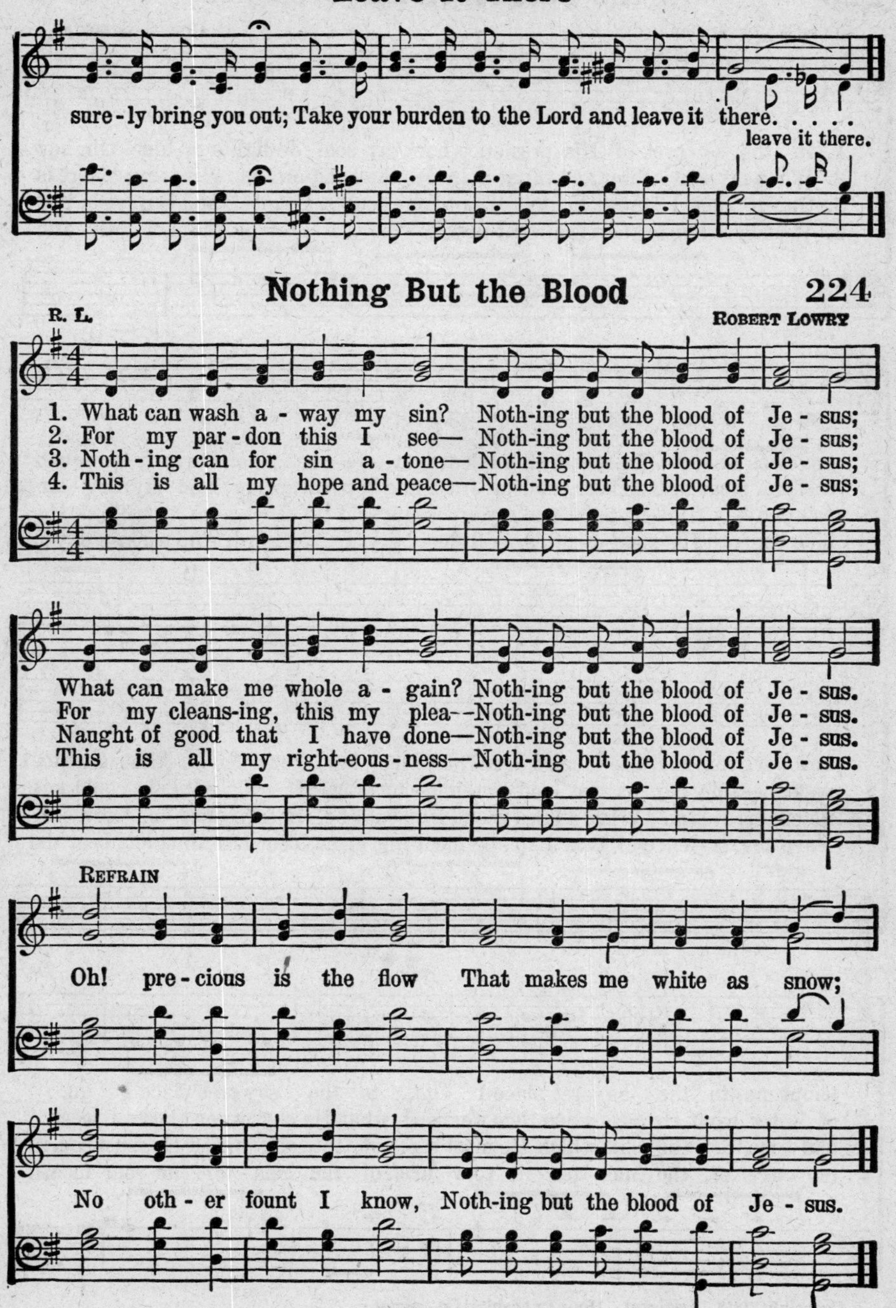
sure-ly bring you out; Take your burden to the Lord and leave it there. . . . .
leave it there.
Nothing But the Blood
224
R. L.
ROBERT LOWRY
1. What can wash a-way my sin? Noth-ing but the blood of Je-sus;
2. For my par-don this I see— Noth-ing but the blood of Je-sus;
3. Noth-ing can for sin a-tone— Noth-ing but the blood of Je-sus;
4. This is all my hope and peace—Noth-ing but the blood of Je-sus;
What can make me whole a-gain? Noth-ing but the blood of Je-sus.
For my cleans-ing, this my plea--Noth-ing but the blood of Je-sus.
Naught of good that I have done—Noth-ing but the blood of Je-sus.
This is all my right-eous-ness—Noth-ing but the blood of Je-sus.
REFRAIN
Oh! pre-cious is the flow That makes me white as snow;
No oth-er fount I know, Noth-ing but the blood of Je-sus.

225 In the Secret of His Presence

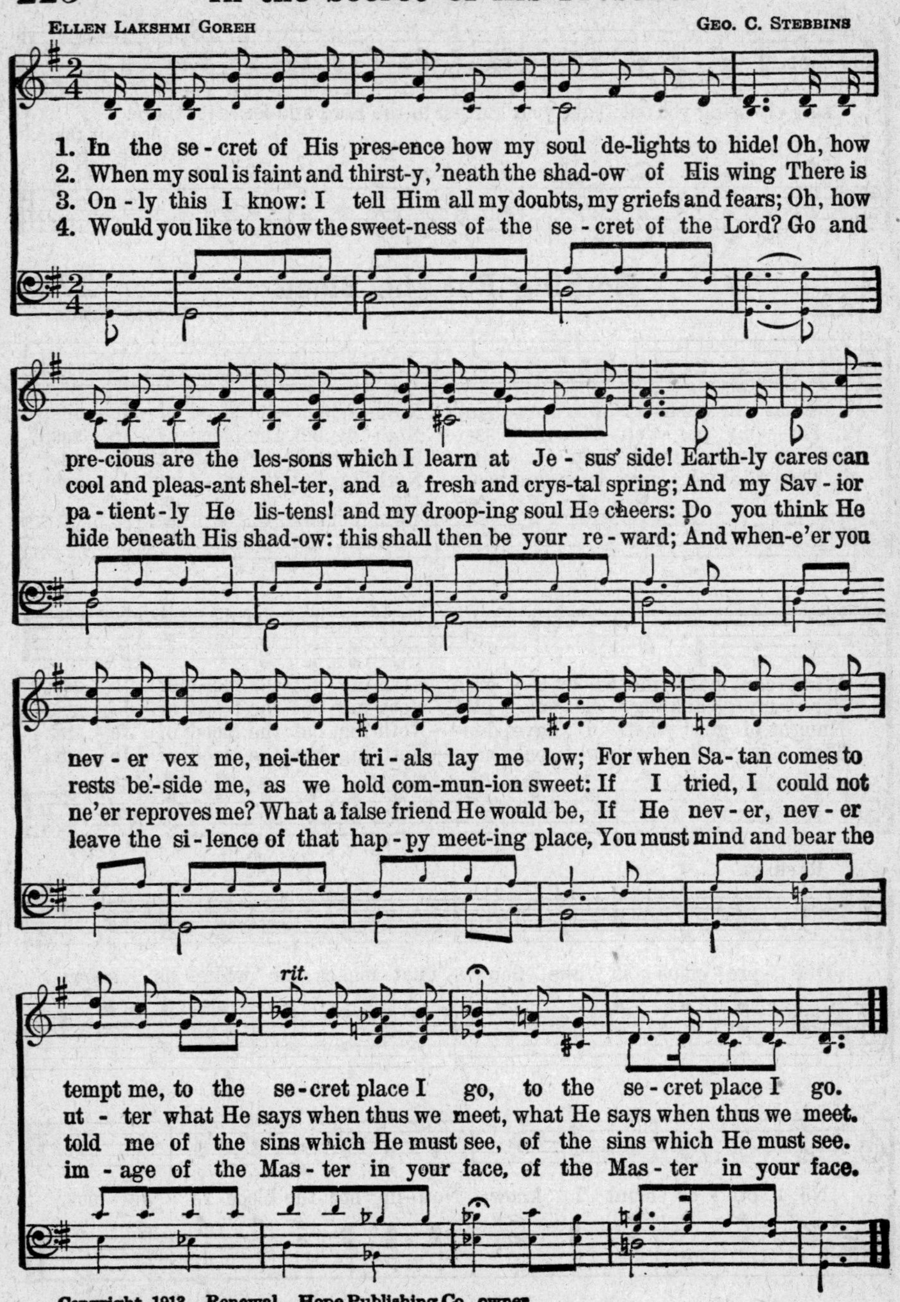

Ellen Lakshmi Goreh
Geo. C. Stebbins
1. In the se-cret of His pres-ence how my soul de-lights to hide! Oh, how
2. When my soul is faint and thirst-y, 'neath the shad-ow of His wing There is
3. On-ly this I know: I tell Him all my doubts, my griefs and fears; Oh, how
4. Would you like to know the sweet-ness of the se-cret of the Lord? Go and
pre-cious are the les-sons which I learn at Je-sus' side! Earth-ly cares can
cool and pleas-ant shel-ter, and a fresh and crys-tal spring; And my Sav-ior
pa-tient-ly He lis-tens! and my droop-ing soul He cheers: Do you think He
hide beneath His shad-ow: this shall then be your re-ward; And when-e'er you
nev-er vex me, nei-ther tri-als lay me low; For when Sa-tan comes to
rests be-side me, as we hold com-mun-ion sweet: If I tried, I could not
ne'er reproves me? What a false friend He would be, If He nev-er, nev-er
leave the si-lence of that hap-py meet-ing place, You must mind and bear the
rit.
tempt me, to the se-cret place I go, to the se-cret place I go.
ut-ter what He says when thus we meet, what He says when thus we meet.
told me of the sins which He must see, of the sins which He must see.
im-age of the Mas-ter in your face, of the Mas-ter in your face.

Copyright, 1913. Renewal. Hope Publishing Co., owner

Let Him In

J. B. Atchinson — E. O. Excell

1. There's a Stran-ger at the door, Let Him in;
2. O - pen now to Him your heart, Let Him in;
3. Hear you now His lov-ing voice? Let Him in;
4. Now ad-mit the heav'n-ly Guest, Let Him in;
Let the Sav-ior in, Let the Sav-ior in;
He has been there oft be-fore, Let Him in;
If you wait He will de-part, Let Him in;
Now, oh, now make Him your choice, Let Him in;
He will make for you a feast, Let Him in;
Let the Sav-ior in, Let the Sav-ior in;
Let Him in, ere He is gone, Let Him in, the Ho-ly One, Je-sus
Let Him in, He is your Friend, He your soul will sure de-fend, He will
He is stand-ing at your door, Joy to you He will re-store, And His
He will speak your sins for-giv'n, And when earth ties all are riv'n, He will
Christ, the Fa-ther's Son, Let Him in.
keep you to the end, Let Him in.
name you will a-dore, Let Him in.
take you home to heav'n, Let Him in.
Let the Sav-ior in, Let the Sav-ior in.

227 More Like the Master

C. H. G. — Chas. H. Gabriel

1. More like the Mas-ter I would ev-er be, More of His meek-ness, more hu-mil-i-ty; More zeal to la-bor, more cour-age to be true, More con-se-cra-tion for work He bids me do. . . . . .
2. More like the Mas-ter is my dai-ly prayer; More strength to car-ry cross-es I must bear; More ear-nest ef-fort to bring His kingdom in; More of His Spir-it, the wan-der-er to win. . . . .
3. More like the Mas-ter I would live and grow; More of His love to oth-ers I would show; More self-de-ni-al, like His in Gal-i-lee, More like the Mas-ter I long to ev-er be. . . . .
rit.
CHORUS.
Take Thou my heart, . . I would be Thine a-lone; . . Take Thou my heart . . and make it all Thine own; . . Purge me from sin, . . . O Lord, I now im-
Take my heart, O take my heart, I would be Thine a-lone; Take my heart, O take my heart and make it all Thine own; Purge Thou me from ev'ry sin, O Lord, I

Copyright, 1934. Renewal. Homer A. Rodeheaver, owner. Used by permission.

More Like the Master

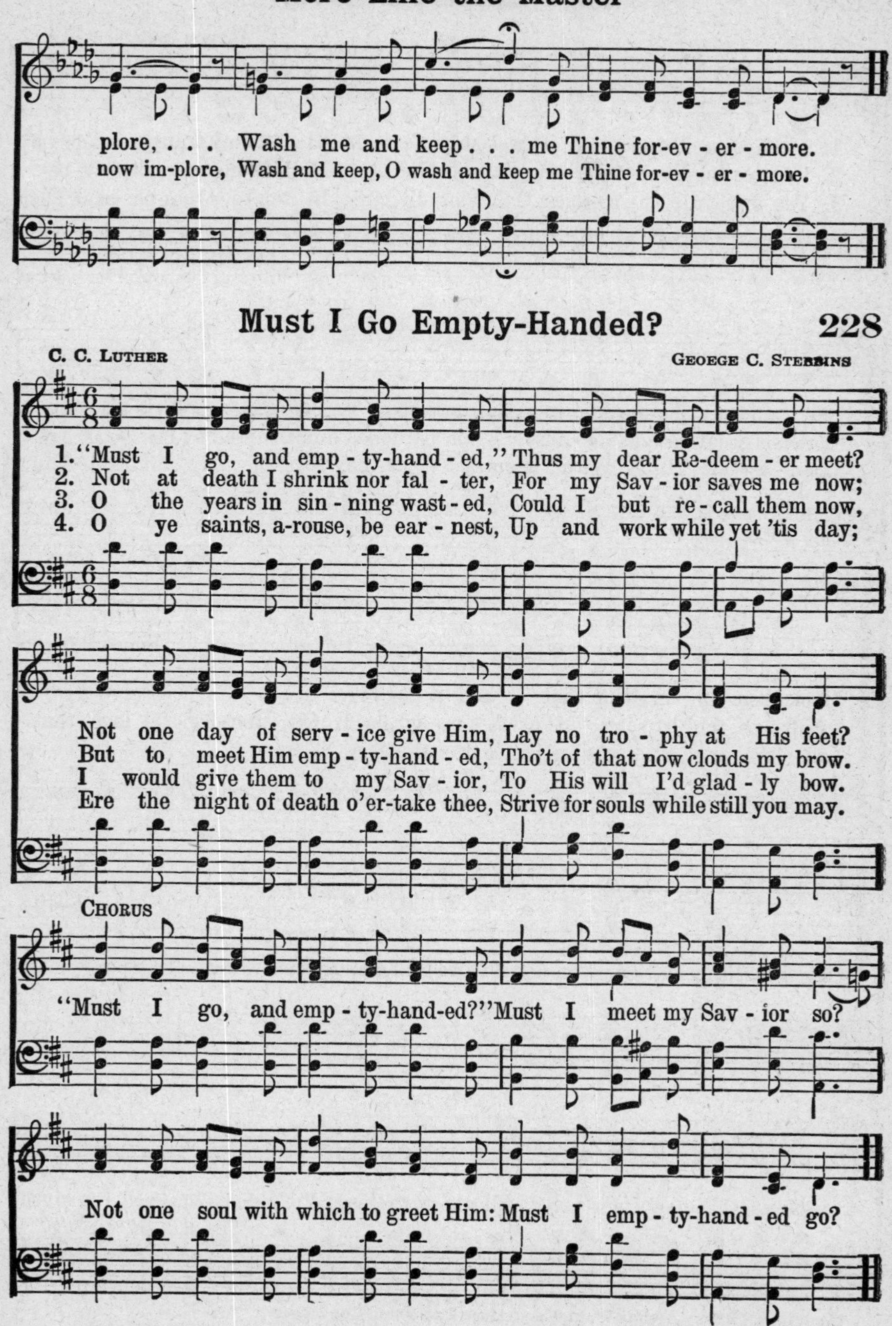

plore, . . . Wash me and keep . . . me Thine for-ev - er - more.
now im-plore, Wash and keep, O wash and keep me Thine for-ev - er - more.
Must I Go Empty-Handed?
228
C. C. Luther
Geoege C. Stebbins
1. "Must I go, and emp - ty-hand - ed," Thus my dear Re-deem - er meet?
2. Not at death I shrink nor fal - ter, For my Sav - ior saves me now;
3. O the years in sin - ning wast - ed, Could I but re - call them now,
4. O ye saints, a-rouse, be ear - nest, Up and work while yet 'tis day;
Not one day of serv - ice give Him, Lay no tro - phy at His feet?
But to meet Him emp - ty-hand - ed, Tho't of that now clouds my brow.
I would give them to my Sav - ior, To His will I'd glad - ly bow.
Ere the night of death o'er-take thee, Strive for souls while still you may.
Chorus
"Must I go, and emp - ty-hand-ed?" Must I meet my Sav - ior so?
Not one soul with which to greet Him: Must I emp - ty-hand - ed go?

229 Oh, Wonderful Love!

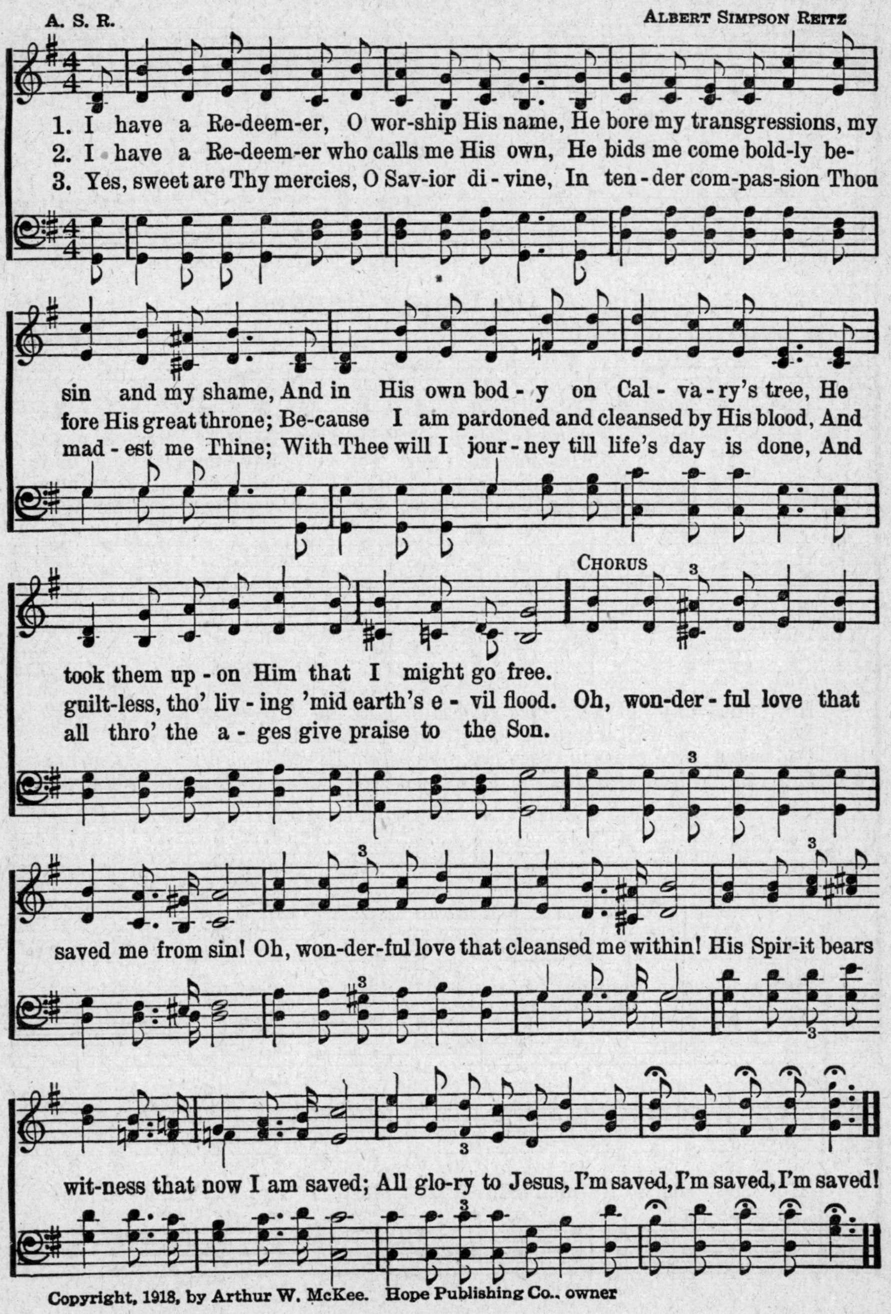
A. S. R.
Albert Simpson Reitz
1. I have a Re-deem-er, O wor-ship His name, He bore my transgressions, my
2. I have a Re-deem-er who calls me His own, He bids me come bold-ly be-
3. Yes, sweet are Thy mercies, O Sav-ior di-vine, In ten-der com-pas-sion Thou
sin and my shame, And in His own bod-y on Cal-va-ry's tree, He
fore His great throne; Be-cause I am pardoned and cleansed by His blood, And
mad-est me Thine; With Thee will I jour-ney till life's day is done, And
Chorus
took them up-on Him that I might go free.
guilt-less, tho' liv-ing 'mid earth's e-vil flood. Oh, won-der-ful love that
all thro' the a-ges give praise to the Son.
saved me from sin! Oh, won-der-ful love that cleansed me within! His Spir-it bears
wit-ness that now I am saved; All glo-ry to Jesus, I'm saved, I'm saved, I'm saved!

Copyright, 1918, by Arthur W. McKee. Hope Publishing Co., owner

He Included Me

Rev. J. Oatman, Jr. | Hamp Sewell

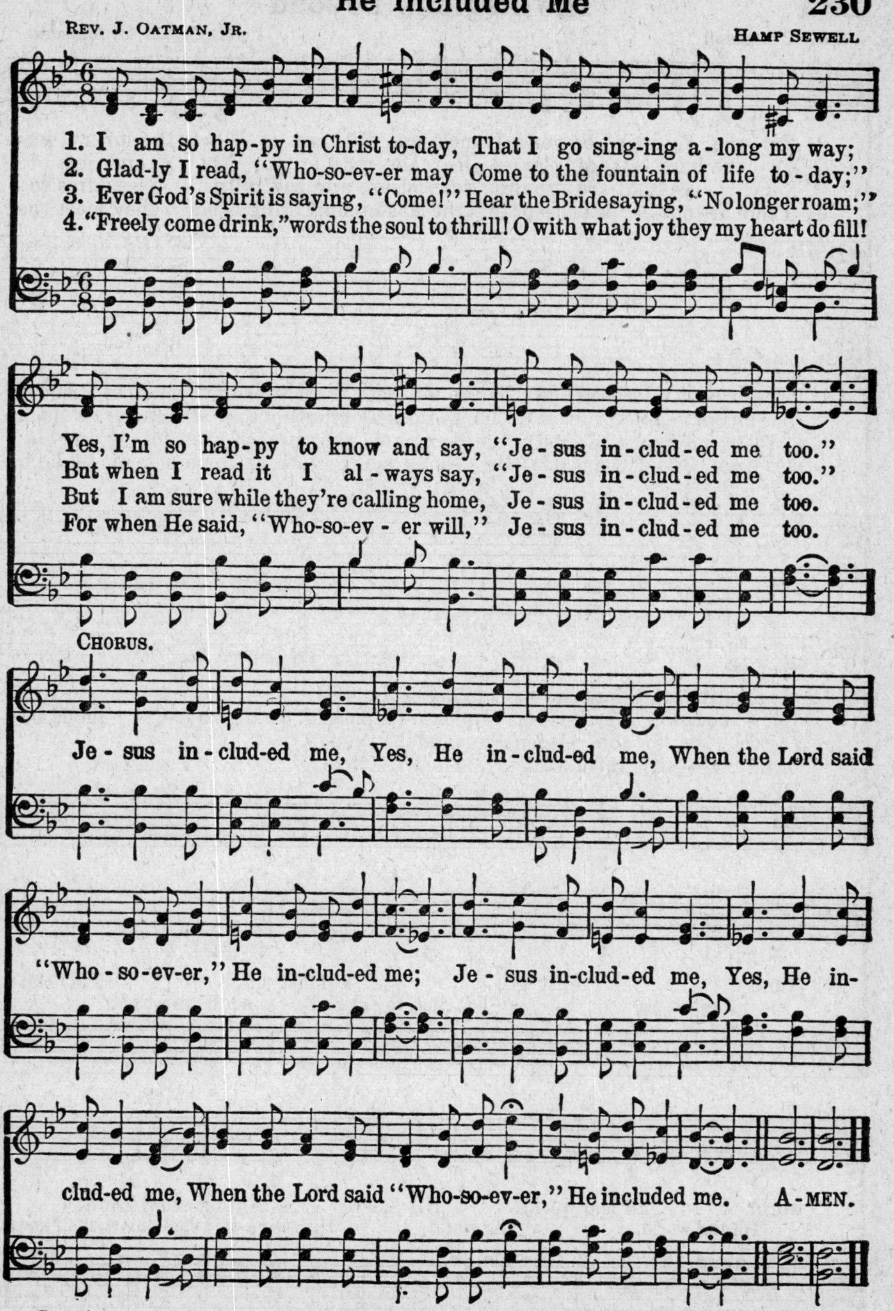
1. I am so hap-py in Christ to-day, That I go sing-ing a-long my way;
2. Glad-ly I read, "Who-so-ev-er may Come to the fountain of life to-day;"
3. Ever God's Spirit is saying, "Come!" Hear the Bridesaying, "Nolongerroam;"
4. "Freely come drink," words the soul to thrill! O with what joy they my heart do fill!
Yes, I'm so hap-py to know and say, "Je-sus in-clud-ed me too."
But when I read it I al-ways say, "Je-sus in-clud-ed me too."
But I am sure while they're calling home, Je-sus in-clud-ed me too.
For when He said, "Who-so-ev-er will," Je-sus in-clud-ed me too.
CHORUS.
Je-sus in-clud-ed me, Yes, He in-clud-ed me, When the Lord said
"Who-so-ev-er," He in-clud-ed me; Je-sus in-clud-ed me, Yes, He in-
clud-ed me, When the Lord said "Who-so-ev-er," He included me. A-MEN.

Copyright, 1941, Renewal. John T. Benson, Jr., owner, Nashville, Tenn. Used by permission.

231 The Regions Beyond

A. B. Simpson — Margaret M. Simpson

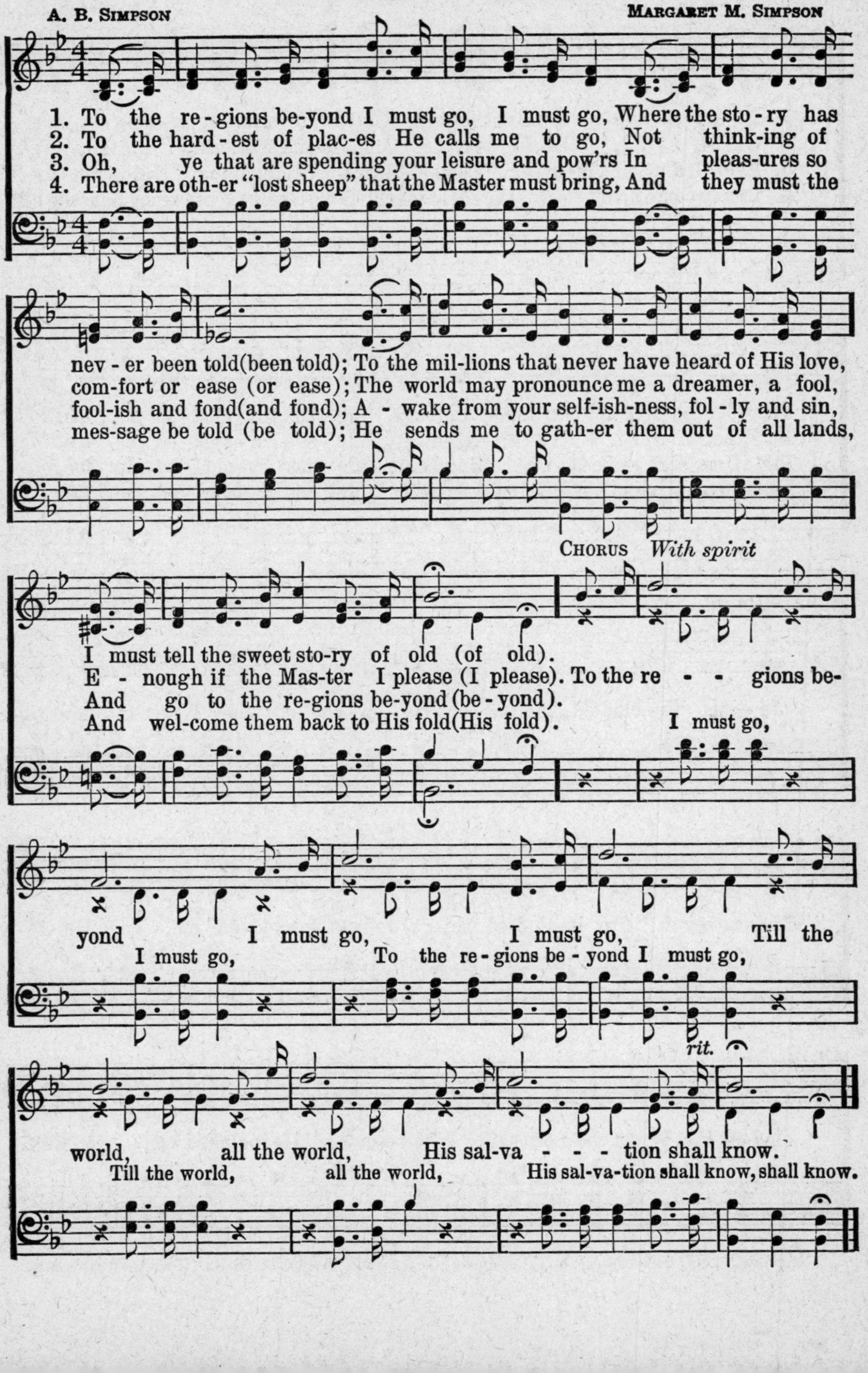

1. To the re-gions be-yond I must go, I must go, Where the sto-ry has nev-er been told (been told); To the mil-lions that never have heard of His love, I must tell the sweet sto-ry of old (of old).
2. To the hard-est of plac-es He calls me to go, Not think-ing of com-fort or ease (or ease); The world may pronounce me a dreamer, a fool, E-nough if the Mas-ter I please (I please).
3. Oh, ye that are spending your leisure and pow'rs In pleas-ures so fool-ish and fond (and fond); A-wake from your self-ish-ness, fol-ly and sin, And go to the re-gions be-yond (be-yond).
4. There are oth-er "lost sheep" that the Master must bring, And they must the mes-sage be told (be told); He sends me to gath-er them out of all lands, And wel-come them back to His fold (His fold).

CHORUS *With spirit*

To the re-gions be-yond I must go, I must go, Till the world, all the world, His sal-va-tion shall know.

(I must go, I must go, To the re-gions be-yond I must go, Till the world, all the world, His sal-va-tion shall know, shall know.)

Great is Thy Faithfulness

T. O. CHISHOLM | WILLIAM M. RUNYAN

1. "Great is Thy faith-ful-ness," O God my Fa - ther, There is no shad-ow of
2. Sum-mer and win - ter, and spring-time and harvest, Sun, moon and stars in their
3. Par - don for sin and a peace that en-dur - eth, Thy own dear presence to
turn - ing with Thee; Thou chang-est not, Thy com-pas-sions, they fail not;
cours - es a - bove, Join with all na - ture in man - i - fold wit - ness,
cheer and to guide; Strength for to - day and bright hope for to-mor - row,
As Thou hast been Thou for - ev - er wilt be.
To Thy great faith-ful - ness, mer-cy and love.
Blessings all mine, with ten thou-sand be - side!
CHORUS
"Great is Thy faith-ful-ness!
Great is Thy faithfulness!" Morning by morning new mercies I see; All I have
rall.
need-ed Thy hand hath provided—"Great is Thy faithfulness," Lord, un-to me!

Copyright, 1923, by W. M. Runyan. Hope Publishing Co., owner.

233 I've Found a Friend

J. G. SMALL GEO. C. STEBBINS

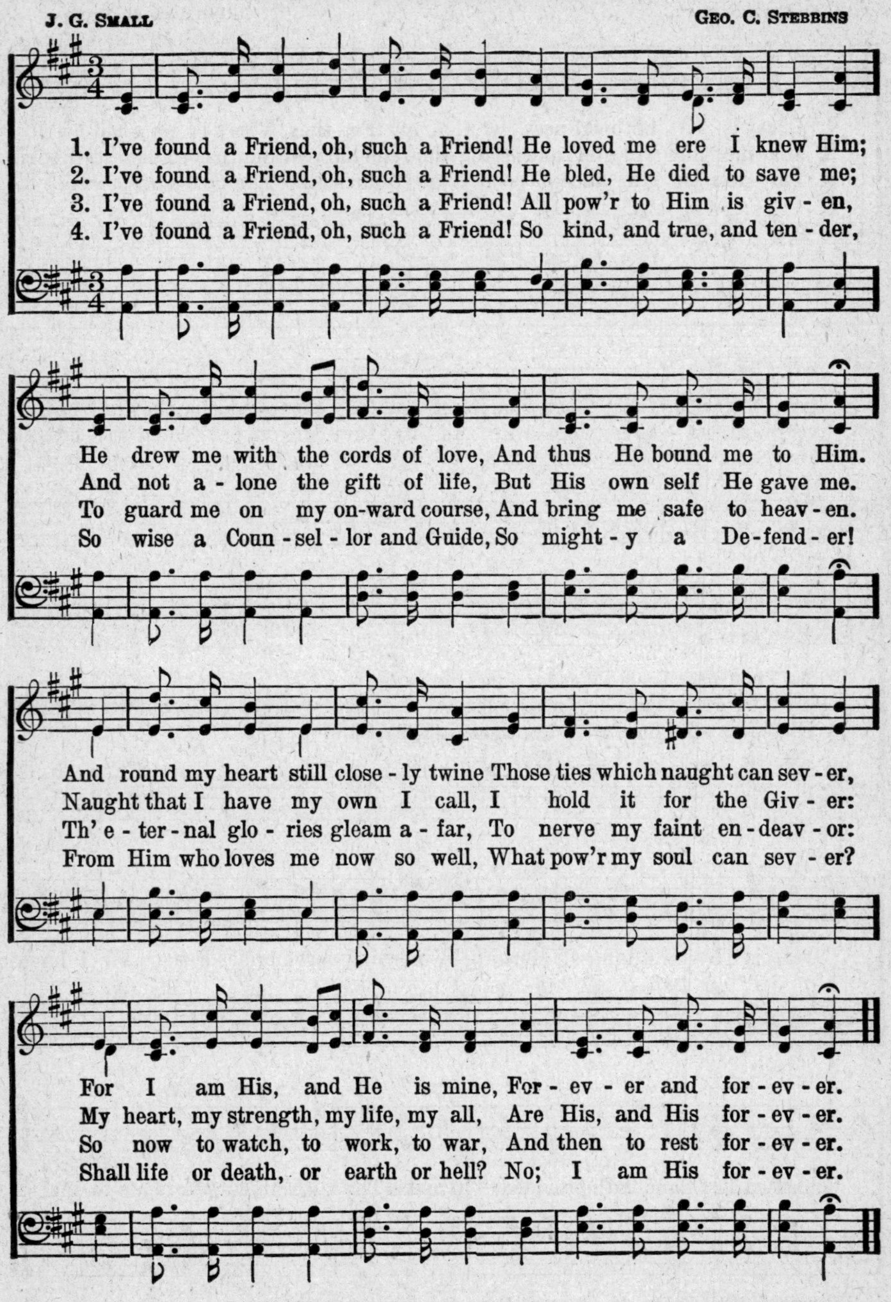
1. I've found a Friend, oh, such a Friend! He loved me ere I knew Him;
2. I've found a Friend, oh, such a Friend! He bled, He died to save me;
3. I've found a Friend, oh, such a Friend! All pow'r to Him is giv - en,
4. I've found a Friend, oh, such a Friend! So kind, and true, and ten - der,
He drew me with the cords of love, And thus He bound me to Him.
And not a - lone the gift of life, But His own self He gave me.
To guard me on my on-ward course, And bring me safe to heav - en.
So wise a Coun - sel - lor and Guide, So might - y a De-fend - er!
And round my heart still close - ly twine Those ties which naught can sev - er,
Naught that I have my own I call, I hold it for the Giv - er:
Th' e - ter - nal glo - ries gleam a - far, To nerve my faint en - deav - or:
From Him who loves me now so well, What pow'r my soul can sev - er?
For I am His, and He is mine, For - ev - er and for - ev - er.
My heart, my strength, my life, my all, Are His, and His for - ev - er.
So now to watch, to work, to war, And then to rest for - ev - er.
Shall life or death, or earth or hell? No; I am His for - ev - er.

Savior, Like a Shepherd Lead Us

Anonymous — William B. Bradbury

1. Sav - ior, like a shep-herd lead us, Much we need Thy ten- der care;
2. We are Thine; do Thou be - friend us, Be the Guardian of our way;
3. Thou hast promised to re - ceive us, Poor and sin- ful though we be;
4. Ear - ly let us seek Thy fa - vor; Ear - ly let us do Thy will;
In Thy pleas-ant pas-tures feed us, For our use Thy folds pre-pare:
Keep Thy flock, from sin de - fend us, Seek us when we go a - stray:
Thou hast mer - cy to re - lieve us, Grace to cleanse, and pow'r to free:
Bless - ed Lord and on - ly Sav - ior, With Thy love our bos- oms fill:
Bless-ed Je - sus, Bless-ed Je - sus, Thou hast bought us, Thine we are;
Bless-ed Je - sus, Bless-ed Je - sus, Hear Thy chil- dren when they pray;
Bless-ed Je - sus, Bless-ed Je - sus, Ear - ly let us turn to Thee;
Bless-ed Je - sus, Bless-ed Je - sus, Thou hast loved us, love us still;
Bless-ed Je - sus, Bless-ed Je - sus, Thou hast bought us, Thine we are.
Bless-ed Je - sus, Bless-ed Je - sus, Hear Thy chil-dren when they pray.
Bless-ed Je - sus, Bless-ed Je - sus, Ear - ly let us turn to Thee.
Bless-ed Je - sus, Bless-ed Je - sus, Thou hast loved us, love us still.

235 O Worship the King

ROBERT GRANT — FRANCIS JOSEPH HAYDN

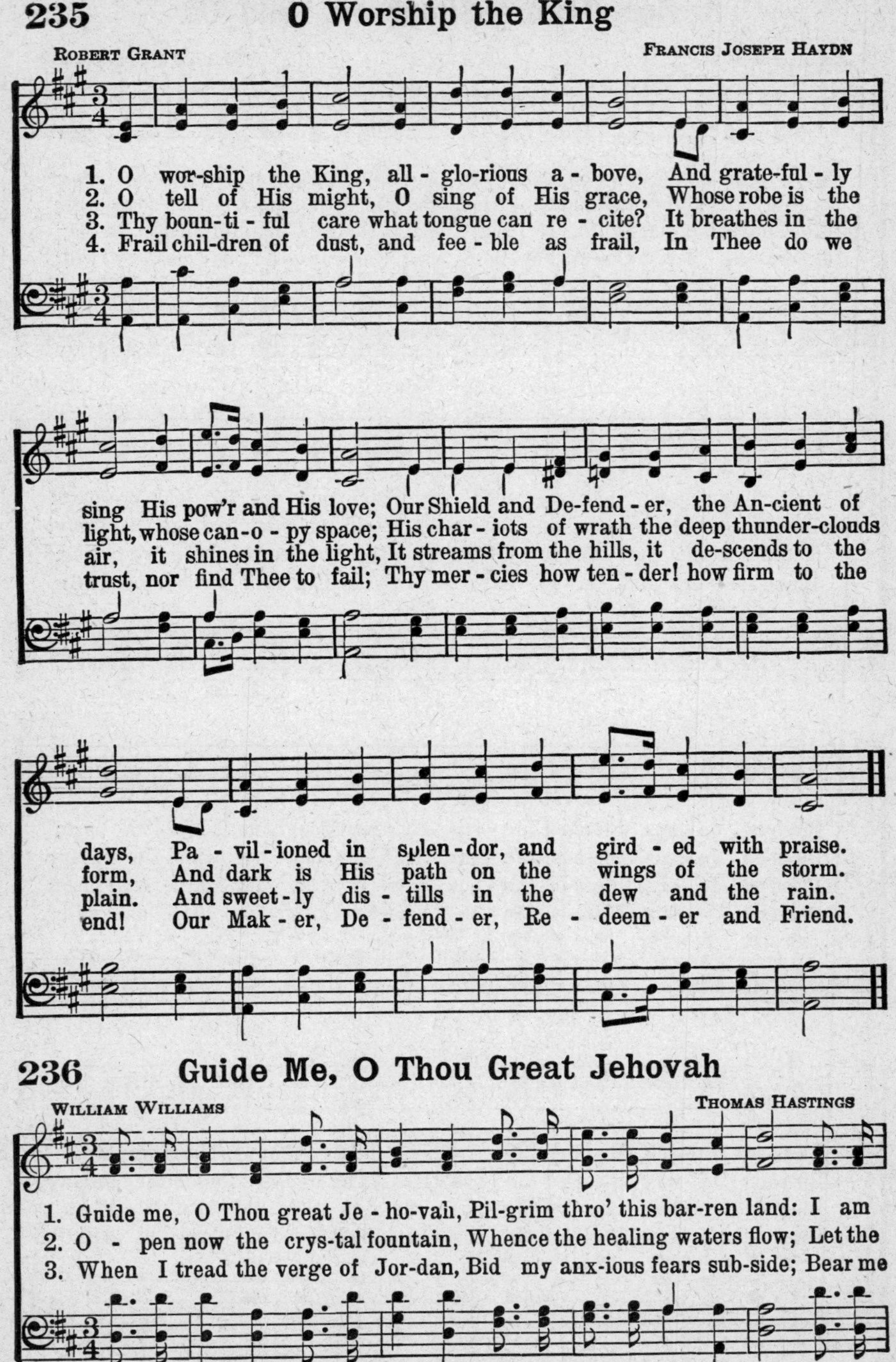

1. O wor-ship the King, all - glo-rious a - bove, And grate-ful - ly
2. O tell of His might, O sing of His grace, Whose robe is the
3. Thy boun-ti - ful care what tongue can re - cite? It breathes in the
4. Frail chil-dren of dust, and fee - ble as frail, In Thee do we
sing His pow'r and His love; Our Shield and De-fend - er, the An-cient of
light, whose can-o - py space; His char - iots of wrath the deep thunder-clouds
air, it shines in the light, It streams from the hills, it de-scends to the
trust, nor find Thee to fail; Thy mer - cies how ten - der! how firm to the
days, Pa - vil - ioned in splen - dor, and gird - ed with praise.
form, And dark is His path on the wings of the storm.
plain. And sweet - ly dis - tills in the dew and the rain.
end! Our Mak - er, De - fend - er, Re - deem - er and Friend.

236 Guide Me, O Thou Great Jehovah

WILLIAM WILLIAMS — THOMAS HASTINGS

1. Guide me, O Thou great Je - ho-vah, Pil-grim thro' this bar-ren land: I am
2. O - pen now the crys-tal fountain, Whence the healing waters flow; Let the
3. When I tread the verge of Jor-dan, Bid my anx-ious fears sub-side; Bear me

Guide Me, O Thou Great Jehovah
weak, but Thou art mighty; Hold me with Thy pow'r-ful hand: Bread of heav-en,
fi - ery, cloud-y pil - lar Lead me all my jour - ney thro': Strong De-liv-'rer,
thro' the swelling cur-rent, Land me safe on Ca-naan's side: Songs of praises
Feed me till I want no more; Bread of heav-en, Feed me till I want no more.
Be Thou still my strength and shield;Strong Deliv'rer,Be Thou still my strength and shield.
I will ev - er give to Thee; Songs of prais-es I will ev - er give to Thee.
Stand Up for Jesus
237
G. DUFFIELD
G. J. WEBB
1. Stand up, stand up for Je - sus, Ye sol - diers of the cross, Lift high His
2. Stand up, stand up for Je - sus, The trum-pet call o - bey; Forth to the
3. Stand up, stand up for Je - sus, Stand in His strength a-lone; The arm of
roy - al ban - ner, It must not suf - fer loss; From vic-t'ry un - to vic - t'ry, His
might-y con - flict, In this His glorious day. "Ye that are men now serve Him," A-
flesh will fail you—Ye dare not trust your own; Put on the gos-pel ar-mor, And,
ar - my shall He lead, Till ev-'ry foe is vanquished And Christ is Lord in-deed.
gainst unnumbered foes; Let courage rise with danger, And strength to strength oppose.
watch-ing un - to prayer, Where du-ty calls, or dan-ger, Be nev-er want-ing there.

238 A Mighty Fortress Is Our God

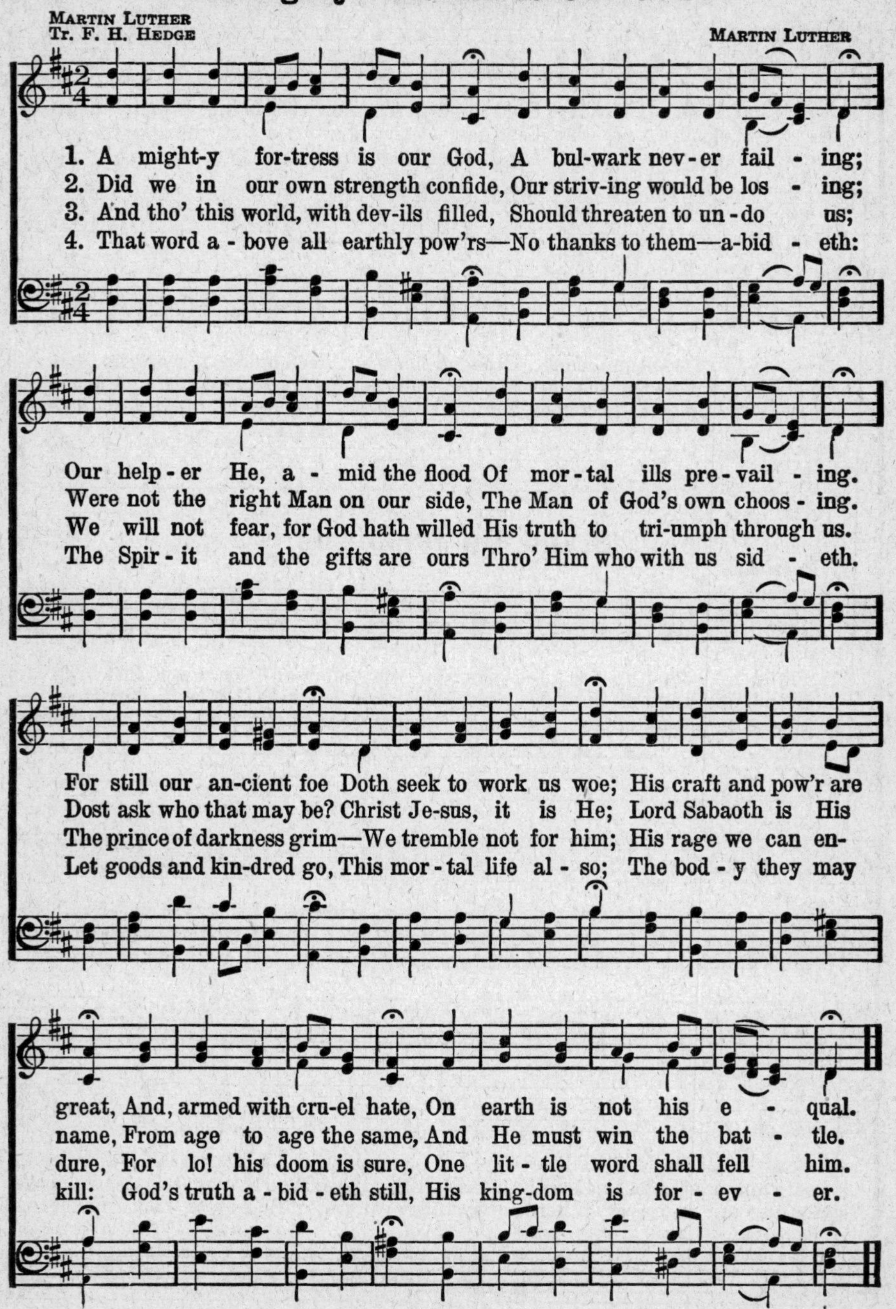
MARTIN LUTHER
TR. F. H. HEDGE
MARTIN LUTHER
1. A might-y for-tress is our God, A bul-wark nev-er fail - ing;
2. Did we in our own strength confide, Our striv-ing would be los - ing;
3. And tho' this world, with dev-ils filled, Should threaten to un-do us;
4. That word a - bove all earthly pow'rs—No thanks to them—a-bid - eth:
Our help-er He, a - mid the flood Of mor-tal ills pre-vail - ing.
Were not the right Man on our side, The Man of God's own choos - ing.
We will not fear, for God hath willed His truth to tri-umph through us.
The Spir - it and the gifts are ours Thro' Him who with us sid - eth.
For still our an-cient foe Doth seek to work us woe; His craft and pow'r are
Dost ask who that may be? Christ Je-sus, it is He; Lord Sabaoth is His
The prince of darkness grim—We tremble not for him; His rage we can en-
Let goods and kin-dred go, This mor - tal life al - so; The bod - y they may
great, And, armed with cru-el hate, On earth is not his e - qual.
name, From age to age the same, And He must win the bat - tle.
dure, For lo! his doom is sure, One lit - tle word shall fell him.
kill: God's truth a - bid - eth still, His king-dom is for - ev - er.

Glorious Things of Thee Are Spoken 239

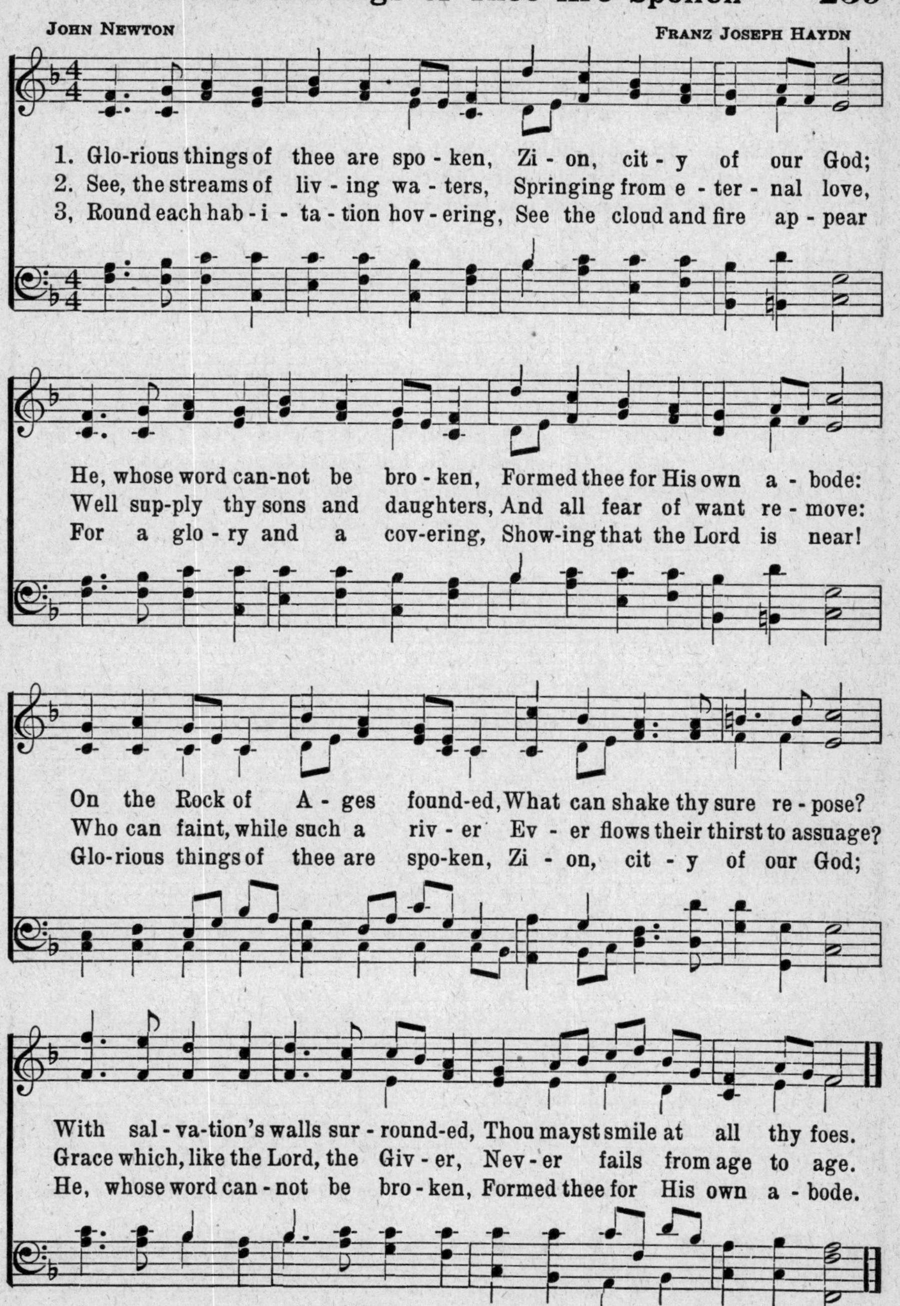

JOHN NEWTON
FRANZ JOSEPH HAYDN
1. Glo-rious things of thee are spo - ken, Zi - on, cit - y of our God;
2. See, the streams of liv - ing wa - ters, Springing from e - ter - nal love,
3, Round each hab - i - ta - tion hov - ering, See the cloud and fire ap - pear
He, whose word can-not be bro - ken, Formed thee for His own a - bode:
Well sup-ply thy sons and daughters, And all fear of want re - move:
For a glo - ry and a cov-ering, Show-ing that the Lord is near!
On the Rock of A - ges found-ed, What can shake thy sure re - pose?
Who can faint, while such a riv - er Ev - er flows their thirst to assuage?
Glo-rious things of thee are spo-ken, Zi - on, cit - y of our God;
With sal - va-tion's walls sur - round-ed, Thou mayst smile at all thy foes.
Grace which, like the Lord, the Giv - er, Nev - er fails from age to age.
He, whose word can - not be bro - ken, Formed thee for His own a - bode.

240 When We Reach the Glory Land

RODNEY CHIRPE — ROGER M. HICKMAN

1. What a won-der-ful Sav-ior is Je-sus, Who suf-fered with
2. O the Sav-ior is call-ing the sin-ner, To join with that
3. In the glo-ri-ous, won-der-ful cit-y, Where Je-sus shall
nail-pierced hand; O yes, 'twill be heav-en to see Him,
glo-rious band Of saved who will praise Him for-ev-er,
have com-mand, We'll dwell with the Sav-ior for-ev-er,
When we reach the glo-ry land.
CHORUS
When we reach the glo-ry
land, When we reach the glo-ry land,
the glo-ry land, the glo-ry land,
We'll walk and we'll talk with the Sav-ior When we reach the glo-ry land.

Copyright, 1918. Hope Publishing Company, owner

There is a Green Hill Far Away

Cecil F. Alexander — Geo. C. Stebbins

1. There is a green hill far a-way, With-out a cit-y wall,
2. We may not know, we can-not tell What pains He had to bear;
3. He died that we might be for-giv'n, He died to make us good,
4. There was no oth-er good e-nough, To pay the price of sin;
Where the dear Lord was cru-ci-fied, Who died to save us all.
But we be-lieve it was for us He hung and suf-fered there.
That we might go at last to Heav'n, Saved by His pre-cious blood.
He on-ly could un-lock the gate Of Heav'n and let us in.
Chorus
Oh, dear-ly, dear-ly has He loved, And we must love Him, too;
rit . . .
And trust in His re-deem-ing blood, And try His works to do.

242 Nearer, My God, to Thee

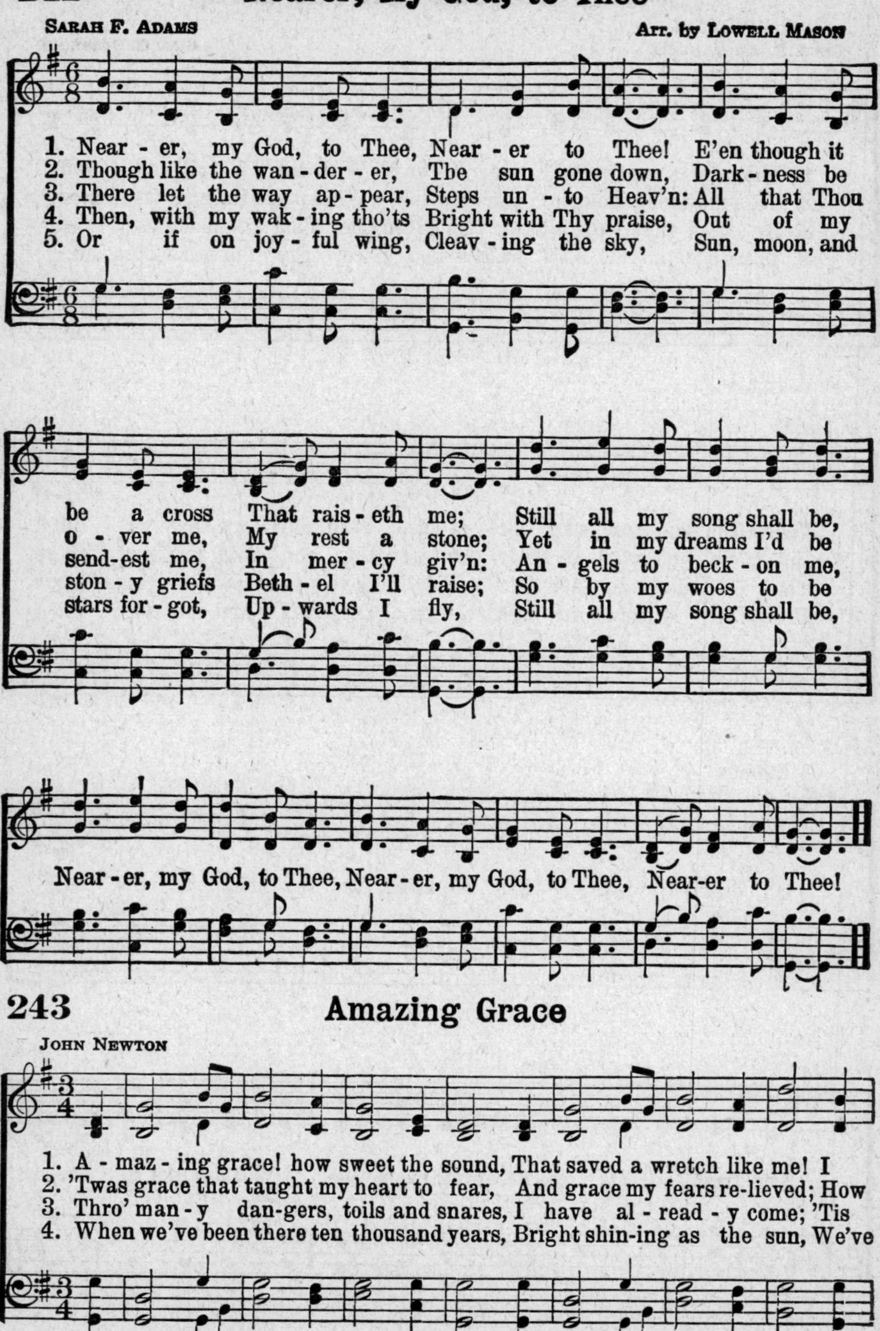

Sarah F. Adams
Arr. by Lowell Mason
1. Near - er, my God, to Thee, Near - er to Thee! E'en though it be a cross That rais - eth me; Still all my song shall be,
2. Though like the wan - der - er, The sun gone down, Dark - ness be o - ver me, My rest a stone; Yet in my dreams I'd be
3. There let the way ap - pear, Steps un - to Heav'n: All that Thou send - est me, In mer - cy giv'n: An - gels to beck - on me,
4. Then, with my wak - ing tho'ts Bright with Thy praise, Out of my ston - y griefs Beth - el I'll raise; So by my woes to be
5. Or if on joy - ful wing, Cleav - ing the sky, Sun, moon, and stars for - got, Up - wards I fly, Still all my song shall be,
Near - er, my God, to Thee, Near - er, my God, to Thee, Near - er to Thee!
243
Amazing Grace
John Newton
1. A - maz - ing grace! how sweet the sound, That saved a wretch like me! I
2. 'Twas grace that taught my heart to fear, And grace my fears re - lieved; How
3. Thro' man - y dan - gers, toils and snares, I have al - read - y come; 'Tis
4. When we've been there ten thousand years, Bright shin - ing as the sun, We've

Amazing Grace

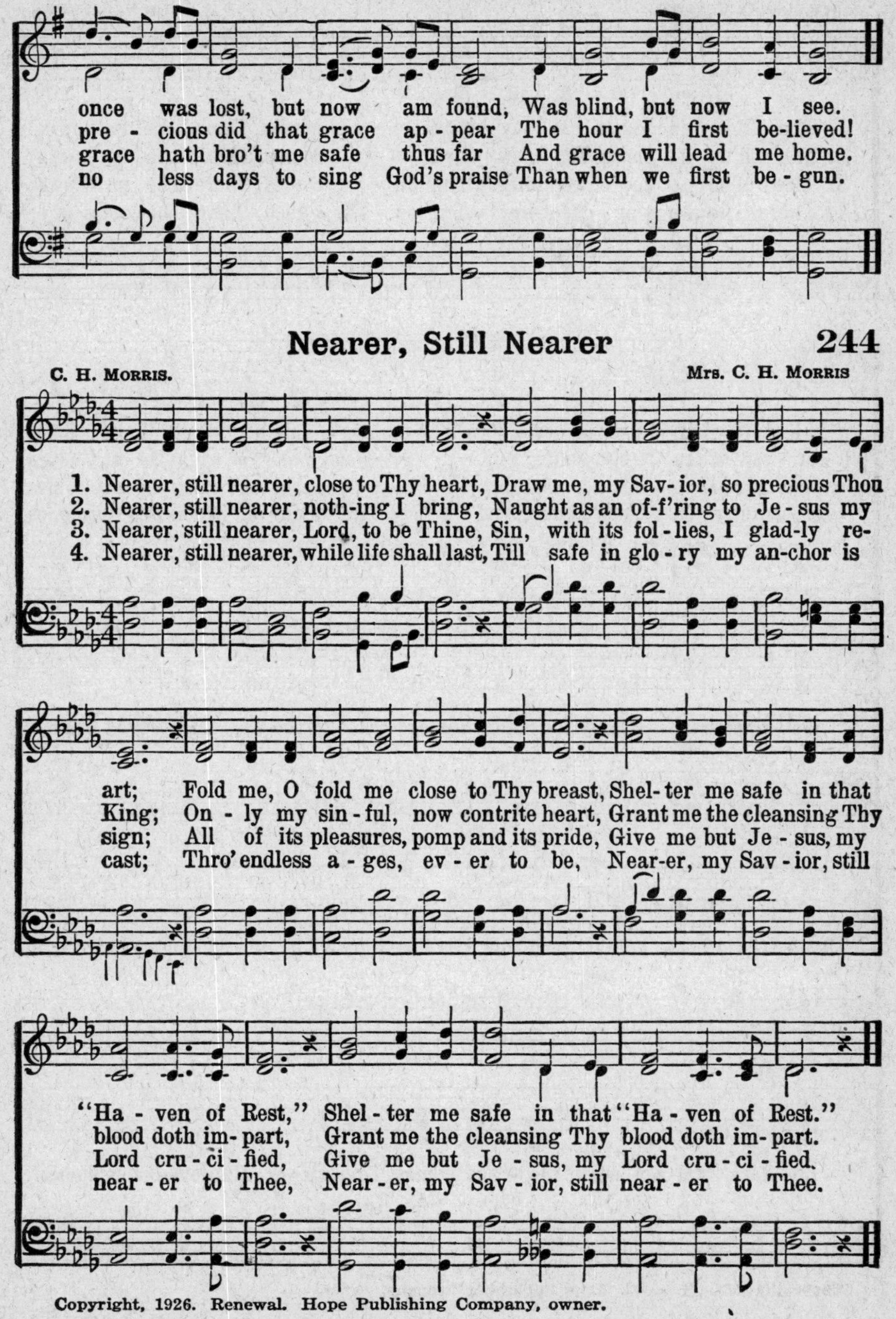
once was lost, but now am found, Was blind, but now I see.
pre - cious did that grace ap - pear The hour I first be-lieved!
grace hath bro't me safe thus far And grace will lead me home.
no less days to sing God's praise Than when we first be - gun.
Nearer, Still Nearer
244
C. H. Morris.
Mrs. C. H. Morris
1. Nearer, still nearer, close to Thy heart, Draw me, my Sav- ior, so precious Thou art; Fold me, O fold me close to Thy breast, Shel- ter me safe in that "Ha - ven of Rest," Shel - ter me safe in that "Ha - ven of Rest."
2. Nearer, still nearer, noth-ing I bring, Naught as an of-f'ring to Je - sus my King; On - ly my sin - ful, now contrite heart, Grant me the cleansing Thy blood doth im- part, Grant me the cleansing Thy blood doth im- part.
3. Nearer, still nearer, Lord, to be Thine, Sin, with its fol - lies, I glad-ly re- sign; All of its pleasures, pomp and its pride, Give me but Je - sus, my Lord cru - ci - fied, Give me but Je - sus, my Lord cru - ci - fied.
4. Nearer, still nearer, while life shall last, Till safe in glo - ry my an-chor is cast; Thro' endless a - ges, ev - er to be, Near-er, my Sav - ior, still near - er to Thee, Near - er, my Sav - ior, still near - er to Thee.

Copyright, 1926. Renewal. Hope Publishing Company, owner.

245 There'll Be No Dark Valley

William O. Cushing   Ira D. Sankey

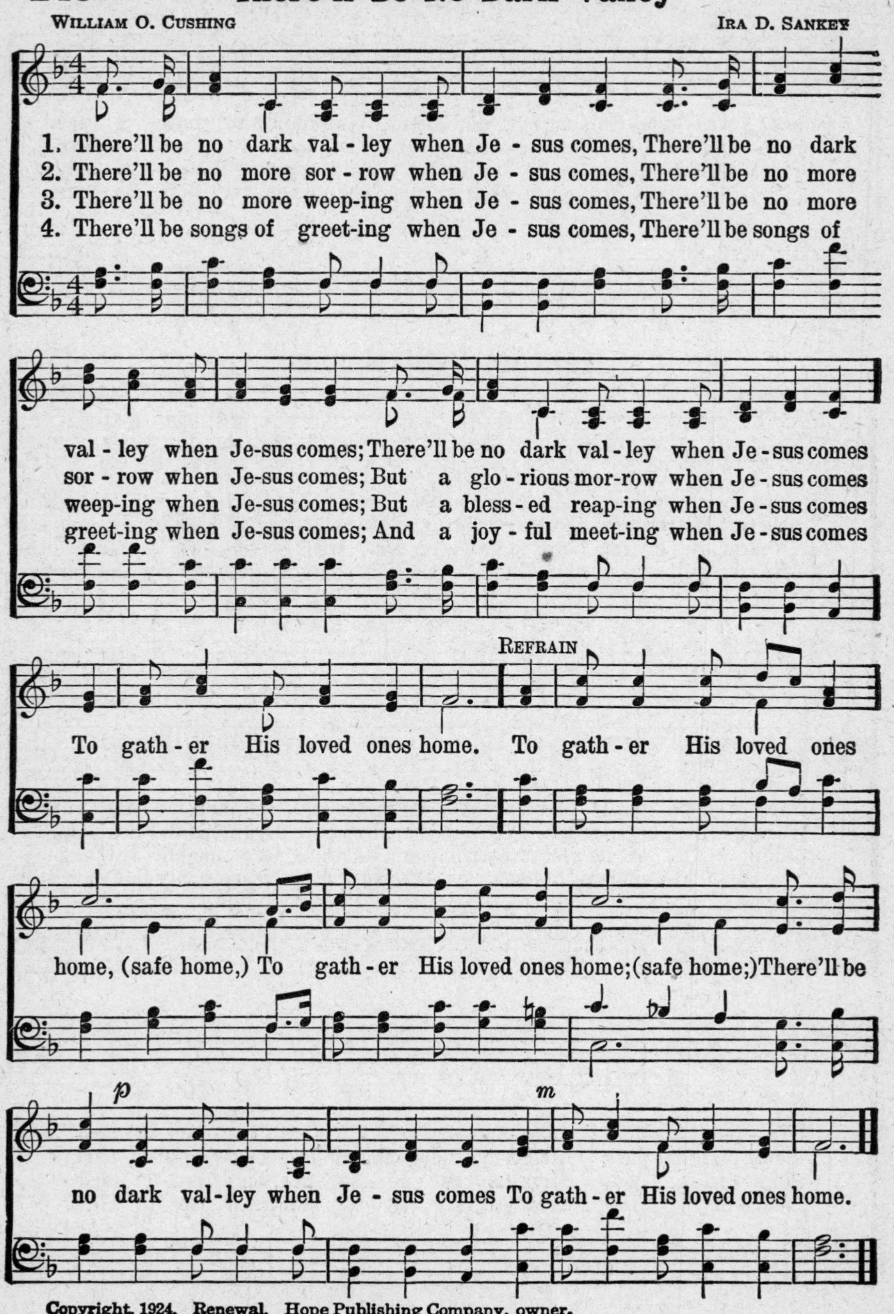

Copyright, 1924. Renewal. Hope Publishing Company, owner.

Safe in the Arms of Jesus
246
Fanny J. Crosby
W. H. Doane
1. Safe in the arms of Je - sus, Safe on His gen-tle breast, There by His
2. Safe in the arms of Je - sus, Safe from cor-rod-ing care, Safe from the
3. Je-sus, my heart's dear ref - uge, Je - sus has died for me; Firm on the
love o'er-shad - ed, Sweet-ly my soul shall rest. Hark! 'tis the voice of
world's temp-ta - tions, Sin can-not harm me there. Free from the blight of
Rock of A - ges, Ev - er my trust shall be. Here let me wait with
an - gels, Borne in a song to me,.. O - ver the fields of glo - ry,
sor - row, Free from my doubts and fears; On - ly a few more tri - als,
pa - tience, Wait till the night is o'er; Wait till I see the morn - ing
O - ver the jas - per sea.......
On - ly a few more tears!.....
Break on the gold - en shore.....
Chorus
Safe in the arms of Je - sus, Safe on His
gen - tle breast, There by His love o'er - shad - ed, Sweetly my soul shall rest.

247 Go Ye Into All the World

J. McG. JAMES McGRANAHAN

1. Far, far a-way, in hea-then darkness dwell-ing, Mil-lions of souls for-ev-er may be lost; Who, who will go, sal-va-tion's sto-ry tell-ing, Look-ing to Je-sus, minding not the cost?
2. See o'er the world wide-o-pen doors in-vit-ing, Sol-diers of Christ, a-rise and en-ter in! Chris-tians, a-wake! your forc-es all u-nit-ing, Send forth the gospel, break the chains of sin.
3. "Why will ye die?" the voice of God is call-ing, "Why will ye die?" re-ech-o in His name; Je-sus hath died to save from death ap-pall-ing, Life and sal-va-tion therefore go pro-claim.
4. God speed the day, when those of ev-'ry na-tion "Glo-ry to God!" tri-um-phant-ly shall sing; Ran-somed, redeemed, re-joic-ing in sal-va-tion, Shout Hal-le-lu-jah, for the Lord is King.
CHORUS
"All pow'r is giv-en un-to Me, All pow'r is giv-en un-to Me, Go ye in-to all the world and preach the gos-pel, And lo, I am with you al-way."

Copyright, 1914. Renewal. Hope Publishing Co., owner.

Anywhere With Jesus

Jessie H. Brown and Mrs. C. M. Alexander — D. B. Towner

1. An - y-where with Je - sus I can safe - ly go; An - y-where He leads me in this world be - low; An - y-where with-out Him dear-est joys would fade; An - y-where with Je - sus I am not a - fraid.
2. An - y-where with Je - sus I am not a - lone; Oth - er friends may fail me, He is still my own; Tho' His hand may lead me o - ver drear - y ways, An - y-where with Je - sus is a house of praise.
3. An - y-where with Je - sus o - ver land and sea, Tell - ing souls in dark-ness of sal - va - tion free; Read - y as He sum-mons me to go or stay, An - y-where with Je - sus when He points the way.
4. An - y-where with Je - sus I can go to sleep, When the dark-'ning shad-ows round a - bout me creep; Know-ing I shall wak - en nev - er more to roam, An - y-where with Je - sus will be home, sweet home.
Chorus
An - y-where! an - y - where! Fear I can - not know;
An - y - where with Je - sus I can safe - ly go.

Copyright, 1915. Renewal. Hope Publishing Company, owner

249 I Surrender All

J. W. VAN DEVENTER | W. S. WEEDEN

1. All to Je - sus I sur-ren - der, All to Him I free - ly give;
2. All to Je - sus I sur-ren - der, Hum - bly at His feet I bow,
3. All to Je - sus I sur-ren - der, Make me, Sav - ior, whol - ly Thine;
4. All to Je - sus I sur-ren - der, Lord, I give my - self to Thee;
I will ev - er love and trust Him, In His pres-ence dai - ly live.
World-ly pleas-ures all for-sak - en, Take me, Je - sus, take me now.
Let me feel the Ho - ly Spir - it,— Tru - ly know that Thou art mine.
Fill me with Thy love and pow - er, Let Thy bless-ing fall on me.
CHORUS
I sur-ren-der all, I sur-ren-der all.
I sur-ren-der all, I sur-ren-der all.
All to Thee, my bless - ed Sav - ior, I sur - ren - der all.

What a Wonderful Savior! 250

ELISHA A. HOFFMAN | ELISHA A. HOFFMAN

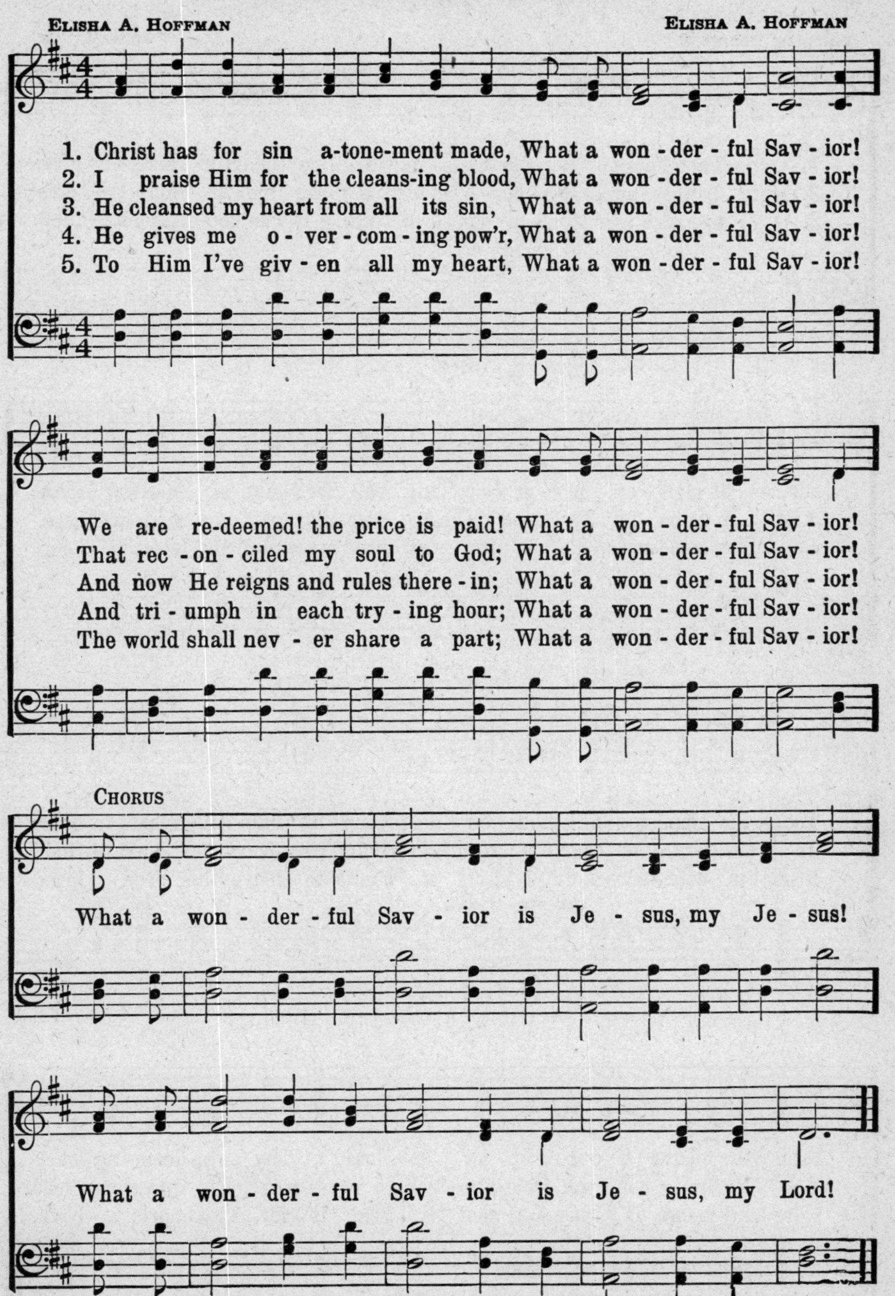
1. Christ has for sin a-tone-ment made, What a won - der - ful Sav - ior!
2. I praise Him for the cleans-ing blood, What a won - der - ful Sav - ior!
3. He cleansed my heart from all its sin, What a won - der - ful Sav - ior!
4. He gives me o - ver - com - ing pow'r, What a won - der - ful Sav - ior!
5. To Him I've giv - en all my heart, What a won - der - ful Sav - ior!
We are re-deemed! the price is paid! What a won - der - ful Sav - ior!
That rec - on - ciled my soul to God; What a won - der - ful Sav - ior!
And now He reigns and rules there - in; What a won - der - ful Sav - ior!
And tri - umph in each try - ing hour; What a won - der - ful Sav - ior!
The world shall nev - er share a part; What a won - der - ful Sav - ior!
CHORUS
What a won - der - ful Sav - ior is Je - sus, my Je - sus!
What a won - der - ful Sav - ior is Je - sus, my Lord!

251 Come, Thou Fount

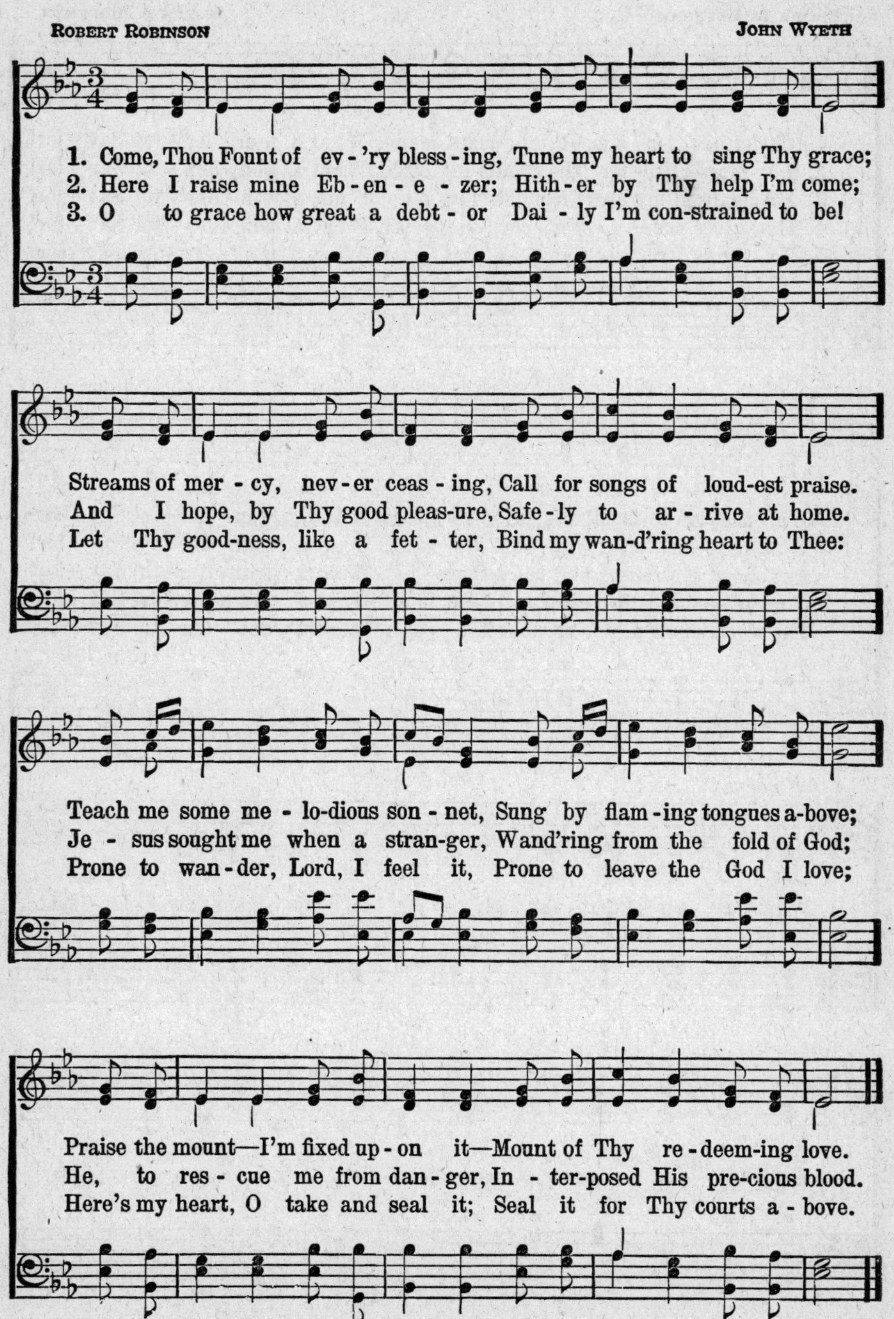
ROBERT ROBINSON
JOHN WYETH
1. Come, Thou Fount of ev - 'ry bless - ing, Tune my heart to sing Thy grace;
2. Here I raise mine Eb - en - e - zer; Hith - er by Thy help I'm come;
3. O to grace how great a debt - or Dai - ly I'm con-strained to be!
Streams of mer - cy, nev - er ceas - ing, Call for songs of loud-est praise.
And I hope, by Thy good pleas-ure, Safe - ly to ar - rive at home.
Let Thy good-ness, like a fet - ter, Bind my wan-d'ring heart to Thee:
Teach me some me - lo-dious son - net, Sung by flam - ing tongues a-bove;
Je - sus sought me when a stran-ger, Wand'ring from the fold of God;
Prone to wan - der, Lord, I feel it, Prone to leave the God I love;
Praise the mount—I'm fixed up - on it—Mount of Thy re - deem-ing love.
He, to res - cue me from dan - ger, In - ter-posed His pre-cious blood.
Here's my heart, O take and seal it; Seal it for Thy courts a - bove.

Jesus, Lover of My Soul 252

CHARLES WESLEY
SIMEON B. MARSH
FINE
1. Jesus, Lover of my soul, Let me to Thy bosom fly,
While the nearer waters roll, While the tempest still is high;
2. Other refuge have I none, Hangs my helpless soul on Thee;
Leave, ah, leave me not alone, Still support and comfort me.
3. Thou, O Christ, art all I want; More than all in Thee I find;
Raise the fallen, cheer the faint, Heal the sick, and lead the blind.
4. Plenteous grace with Thee is found, Grace to cover all my sin;
Let the healing streams abound; Make and keep me pure within.
D.C.—Safe into the haven guide, O receive my soul at last.
D.C.—Cover my defenseless head With the shadow of Thy wing.
D.C.—Vile and full of sin I am, Thou art full of truth and grace.
D.C.—Spring Thou up within my heart, Rise to all eternity.
D. C.
Hide me, O my Savior, hide, Till the storm of life is past;
All my trust on Thee is stayed, All my help from Thee I bring;
Just and holy is Thy name, I am all unrighteousness;
Thou of life the fountain art, Freely let me take of Thee;
Must Jesus Bear the Cross Alone? 253
THOS. SHEPHERD
GEO. N. ALLEN
1. Must Jesus bear the cross alone, And all the world go free?
2. The consecrated cross I'll bear, Till death shall set me free,
3. Upon the crystal pavement, down At Jesus' pierced feet,
4. O precious cross! O glorious crown! O resurrection day!
No; there's a cross for every one, And there's a cross for me.
And then go home my crown to wear, For there's a crown for me.
Joyful, I'll cast my golden crown, And His dear name repeat.
Ye angels, from the stars come down, And bear my soul away.

254 O Jesus, I Have Promised

JOHN E. BODE
ARTHUR H. MANN
1. O Je - sus, I have prom-ised To serve Thee to the end; Be Thou for-ev - er near me, My Mas-ter and my Friend: I shall not fear the bat - tle If Thou art by my side, Nor wan - der from the path-way If Thou wilt be my guide.
2. O let me feel Thee near me, The world is ev - er near; I see the sights that daz - zle, The tempting sounds I hear: My foes are ev - er near me, A-round me and with-in; But, Je - sus, draw Thou near-er, And shield my soul from sin.
3. O Je - sus, Thou hast promised To all who fol - low Thee, That where Thou art in glo - ry, There shall Thy servant be; And, Je-sus, I have promised To serve Thee to the end; O give me grace to fol - low My Mas - ter and my Friend.
255 We Bless the Name of Christ, the Lord
SAMUEL FREDERICK COFFMAN
THOMAS HASTINGS
1. We bless the name of Christ, the Lord, We bless Him for His ho - ly Word,
2. We fol - low Him with pure de-light To sanc - ti - fy His sa-cred rite;
3. Bap-tized in God—the Fa-ther, Son, And Ho - ly Spir-it—Three in One,
4. By grace we "Ab - ba, Fa-ther," cry; By grace the Com-fort-er comes nigh;

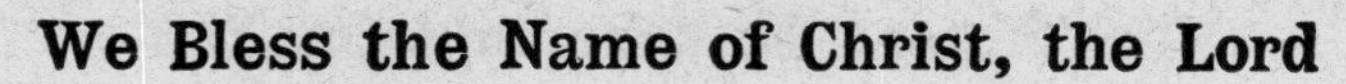
We Bless the Name of Christ, the Lord

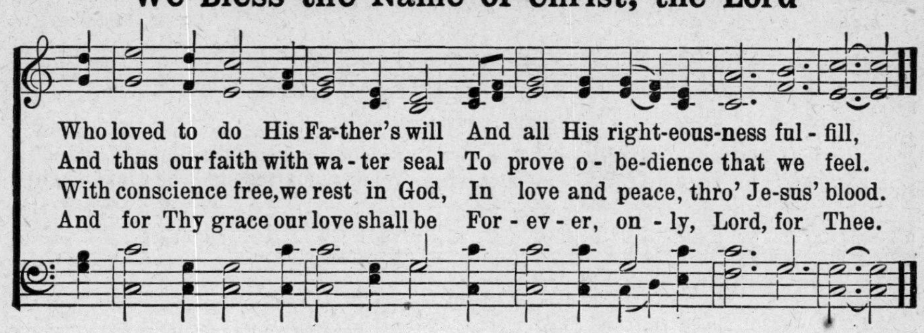
Who loved to do His Fa-ther's will And all His right-eous-ness ful - fill,
And thus our faith with wa - ter seal To prove o - be-dience that we feel.
With conscience free, we rest in God, In love and peace, thro' Je-sus' blood.
And for Thy grace our love shall be For - ev - er, on - ly, Lord, for Thee.

Jesus Bids Us Shine 256

E. O. Excell

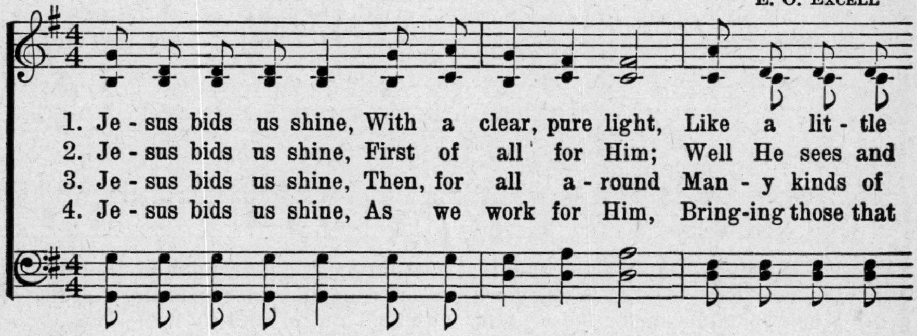

1. Je - sus bids us shine, With a clear, pure light, Like a lit - tle
2. Je - sus bids us shine, First of all for Him; Well He sees and
3. Je - sus bids us shine, Then, for all a - round Man - y kinds of
4. Je - sus bids us shine, As we work for Him, Bring-ing those that

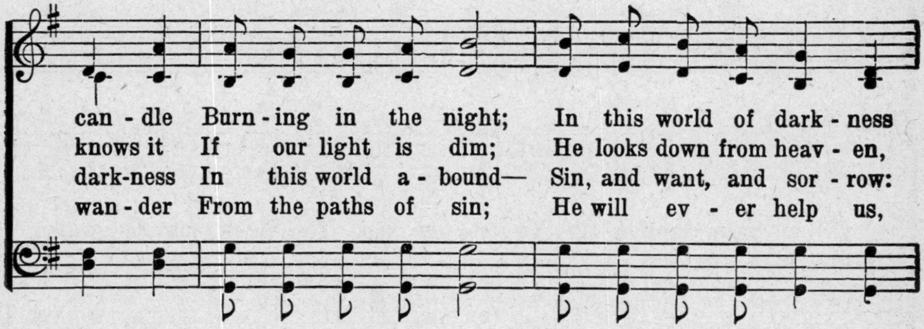

can - dle Burn - ing in the night; In this world of dark - ness
knows it If our light is dim; He looks down from heav - en,
dark-ness In this world a - bound— Sin, and want, and sor - row:
wan - der From the paths of sin; He will ev - er help us,

We must shine, You in your small cor - ner, And I in mine.
Sees us shine, You in your small cor - ner, And I in mine.
We must shine, You in your small cor - ner, And I in mine.
If we shine, You in your small cor - ner, And I in mine.

257 The Victory May Depend On You

George O. Webster J. H. Fillmore

1. Thro' the land a call is sound-ing, And it comes to age and youth;
2. See the might-y hosts of e - vil Spreading death thro'-out the land;
3. Lo, a tri-umph day is com - ing, When our arms shall be laid down;

'Tis a sum-mons to the con - flict, In the cause of right and truth:
Who is there will an - swer quick-ly, And the hosts of sin with-stand!
Then each faith - ful, loy - al sol - dier Shall re - ceive a vic - tor's crown;

To the stand-ard of our Cap-tain, Lo, there comes a faith-ful few; But the
Do not fear to join our standard, For our ranks are tried and true, And the
Would you stand among the vic- tors, With the band of faith-ful few? Then the

vic - to - ry, my brother, May de-pend on you.

CHORUS

The vic-t'ry may de-pend on you, on you, The vic-t'ry may de-pend on you; on you; Dare to stand among the few,

Copyright, 1934 by J. H. Fillmore. Renewal. Lillenas Publishing Co., owner. Used by permission.

The Victory May Depend On You

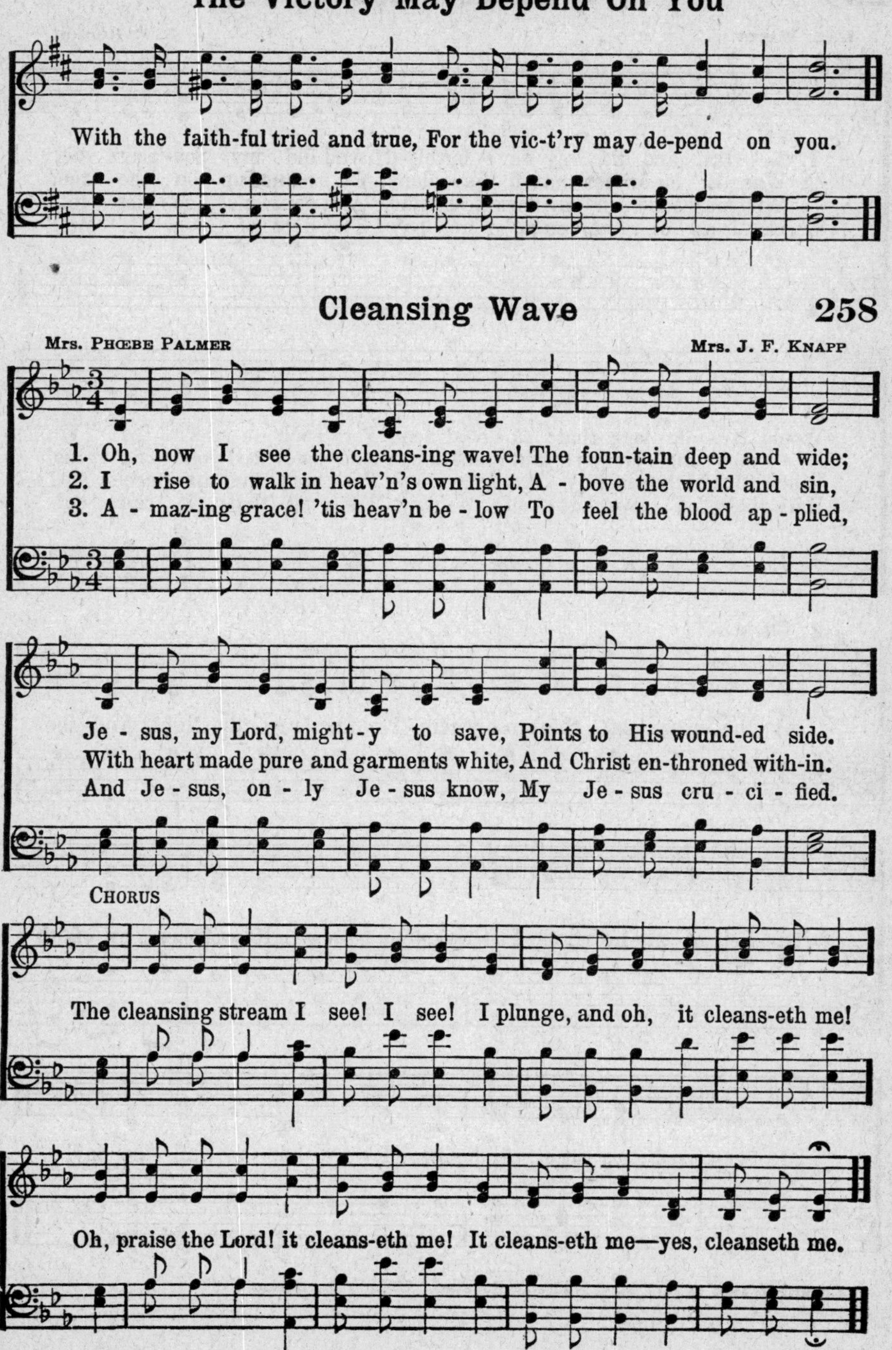
With the faith-ful tried and true, For the vic-t'ry may de-pend on you.
Cleansing Wave
258
Mrs. Phœbe Palmer
Mrs. J. F. Knapp
1. Oh, now I see the cleans-ing wave! The foun-tain deep and wide;
2. I rise to walk in heav'n's own light, A - bove the world and sin,
3. A - maz-ing grace! 'tis heav'n be - low To feel the blood ap - plied,
Je - sus, my Lord, might - y to save, Points to His wound-ed side.
With heart made pure and garments white, And Christ en-throned with-in.
And Je - sus, on - ly Je - sus know, My Je - sus cru - ci - fied.
Chorus
The cleansing stream I see! I see! I plunge, and oh, it cleans-eth me!
Oh, praise the Lord! it cleans-eth me! It cleans-eth me—yes, cleanseth me.

At the Cross

Isaac Watts — R. E. Hudson

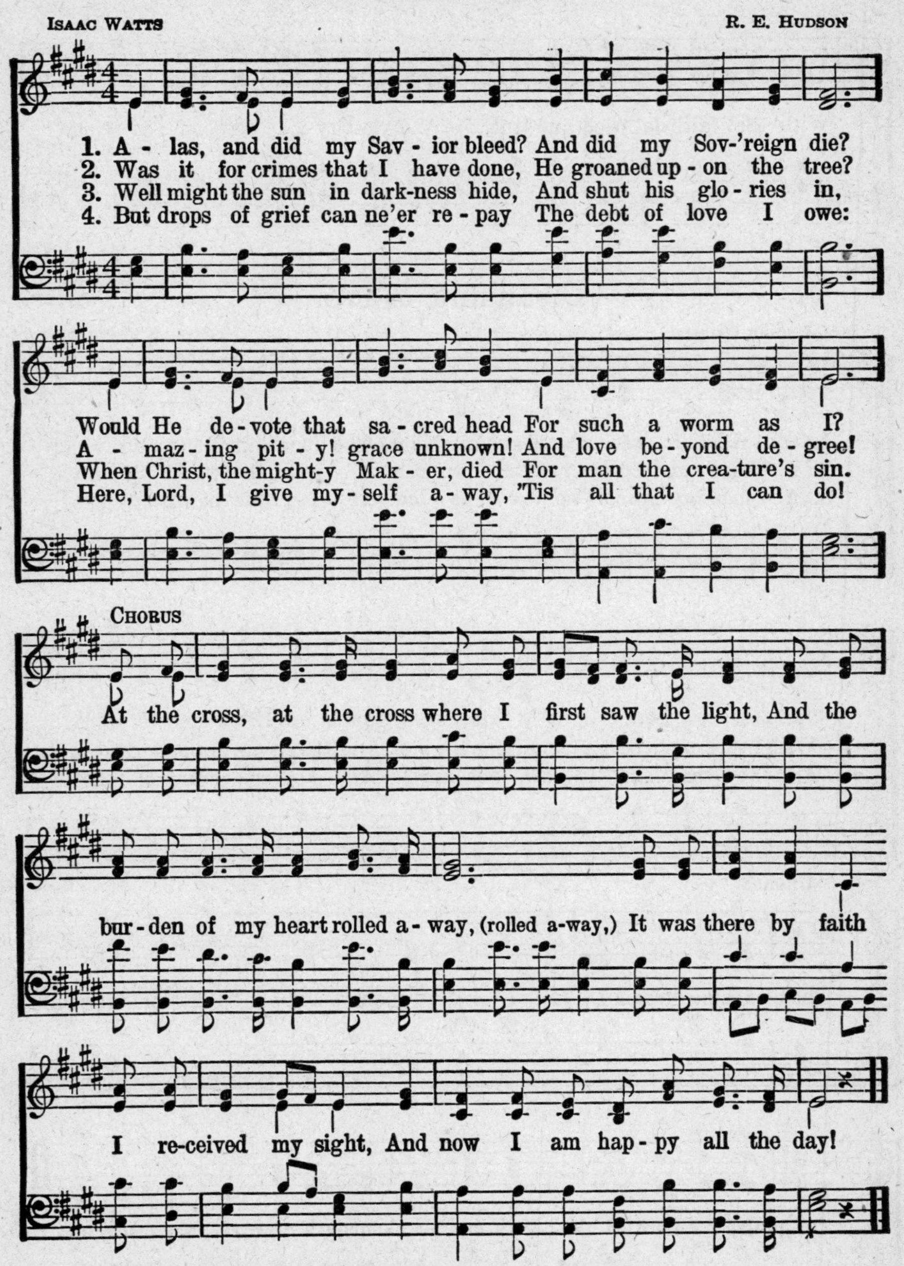
1. A - las, and did my Sav - ior bleed? And did my Sov-'reign die?
2. Was it for crimes that I have done, He groaned up - on the tree?
3. Well might the sun in dark-ness hide, And shut his glo - ries in,
4. But drops of grief can ne'er re - pay The debt of love I owe:
Would He de - vote that sa - cred head For such a worm as I?
A - maz - ing pit - y! grace unknown! And love be - yond de - gree!
When Christ, the might-y Mak - er, died For man the crea-ture's sin.
Here, Lord, I give my - self a - way, 'Tis all that I can do!
Chorus
At the cross, at the cross where I first saw the light, And the
bur - den of my heart rolled a - way, (rolled a-way,) It was there by faith
I re-ceived my sight, And now I am hap - py all the day!

Copyright, 1916, by Mrs. Mary Hudson. Renewal. Used by permission

The Name of Jesus

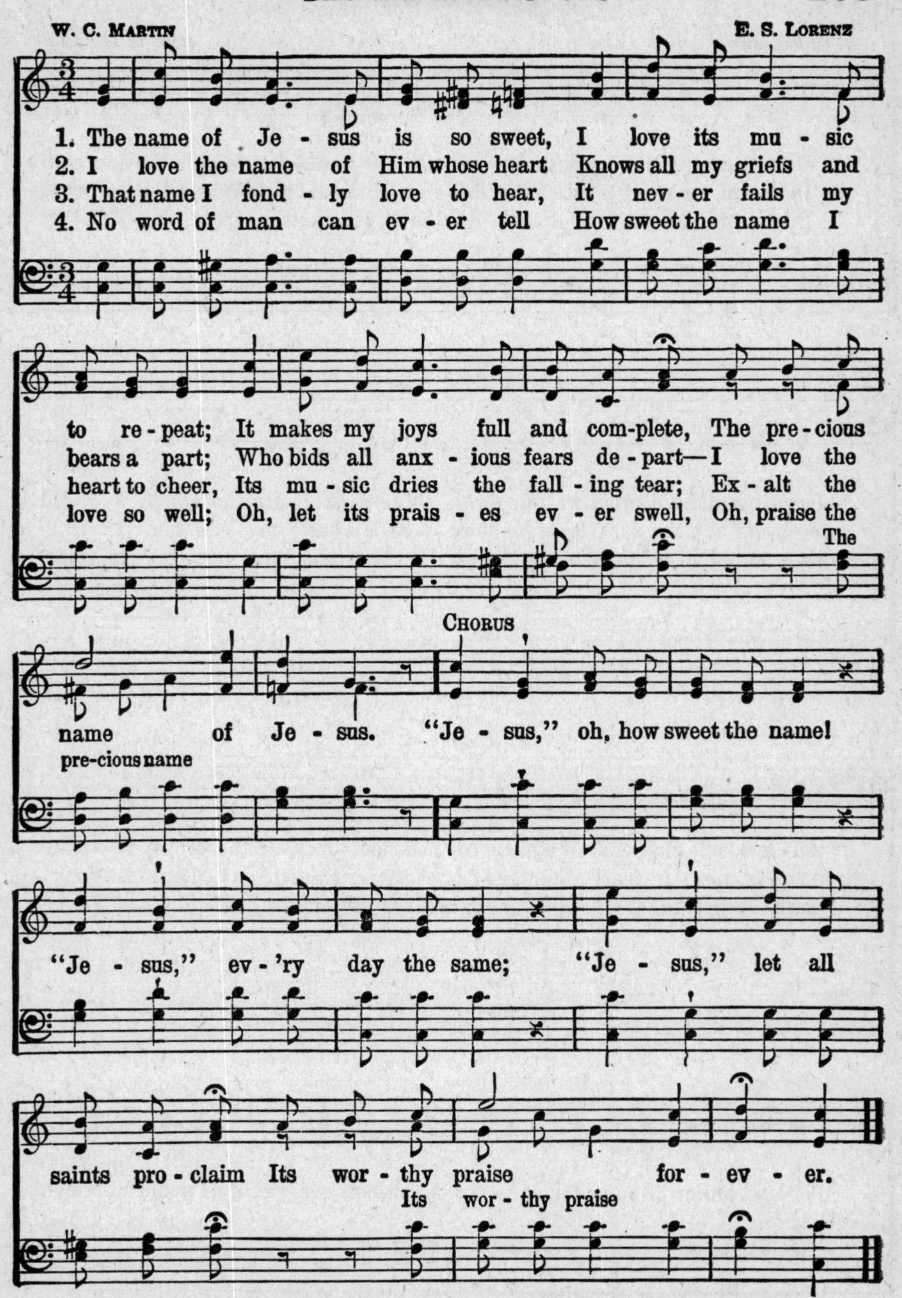
W. C. Martin
E. S. Lorenz
1. The name of Je - sus is so sweet, I love its mu - sic to re - peat; It makes my joys full and com-plete, The pre-cious name of Je - sus.
2. I love the name of Him whose heart Knows all my griefs and bears a part; Who bids all anx - ious fears de - part— I love the name of Je - sus.
3. That name I fond - ly love to hear, It nev - er fails my heart to cheer, Its mu - sic dries the fall - ing tear; Ex - alt the name of Je - sus.
4. No word of man can ev - er tell How sweet the name I love so well; Oh, let its prais - es ev - er swell, Oh, praise the name of Je - sus.
The pre-cious name
Chorus
"Je - sus," oh, how sweet the name! "Je - sus," ev - 'ry day the same; "Je - sus," let all saints pro - claim Its wor - thy praise for - ev - er.
Its wor - thy praise

Copyright, 1901 and 1902, by F. S. Lorenz. Renewal secured. Used by permission.

261

Follow On

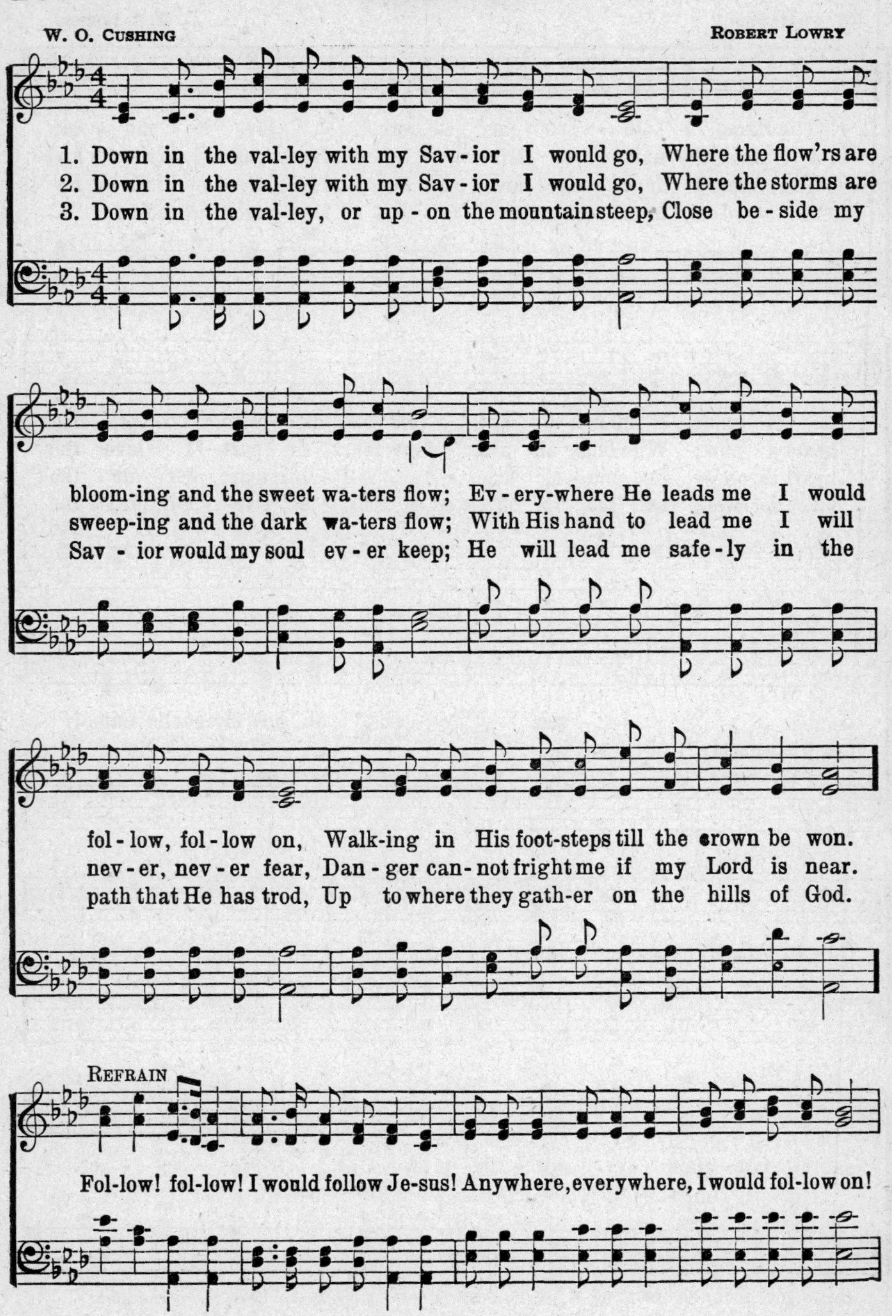
W. O. Cushing
Robert Lowry
1. Down in the val-ley with my Sav-ior I would go, Where the flow'rs are bloom-ing and the sweet wa-ters flow; Ev-ery-where He leads me I would fol-low, fol-low on, Walk-ing in His foot-steps till the crown be won.
2. Down in the val-ley with my Sav-ior I would go, Where the storms are sweep-ing and the dark wa-ters flow; With His hand to lead me I will nev-er, nev-er fear, Dan-ger can-not fright me if my Lord is near.
3. Down in the val-ley, or up-on the mountain steep, Close be-side my Sav-ior would my soul ev-er keep; He will lead me safe-ly in the path that He has trod, Up to where they gath-er on the hills of God.
Refrain
Fol-low! fol-low! I would follow Je-sus! Anywhere, everywhere, I would fol-low on!

Follow On
Fol-low! fol-low! I would follow Jesus! Everywhere He leads me I would follow on!
I Remember Calvary
262
Rev. W. C. Martin
J. M. Black
1. Where He may lead me I will go, For I have learned to trust Him so,
2. O I de-light in His com-mand, Love to be led by His dear hand;
3. On-ward I go, nor doubt nor fear, Hap-py with Christ my Sav-ior near,
And I re-mem-ber 'twas for me, That He was slain on Cal-va-ry.
His di-vine will is sweet to me, Hallowed by blood-stained Cal-va-ry.
Trust-ing that I some day shall see Je-sus my Friend of Cal-va-ry.
Chorus
Je-sus shall lead me night and day, Je-sus shall lead me all the way,
He is the tru-est Friend to me, For I re-mem-ber Cal-va-ry.
Copyright. 1928. Renewal. Hope Publishing Company, owner

263 Just As I Am

CHARLOTTE ELLIOTT — WILLIAM B. BRADBURY

1. Just as I am, with-out one plea, But that Thy blood was shed for me,
2. Just as I am, and wait-ing not To rid my soul of one dark blot,
3. Just as I am, tho' tossed a-bout With many a con-flict, many a doubt,
4. Just as I am, poor, wretched, blind; Sight, riches, heal-ing of the mind,
5. Just as I am, Thou wilt re-ceive, Wilt welcome, pardon, cleanse, relieve;

And that Thou bidd'st me come to Thee, O Lamb of God, I come! I come!
To Thee whose blood can cleanse each spot, O Lamb of God, I come! I come!
Fight-ings and fears with-in, with-out, O Lamb of God, I come! I come!
Yea, all I need, in Thee to find, O Lamb of God, I come! I come!
Be-cause Thy prom-ise I be-lieve, O Lamb of God, I come! I come!

264 O Happy Day

PHILIP DODDRIDGE — E. F. RIMBAULT

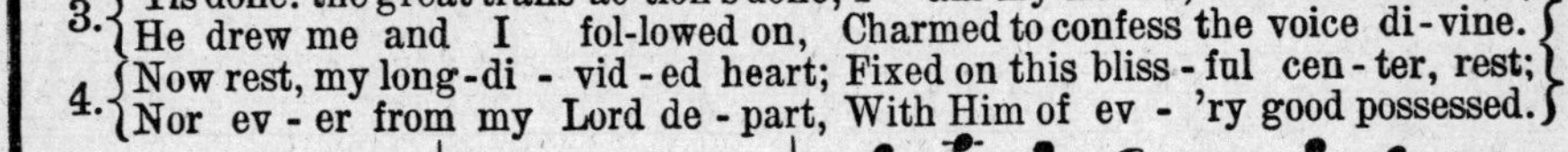

1. {O hap-py day that fixed my choice On Thee, my Sav-ior and my God!
Well may this glow-ing heart re-joice, And tell its rap-tures all a-broad.}
2. {O hap-py bond, that seals my vows To Him who mer-its all my love!
Let cheer-ful an-thems fill His house, While to that sa-cred shrine I move.}
3. {'Tis done: the great trans-ac-tion's done; I am my Lord's, and He is mine;
He drew me and I fol-lowed on, Charmed to confess the voice di-vine.}
4. {Now rest, my long-di-vid-ed heart; Fixed on this bliss-ful cen-ter, rest;
Nor ev-er from my Lord de-part, With Him of ev-'ry good possessed.}

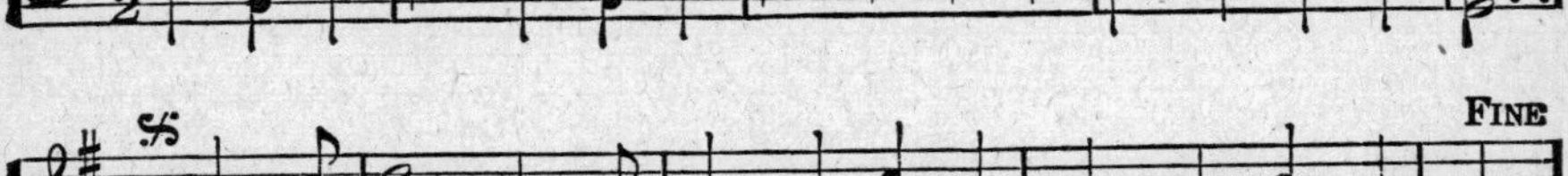

FINE

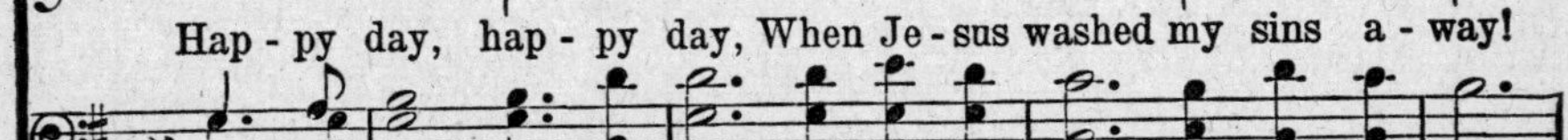

Hap-py day, hap-py day, When Je-sus washed my sins a-way!

O Happy Day

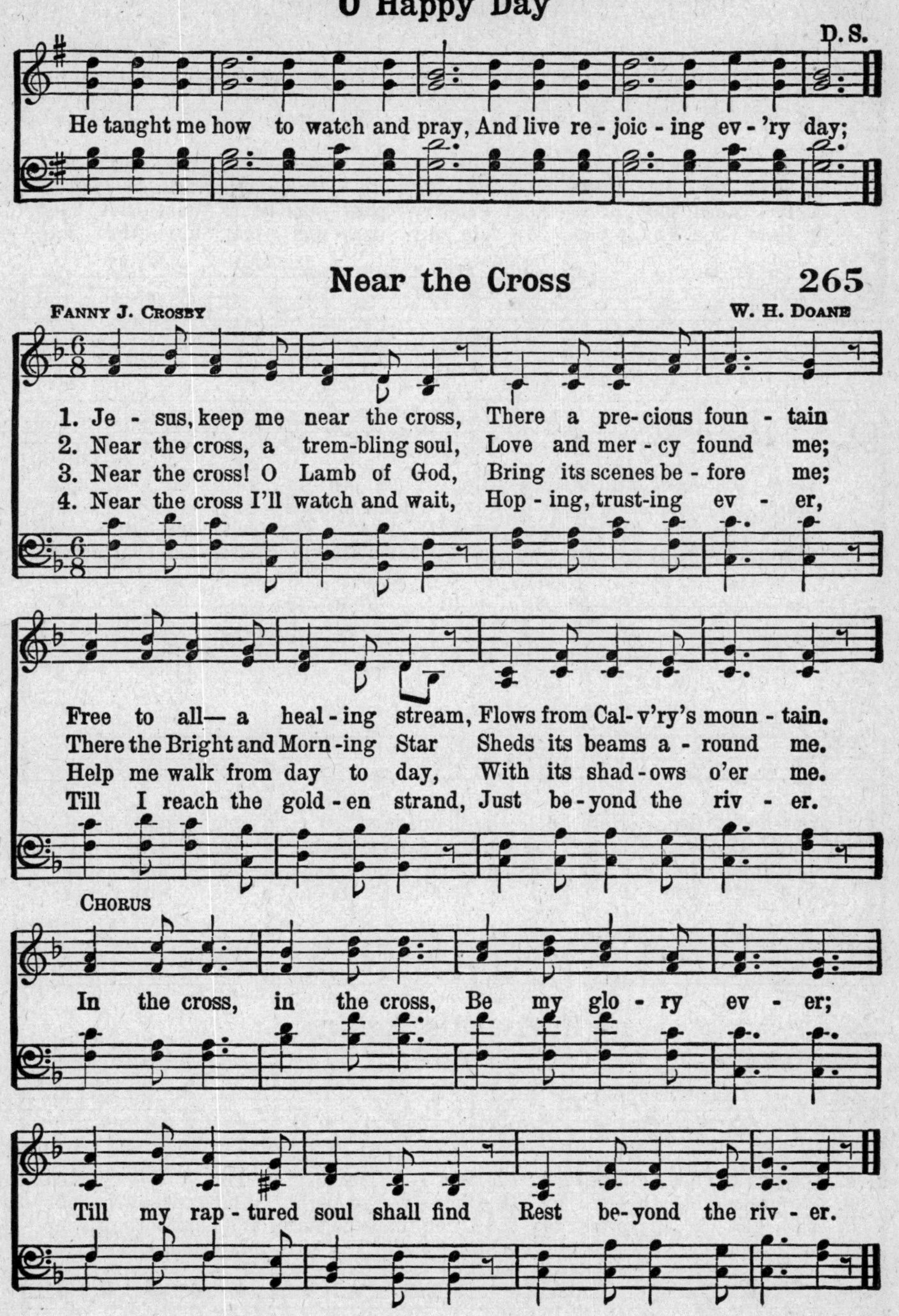
D. S.
He taught me how to watch and pray, And live re - joic - ing ev - 'ry day;
Near the Cross
265
Fanny J. Crosby
W. H. Doane
1. Je - sus, keep me near the cross, There a pre - cious foun - tain
2. Near the cross, a trem-bling soul, Love and mer - cy found me;
3. Near the cross! O Lamb of God, Bring its scenes be - fore me;
4. Near the cross I'll watch and wait, Hop - ing, trust-ing ev - er,
Free to all— a heal - ing stream, Flows from Cal - v'ry's moun - tain.
There the Bright and Morn - ing Star Sheds its beams a - round me.
Help me walk from day to day, With its shad - ows o'er me.
Till I reach the gold - en strand, Just be - yond the riv - er.
Chorus
In the cross, in the cross, Be my glo - ry ev - er;
Till my rap - tured soul shall find Rest be - yond the riv - er.

266 Abide With Me

H. F. LYTE | W. H. MONK

1. A - bide with me: fast falls the e - ven - tide; The dark - ness
2. Swift to its close ebbs out life's lit - tle day; Earth's joys grow
3. I need Thy pres - ence ev - 'ry pass - ing hour: What but Thy
4. Hold Thou Thy cross be - fore my clos - ing eyes; Shine thro' the

deep - ens; Lord, with me a - bide: When oth - er help - ers fail, and
dim, its glo - ries pass a - way; Change and de - cay in all a-
grace can foil the tempter's pow'r? Who like Thy - self my guide and
gloom, and point me to the skies: Heav'n's morning breaks, and earth's vain

com - forts flee, Help of the help - less, O a - bide with me!
round I see; O Thou who chang - est not, a - bide with me!
stay can be? Thro' cloud and sun - shine, O a - bide with me!
shad - ows flee: In life, in death, O Lord, a - bide with me!

267 Revive Us Again

WM. P. MACKAY | JOHN J. HUSBAND

1. We praise Thee, O God! for the Son of Thy love, For Je - sus who
2. We praise Thee, O God! for Thy Spir - it of light, Who has shown us our
3. All glo - ry and praise to the Lamb that was slain, Who has borne all our
4. Re - vive us a - gain; fill each heart with Thy love; May each soul be re-

Revive Us Again

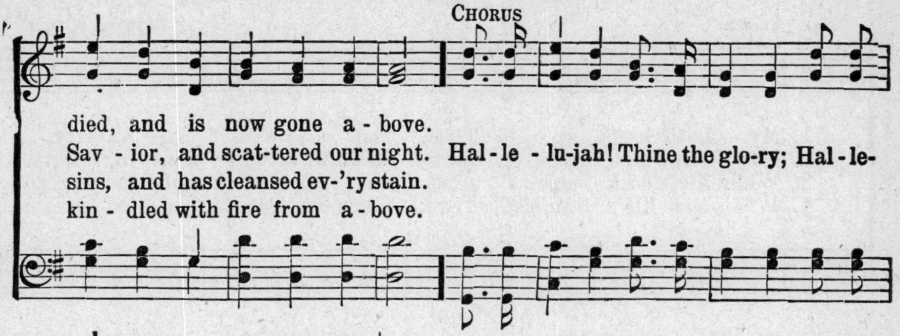

CHORUS

died, and is now gone a - bove.
Sav - ior, and scat-tered our night. Hal - le - lu-jah! Thine the glo-ry; Hal - le-
sins, and has cleansed ev-'ry stain.
kin - dled with fire from a - bove.

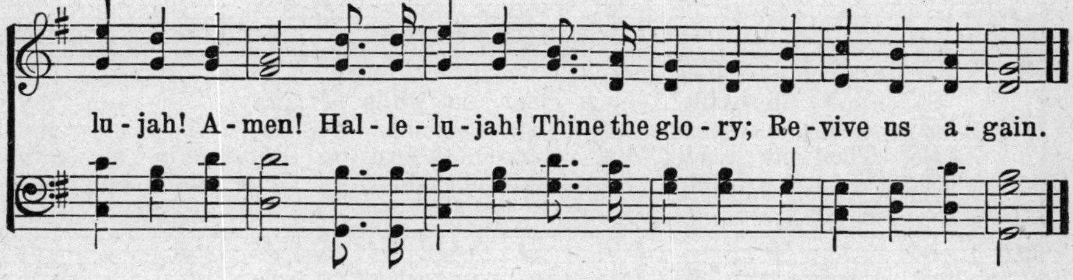

lu - jah! A - men! Hal - le - lu - jah! Thine the glo - ry; Re - vive us a - gain.

Holy Ghost, with Light Divine 268

ANDREW REED

LOUIS M. GOTTSCHALK
Arr. by Edwin P. Parker

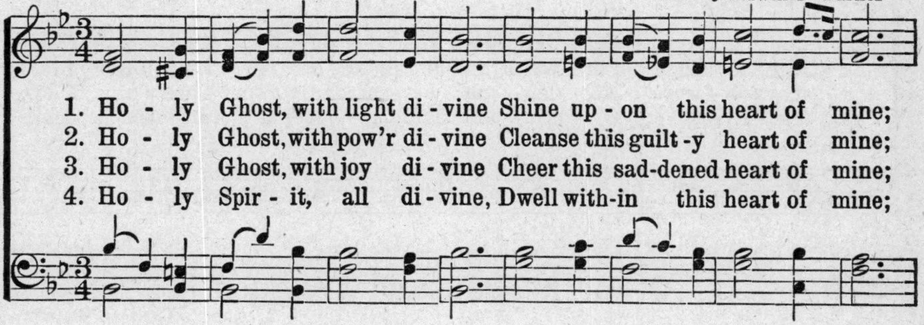

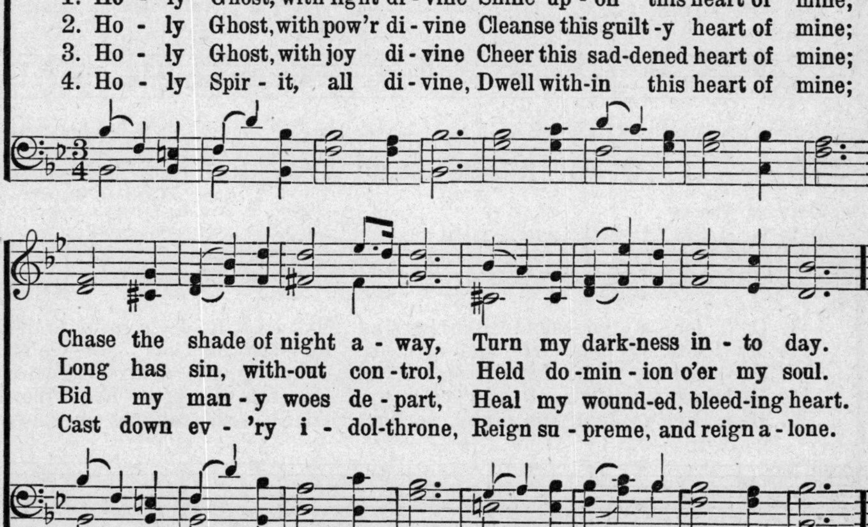
1. Ho - ly Ghost, with light di - vine Shine up - on this heart of mine;
2. Ho - ly Ghost, with pow'r di - vine Cleanse this guilt - y heart of mine;
3. Ho - ly Ghost, with joy di - vine Cheer this sad-dened heart of mine;
4. Ho - ly Spir - it, all di - vine, Dwell with-in this heart of mine;
Chase the shade of night a - way, Turn my dark-ness in - to day.
Long has sin, with-out con - trol, Held do - min - ion o'er my soul.
Bid my man - y woes de - part, Heal my wound-ed, bleed-ing heart.
Cast down ev - 'ry i - dol-throne, Reign su - preme, and reign a - lone.

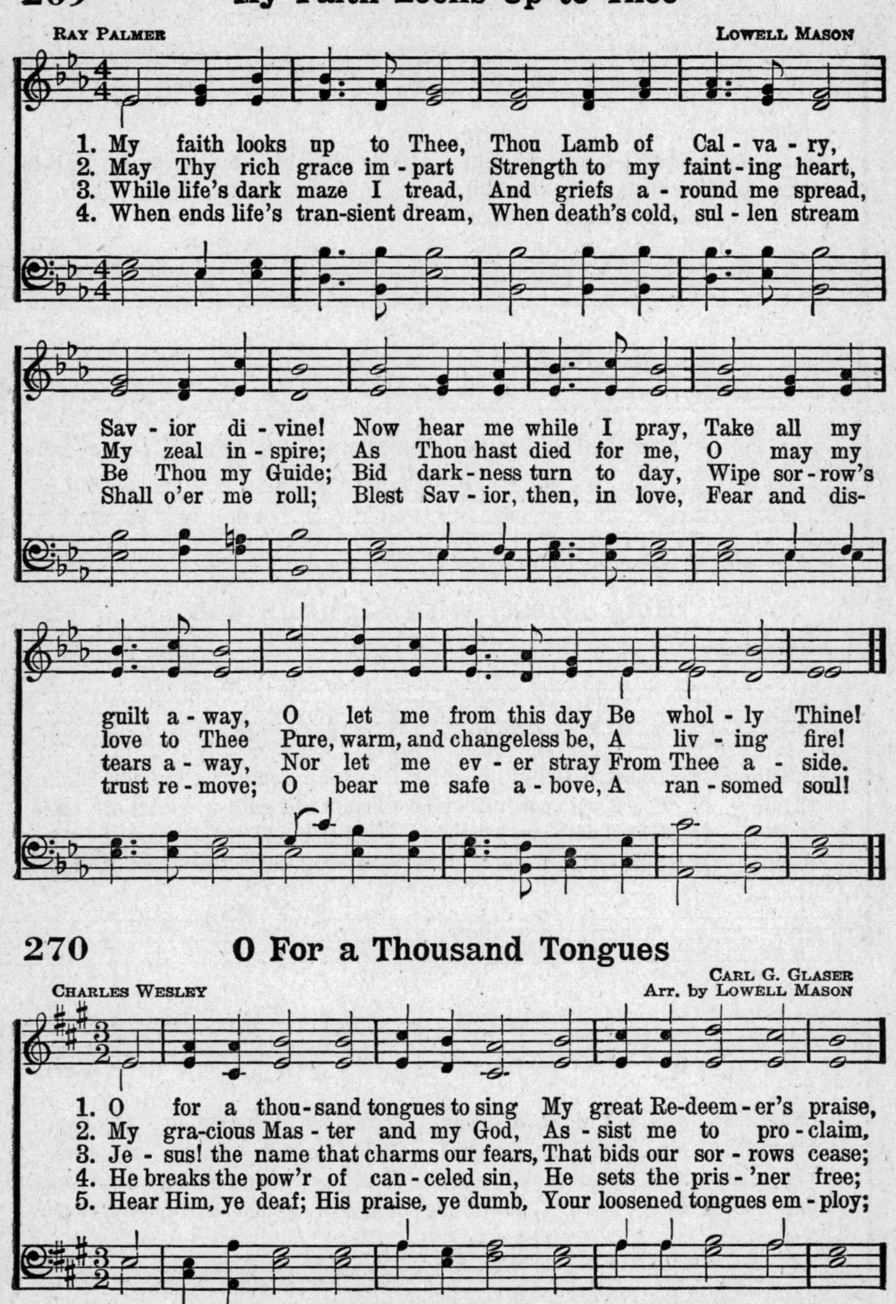
269 My Faith Looks Up to Thee
RAY PALMER
LOWELL MASON
1. My faith looks up to Thee, Thou Lamb of Cal - va - ry,
2. May Thy rich grace im - part Strength to my faint - ing heart,
3. While life's dark maze I tread, And griefs a - round me spread,
4. When ends life's tran-sient dream, When death's cold, sul - len stream
Sav - ior di - vine! Now hear me while I pray, Take all my
My zeal in - spire; As Thou hast died for me, O may my
Be Thou my Guide; Bid dark-ness turn to day, Wipe sor - row's
Shall o'er me roll; Blest Sav - ior, then, in love, Fear and dis-
guilt a - way, O let me from this day Be whol - ly Thine!
love to Thee Pure, warm, and changeless be, A liv - ing fire!
tears a - way, Nor let me ev - er stray From Thee a - side.
trust re - move; O bear me safe a - bove, A ran - somed soul!
270 O For a Thousand Tongues
CARL G. GLASER
CHARLES WESLEY
Arr. by LOWELL MASON
1. O for a thou - sand tongues to sing My great Re-deem - er's praise,
2. My gra-cious Mas - ter and my God, As - sist me to pro - claim,
3. Je - sus! the name that charms our fears, That bids our sor - rows cease;
4. He breaks the pow'r of can - celed sin, He sets the pris - 'ner free;
5. Hear Him, ye deaf; His praise, ye dumb, Your loosened tongues em - ploy;

O For a Thousand Tongues

The glo-ries of my God and King, The tri-umphs of His grace.
To spread thro' all the earth a-broad, The hon-ors of Thy name.
'Tis mu-sic in the sin-ner's ears, 'Tis life, and health, and peace.
His blood can make the foul-est clean; His blood a-vailed for me.
Ye blind, be-hold your Sav-ior come; And leap, ye lame, for joy.
Lead, Kindly Light
271
JOHN H. NEWMAN
JOHN B. DYKES
1. Lead, kindly Light, amid th'encircling gloom, Lead Thou me on! The night is
2. I was not ev-er thus, nor prayed that Thou Shouldst lead me on; I loved to
3. So long Thy pow'r hath blest me, sure it still Will lead me on O'er moor and
dark, and I am far from home; Lead Thou me on! Keep Thou my feet; I
choose and see my path; but now Lead Thou me on! I loved the gar-ish
fen, o'er crag and torrent, till The night is gone, And with the morn those
do not ask to see . . . The dis-tant scene; one step e-nough for me.
day, and, spite of fears, . . Pride ruled my will. Remember not past years!
an-gel fa-ces smile, . Which I have loved long since, and lost a-while!

272
More Love to Thee
Elizabeth Prentiss
W. H. Doane
1. More love to Thee, O Christ, More love to Thee! Hear Thou the
2. Once earth-ly joy I craved, Sought peace and rest; Now Thee a-
3. Let sor-row do its work, Send grief and pain; Sweet are Thy
4. Then shall my lat-est breath Whis-per Thy praise; This be the
prayer I make On bend-ed knee; This is my ear-nest plea:
lone I seek, Give what is best; This all my prayer shall be:
mes-sen-gers, Sweet their re-frain, When they can sing with me,
part-ing cry My heart shall raise; This still its prayer shall be:
More love, O Christ, to Thee, More love to Thee, More love to Thee!
273
Jesus Calls Us
Mrs. Cecil F. Alexander
William H. Jude
1. Je-sus calls us; o'er the tu-mult Of our life's wild, rest-less sea,
2. Je-sus calls us from the wor-ship Of the vain world's gold-en store,
3. In our joys and in our sor-rows, Days of toil and hours of ease,
4. Je-sus calls us: by Thy mer-cies, Sav-ior, may we hear Thy call,

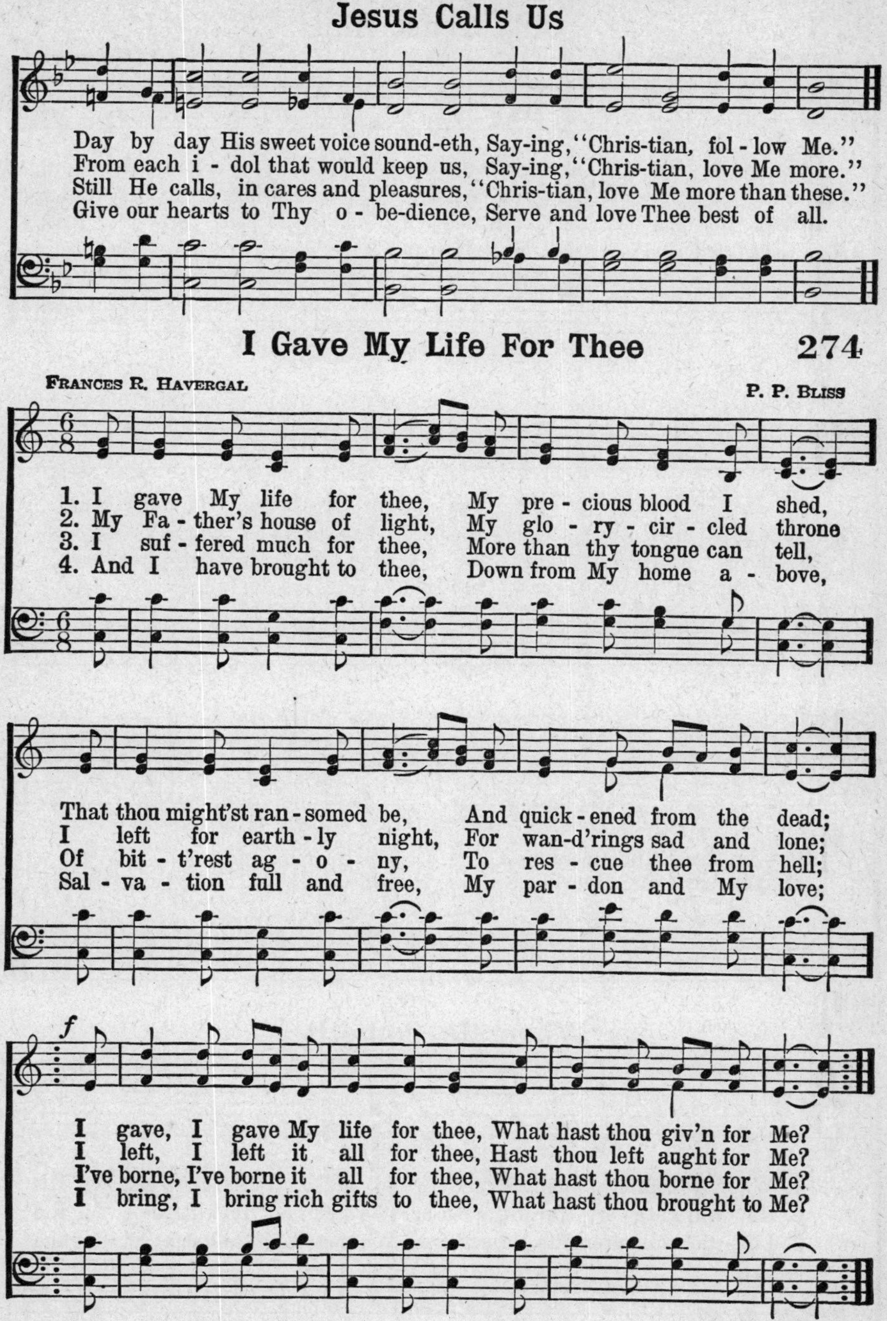
Jesus Calls Us
Day by day His sweet voice sound-eth, Say-ing, "Chris-tian, fol - low Me."
From each i - dol that would keep us, Say-ing, "Chris-tian, love Me more."
Still He calls, in cares and pleasures, "Chris-tian, love Me more than these."
Give our hearts to Thy o - be-dience, Serve and love Thee best of all.
I Gave My Life For Thee
274
Frances R. Havergal
P. P. Bliss
1. I gave My life for thee, My pre - cious blood I shed,
2. My Fa - ther's house of light, My glo - ry - cir - cled throne
3. I suf - fered much for thee, More than thy tongue can tell,
4. And I have brought to thee, Down from My home a - bove,
That thou might'st ran - somed be, And quick - ened from the dead;
I left for earth - ly night, For wan-d'rings sad and lone;
Of bit - t'rest ag - o - ny, To res - cue thee from hell;
Sal - va - tion full and free, My par - don and My love;
f
I gave, I gave My life for thee, What hast thou giv'n for Me?
I left, I left it all for thee, Hast thou left aught for Me?
I've borne, I've borne it all for thee, What hast thou borne for Me?
I bring, I bring rich gifts to thee, What hast thou brought to Me?

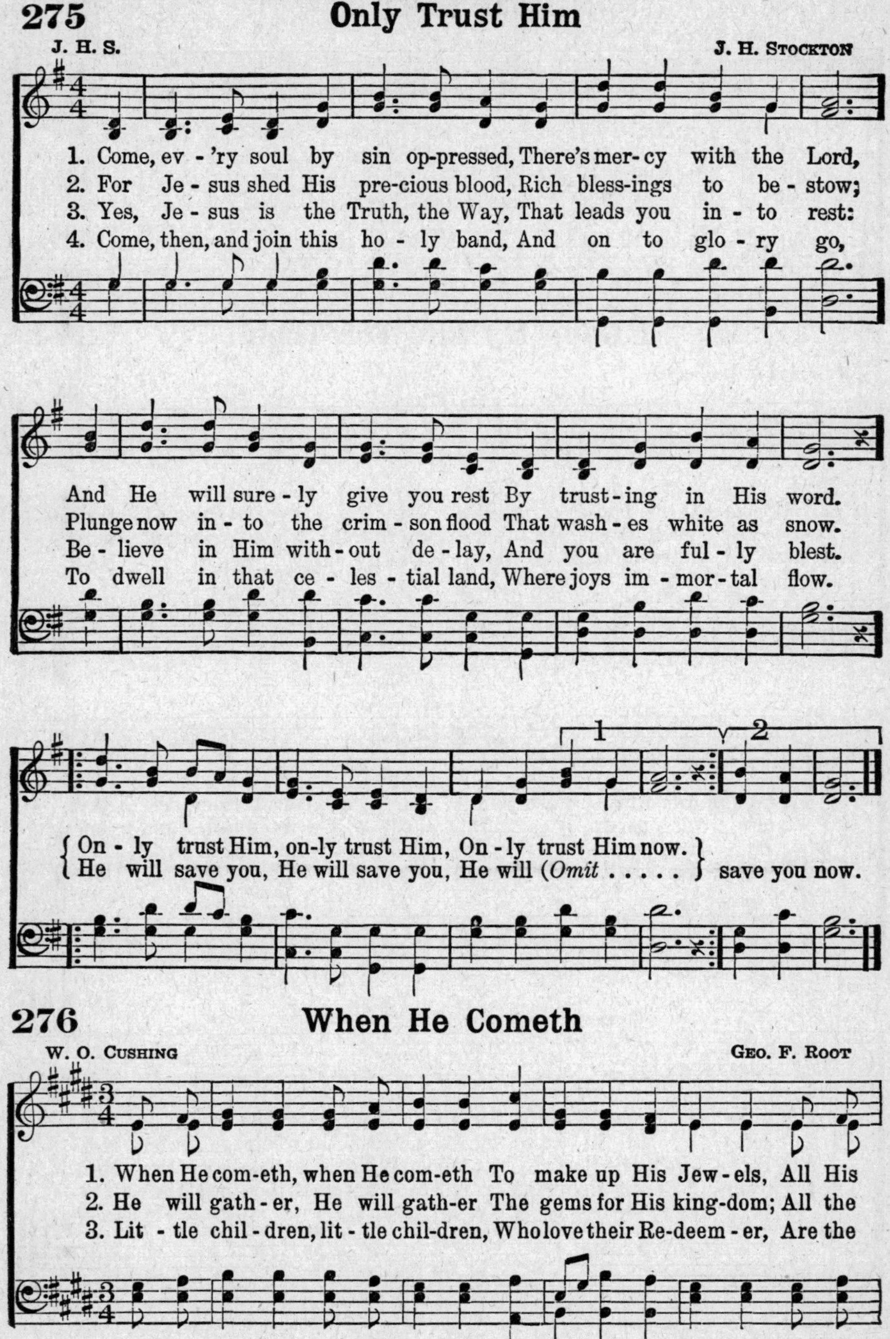
275 Only Trust Him
J. H. S.
J. H. Stockton
1. Come, ev - 'ry soul by sin op-pressed, There's mer-cy with the Lord,
2. For Je - sus shed His pre-cious blood, Rich bless-ings to be - stow;
3. Yes, Je - sus is the Truth, the Way, That leads you in - to rest:
4. Come, then, and join this ho - ly band, And on to glo - ry go,
And He will sure - ly give you rest By trust - ing in His word.
Plunge now in - to the crim - son flood That wash - es white as snow.
Be - lieve in Him with - out de - lay, And you are ful - ly blest.
To dwell in that ce - les - tial land, Where joys im - mor - tal flow.
1
2
On - ly trust Him, on-ly trust Him, On - ly trust Him now.
He will save you, He will save you, He will (Omit . . . . . save you now.
276 When He Cometh
W. O. Cushing
Geo. F. Root
1. When He com-eth, when He com-eth To make up His Jew-els, All His
2. He will gath - er, He will gath-er The gems for His king-dom; All the
3. Lit - tle chil - dren, lit - tle chil-dren, Who love their Re-deem - er, Are the

When He Cometh

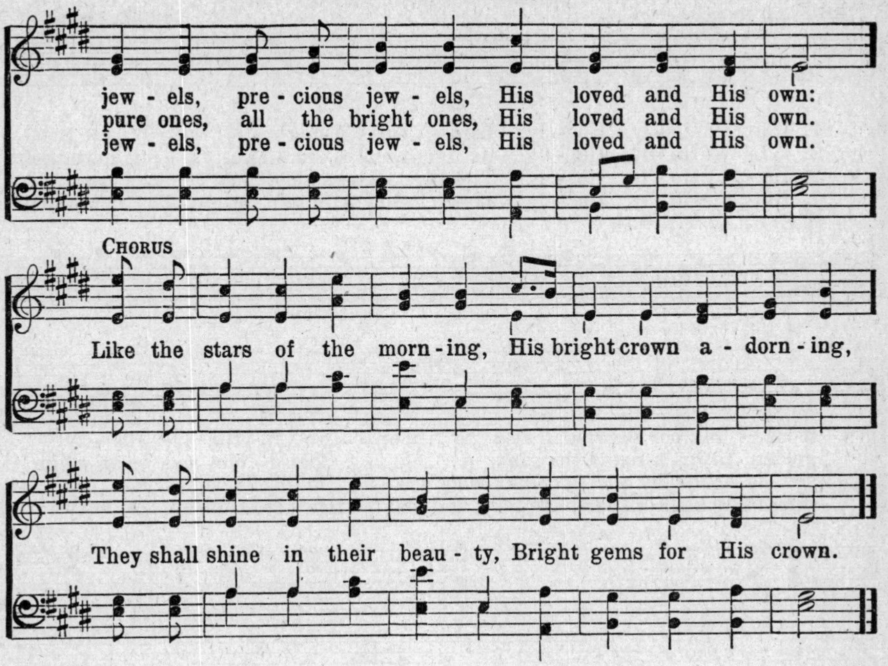

jew - els, pre - cious jew - els, His loved and His own:
pure ones, all the bright ones, His loved and His own.
jew - els, pre - cious jew - els, His loved and His own.

CHORUS

Like the stars of the morn - ing, His bright crown a - dorn - ing,
They shall shine in their beau - ty, Bright gems for His crown.

Majestic Sweetness Sits Enthroned 277

SAMUEL STENNETT THOMAS HASTINGS

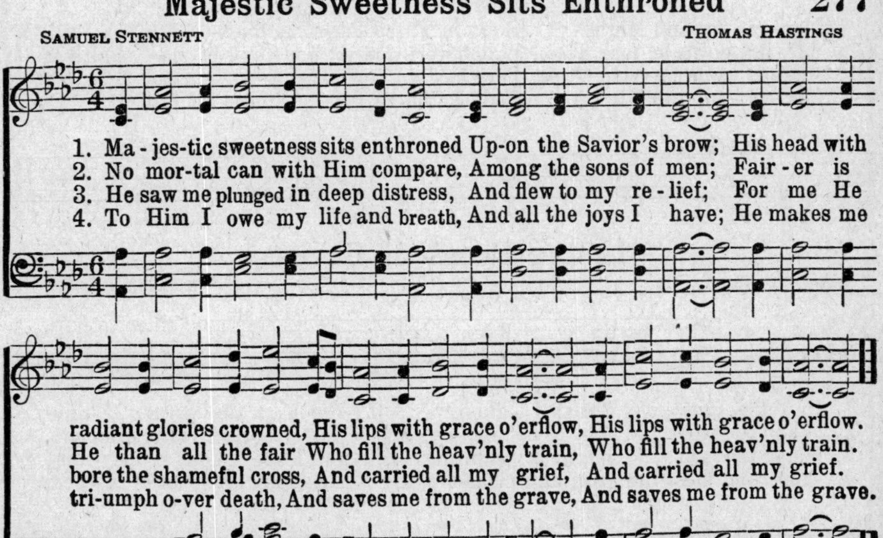
1. Ma - jes-tic sweetness sits enthroned Up-on the Savior's brow; His head with
2. No mor-tal can with Him compare, Among the sons of men; Fair - er is
3. He saw me plunged in deep distress, And flew to my re - lief; For me He
4. To Him I owe my life and breath, And all the joys I have; He makes me
radiant glories crowned, His lips with grace o'erflow, His lips with grace o'erflow.
He than all the fair Who fill the heav'nly train, Who fill the heav'nly train.
bore the shameful cross, And carried all my grief, And carried all my grief.
tri-umph o-ver death, And saves me from the grave, And saves me from the grave.

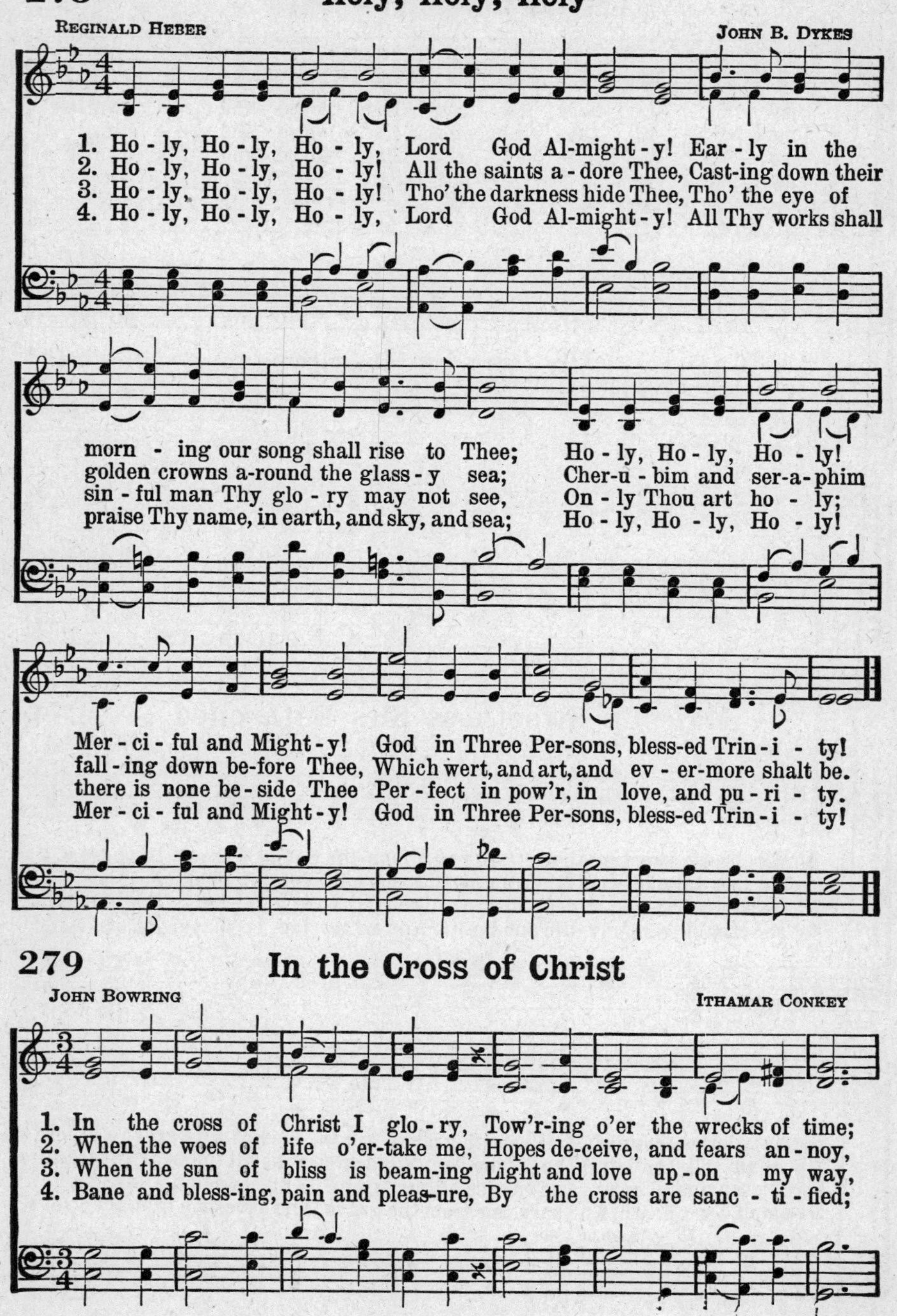
278
Holy, Holy, Holy
Reginald Heber
John B. Dykes
1. Ho - ly, Ho - ly, Ho - ly, Lord God Al-might - y! Ear - ly in the
2. Ho - ly, Ho - ly, Ho - ly! All the saints a - dore Thee, Cast-ing down their
3. Ho - ly, Ho - ly, Ho - ly! Tho' the darkness hide Thee, Tho' the eye of
4. Ho - ly, Ho - ly, Ho - ly, Lord God Al-might - y! All Thy works shall
morn - ing our song shall rise to Thee; Ho - ly, Ho - ly, Ho - ly!
golden crowns a-round the glass - y sea; Cher-u - bim and ser-a-phim
sin - ful man Thy glo - ry may not see, On - ly Thou art ho - ly;
praise Thy name, in earth, and sky, and sea; Ho - ly, Ho - ly, Ho - ly!
Mer - ci - ful and Might - y! God in Three Per-sons, bless-ed Trin - i - ty!
fall - ing down be-fore Thee, Which wert, and art, and ev - er-more shalt be.
there is none be - side Thee Per - fect in pow'r, in love, and pu - ri - ty.
Mer - ci - ful and Might - y! God in Three Per-sons, bless-ed Trin - i - ty!
279
In the Cross of Christ
John Bowring
Ithamar Conkey
1. In the cross of Christ I glo - ry, Tow'r-ing o'er the wrecks of time;
2. When the woes of life o'er-take me, Hopes de-ceive, and fears an - noy,
3. When the sun of bliss is beam-ing Light and love up - on my way,
4. Bane and bless-ing, pain and pleas-ure, By the cross are sanc - ti - fied;

In the Cross of Christ
All the light of sa - cred sto - ry Gath-ers round its head sub-lime.
Nev - er shall the cross for - sake me: Lo! it glows with peace and joy.
From the cross the ra - diance streaming Adds more lus - ter to the day.
Peace is there that knows no meas-ure, Joys that thro' all time a - bide.
Break Thou the Bread of Life
280
Mary Ann Lathbury
William F. Sherwin
1. Break Thou the bread of life, Dear Lord, to me, As Thou didst
2. Bless Thou the truth, dear Lord, To me— to me— As Thou didst
3. Thou art the bread of life, O Lord, to me, Thy ho - ly
4. O send Thy Spir - it, Lord, Now un - to me, That He may
break the loaves Be - side the sea; Be - yond the sa - cred page
bless the bread By Gal - i - lee; Then shall all bond - age cease,
Word the truth That sav - eth me; Give me to eat and live
touch my eyes, And make me see: Show me the truth con-cealed

I seek Thee, Lord; My spir - it pants for Thee, O liv - ing Word.
All fet - ters fall; And I shall find my peace, My All in all.
With Thee a - bove; Teach me to love Thy truth, For Thou art love.
With - in Thy Word, And in Thy book re-vealed I see the Lord.

281 Glory to His Name

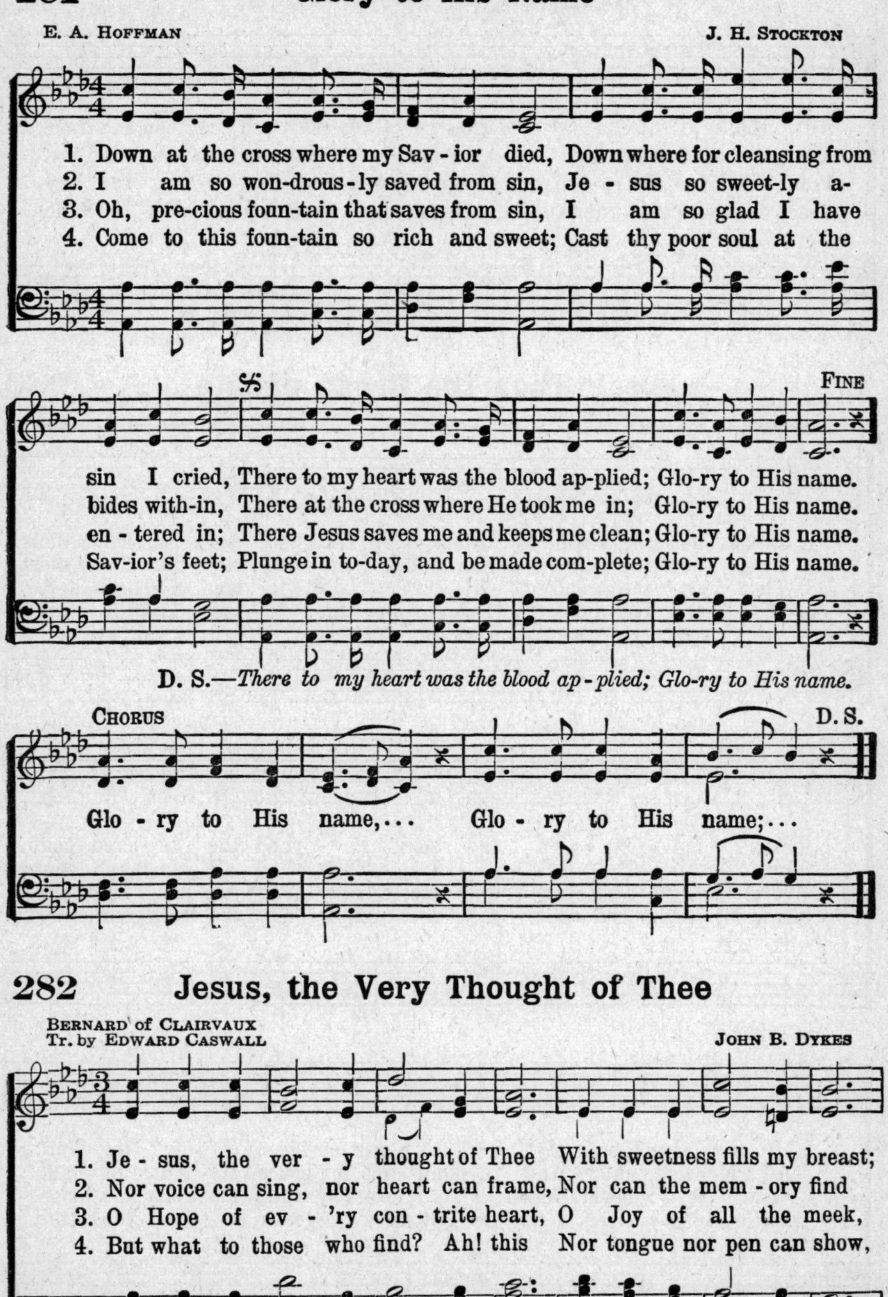
E. A. Hoffman
J. H. Stockton
1. Down at the cross where my Sav-ior died, Down where for cleansing from sin I cried, There to my heart was the blood ap-plied; Glo-ry to His name.
2. I am so won-drous-ly saved from sin, Je-sus so sweet-ly a-bides with-in, There at the cross where He took me in; Glo-ry to His name.
3. Oh, pre-cious foun-tain that saves from sin, I am so glad I have en-tered in; There Jesus saves me and keeps me clean; Glo-ry to His name.
4. Come to this foun-tain so rich and sweet; Cast thy poor soul at the Sav-ior's feet; Plunge in to-day, and be made com-plete; Glo-ry to His name.
Fine
D. S.—There to my heart was the blood ap-plied; Glo-ry to His name.
Chorus
Glo-ry to His name,... Glo-ry to His name;...
D. S.
282 Jesus, the Very Thought of Thee
Bernard of Clairvaux
Tr. by Edward Caswall
John B. Dykes
1. Je-sus, the ver-y thought of Thee With sweetness fills my breast;
2. Nor voice can sing, nor heart can frame, Nor can the mem-ory find
3. O Hope of ev-'ry con-trite heart, O Joy of all the meek,
4. But what to those who find? Ah! this Nor tongue nor pen can show,

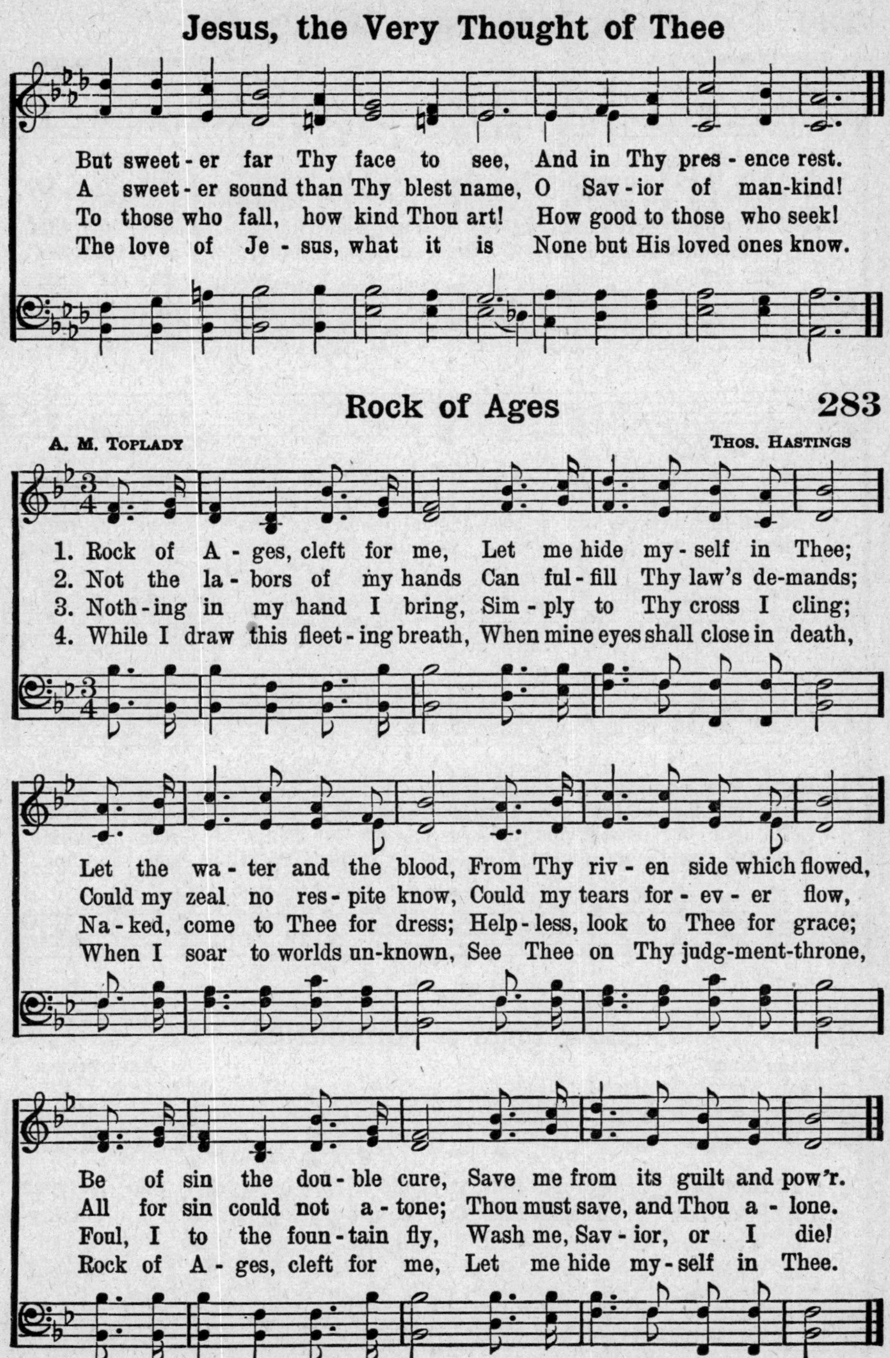
Jesus, the Very Thought of Thee
But sweet-er far Thy face to see, And in Thy pres-ence rest.
A sweet-er sound than Thy blest name, O Sav-ior of man-kind!
To those who fall, how kind Thou art! How good to those who seek!
The love of Je-sus, what it is None but His loved ones know.
Rock of Ages
283
A. M. Toplady
Thos. Hastings
1. Rock of A-ges, cleft for me, Let me hide my-self in Thee;
2. Not the la-bors of my hands Can ful-fill Thy law's de-mands;
3. Noth-ing in my hand I bring, Sim-ply to Thy cross I cling;
4. While I draw this fleet-ing breath, When mine eyes shall close in death,
Let the wa-ter and the blood, From Thy riv-en side which flowed,
Could my zeal no res-pite know, Could my tears for-ev-er flow,
Na-ked, come to Thee for dress; Help-less, look to Thee for grace;
When I soar to worlds un-known, See Thee on Thy judg-ment-throne,
Be of sin the dou-ble cure, Save me from its guilt and pow'r.
All for sin could not a-tone; Thou must save, and Thou a-lone.
Foul, I to the foun-tain fly, Wash me, Sav-ior, or I die!
Rock of A-ges, cleft for me, Let me hide my-self in Thee.

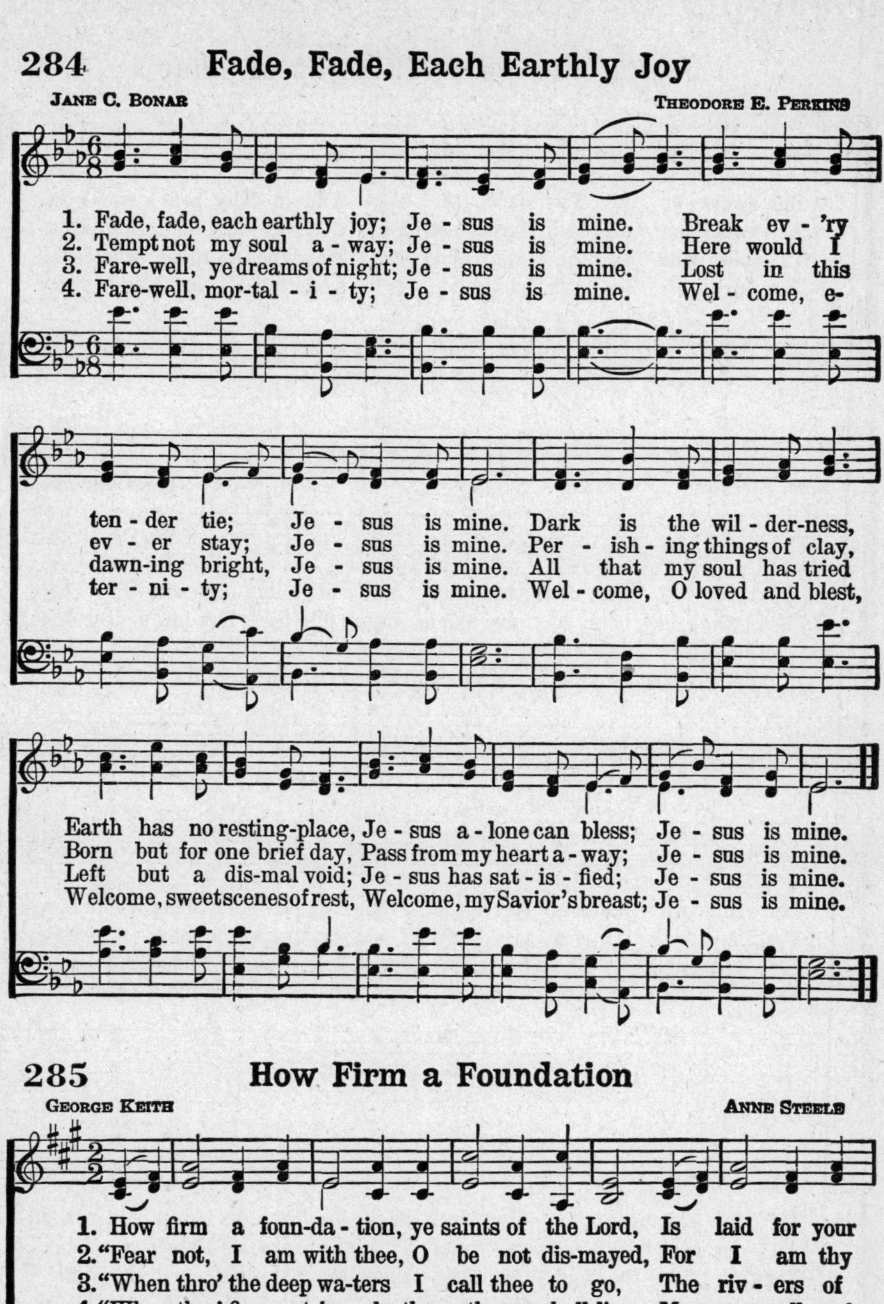
284 Fade, Fade, Each Earthly Joy
Jane C. Bonar
Theodore E. Perkins
1. Fade, fade, each earthly joy; Je - sus is mine. Break ev - 'ry ten - der tie; Je - sus is mine. Dark is the wil - der-ness, Earth has no resting-place, Je - sus a - lone can bless; Je - sus is mine.
2. Tempt not my soul a - way; Je - sus is mine. Here would I ev - er stay; Je - sus is mine. Per - ish - ing things of clay, Born but for one brief day, Pass from my heart a - way; Je - sus is mine.
3. Fare-well, ye dreams of night; Je - sus is mine. Lost in this dawn-ing bright, Je - sus is mine. All that my soul has tried Left but a dis-mal void; Je - sus has sat - is - fied; Je - sus is mine.
4. Fare-well, mor-tal - i - ty; Je - sus is mine. Wel - come, e - ter - ni - ty; Je - sus is mine. Wel - come, O loved and blest, Welcome, sweet scenes of rest, Welcome, my Savior's breast; Je - sus is mine.
285 How Firm a Foundation
George Keith
Anne Steele
1. How firm a foun-da - tion, ye saints of the Lord, Is laid for your
2. "Fear not, I am with thee, O be not dis-mayed, For I am thy
3. "When thro' the deep wa-ters I call thee to go, The riv - ers of
4. "When thro' fier - y tri - als thy path-way shall lie, My grace, all - suf-

How Firm a Foundation

faith in His ex - cel - lent Word! What more can He say than to
God, and will still give thee aid; I'll strength - en thee, help thee, and
sor - row shall not o - ver - flow; For I will be with thee thy
fi - cient, shall be thy sup - ply; The flames shall not hurt thee, I
you He hath said, To you who for ref - uge to Je - sus have fled?
cause thee to stand, Up - held by My gra - cious, om-nip - o - tent hand.
tri - als to bless, And sanc - ti - fy to thee thy deep - est dis - tress.
on - ly de - sign Thy dross to con-sume, and thy gold to re - fine.
[SECOND TUNE]
Portuguese Hymn
Unknown
1. How firm a foun-da-tion, ye saints of the Lord, Is laid for your faith in His
ex-cel-lent Word! What more can He say than to you He hath said, To you, who for
ref - uge to Je - sus have fled? To you, who for ref-uge to Je-sus have fled?

286 Why Do You Wait?

G. F. R. — Geo. F. Root

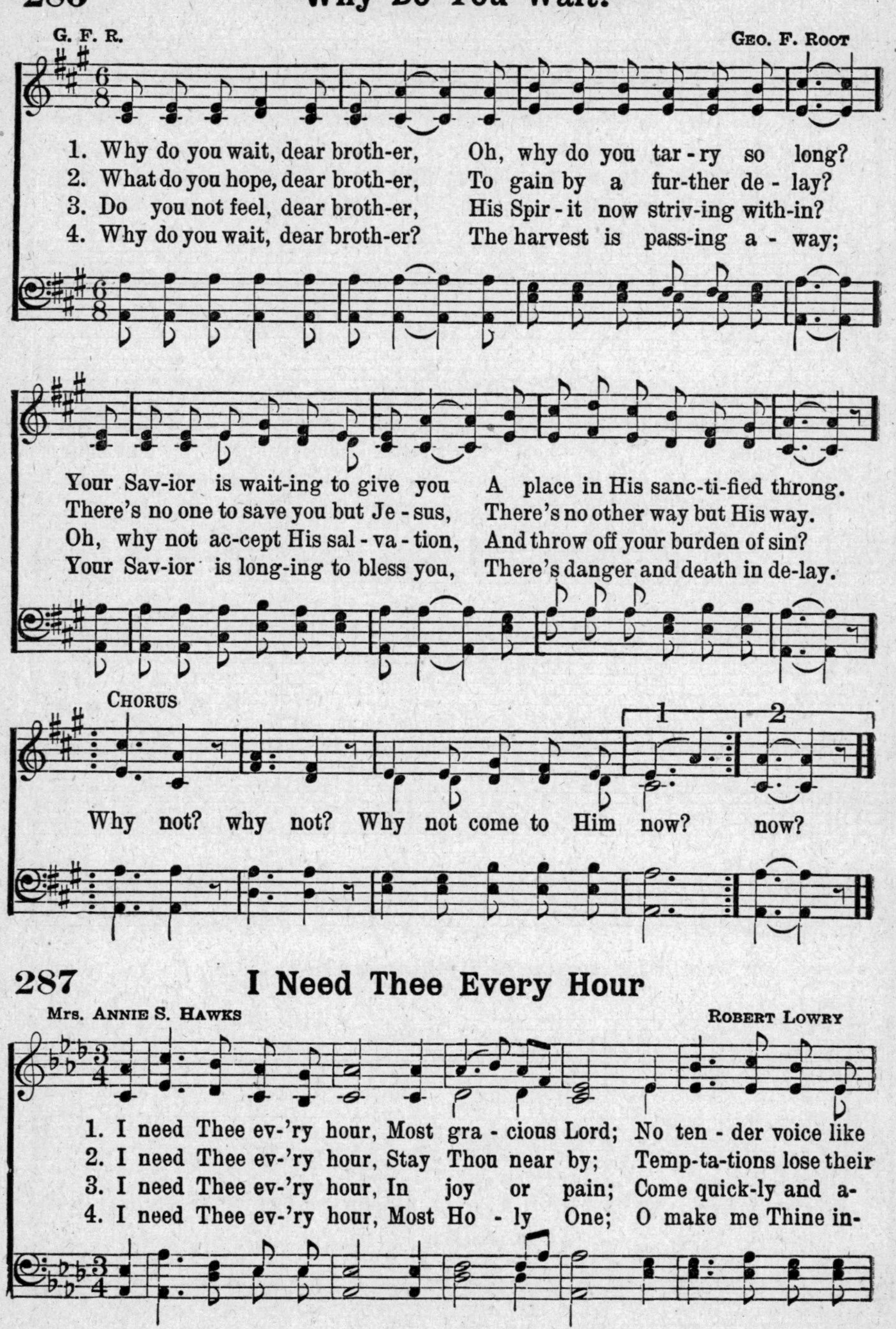
1. Why do you wait, dear broth-er, Oh, why do you tar-ry so long?
2. What do you hope, dear broth-er, To gain by a fur-ther de-lay?
3. Do you not feel, dear broth-er, His Spir-it now striv-ing with-in?
4. Why do you wait, dear broth-er? The harvest is pass-ing a-way;
Your Sav-ior is wait-ing to give you A place in His sanc-ti-fied throng.
There's no one to save you but Je-sus, There's no other way but His way.
Oh, why not ac-cept His sal-va-tion, And throw off your burden of sin?
Your Sav-ior is long-ing to bless you, There's danger and death in de-lay.
Chorus
Why not? why not? Why not come to Him now? now?

287 I Need Thee Every Hour

Mrs. Annie S. Hawks — Robert Lowry

1. I need Thee ev-'ry hour, Most gra-cious Lord; No ten-der voice like
2. I need Thee ev-'ry hour, Stay Thou near by; Temp-ta-tions lose their
3. I need Thee ev-'ry hour, In joy or pain; Come quick-ly and a-
4. I need Thee ev-'ry hour, Most Ho-ly One; O make me Thine in-

I Need Thee Every Hour

CHORUS
Thine Can peace af - ford.
pow'r When Thou art nigh. I need Thee, O I need Thee; Ev-'ry hour I
bide, Or life is vain.
deed, Thou bless-ed Son!
need Thee! O bless me now, my Sav - ior, I come to Thee!
Oh, How I Love Jesus
288
1. There is a name I love to hear, I love to sing its worth; It sounds like
2. It tells me of a Sav-ior's love, Who died to set me free; It tells me
3. It tells me what my Fa-ther hath In store for ev - 'ry day, And tho' I
4. It tells of One whose loving heart Can feel my deep-est woe, Who in each
CHORUS
mu - sic in mine ear, The sweetest name on earth.
of His precious blood, The sin-ner's per-fect plea. Oh, how I love Je - sus,
tread a darksome path, Yields sunshine all the way.
sor - row bears a part, That none can bear be-low.
Oh, how I love Je - sus, Oh, how I love Je - sus, Be-cause He first loved me!

289 Jesus Paid It All
Mrs. H. M. Hall
John T. Grape
1. I hear the Sav-ior say, "Thy strength in-deed is small, Child of weakness, watch and pray, Find in Me thine all in all."
2. Lord, now in-deed I find Thy pow'r, and Thine a-lone, Can change the lep-er's spots, And melt the heart of stone.
3. For noth-ing good have I Where-by Thy grace to claim— I'll wash my garments white In the blood of Cal-v'ry's Lamb.
4. And when, be-fore the throne, I stand in Him com-plete, "Je-sus died my soul to save," My lips shall still re-peat.
Chorus
Je-sus paid it all, All to Him I owe; Sin had left a crimson stain, He washed it white as snow.
290 Lord, I'm Coming Home
W. J. K.
Wm. J. Kirkpatrick
1. I've wan-dered far a-way from God, Now I'm com-ing home;
2. I've wast-ed man-y pre-cious years, Now I'm com-ing home;
3. I've tired of sin and stray-ing, Lord, Now I'm com-ing home;
4. My soul is sick, my heart is sore, Now I'm com-ing home;
Copyright, 1920, Renewal. Hope Publishing Co., owner

Lord, I'm Coming Home
FINE
The paths of sin too long I've trod, Lord, I'm com-ing home.
I now re-pent with bit - ter tears, Lord, I'm com-ing home.
I'll trust Thy love, be-lieve Thy word, Lord, I'm com-ing home.
My strength re-new, my hope re-store, Lord, I'm com-ing home.
D. S.—O - pen wide Thine arms of love, Lord, I'm com - ing home.
CHORUS
D. S.
Com - ing home, com - ing home, Nev - er - more to roam,
Take My Life, and Let It Be
291
FRANCES R. HAVERGAL
CÆSAR MALAN
1. Take my life, and let it be Con-se-crat-ed, Lord, to Thee; Take my hands, and
2. Take my feet, and let them be Swift and beau-ti-ful for Thee; Take my voice, and
3. Take my lips, and let them be Filled with messages for Thee; Take my sil - ver
4. Take my love, my God, I pour At Thy feet its treas-ure store; Take my-self and
let them move At the im-pulse of Thy love, At the im-pulse of Thy love.
let me sing Al-ways, on - ly, for my King, Al-ways, on - ly, for my King.
and my gold, Not a mite would I with-hold, Not a mite would I with-hold.
I will be Ev - er, on - ly, all for Thee, Ev - er, on - ly, all for Thee.

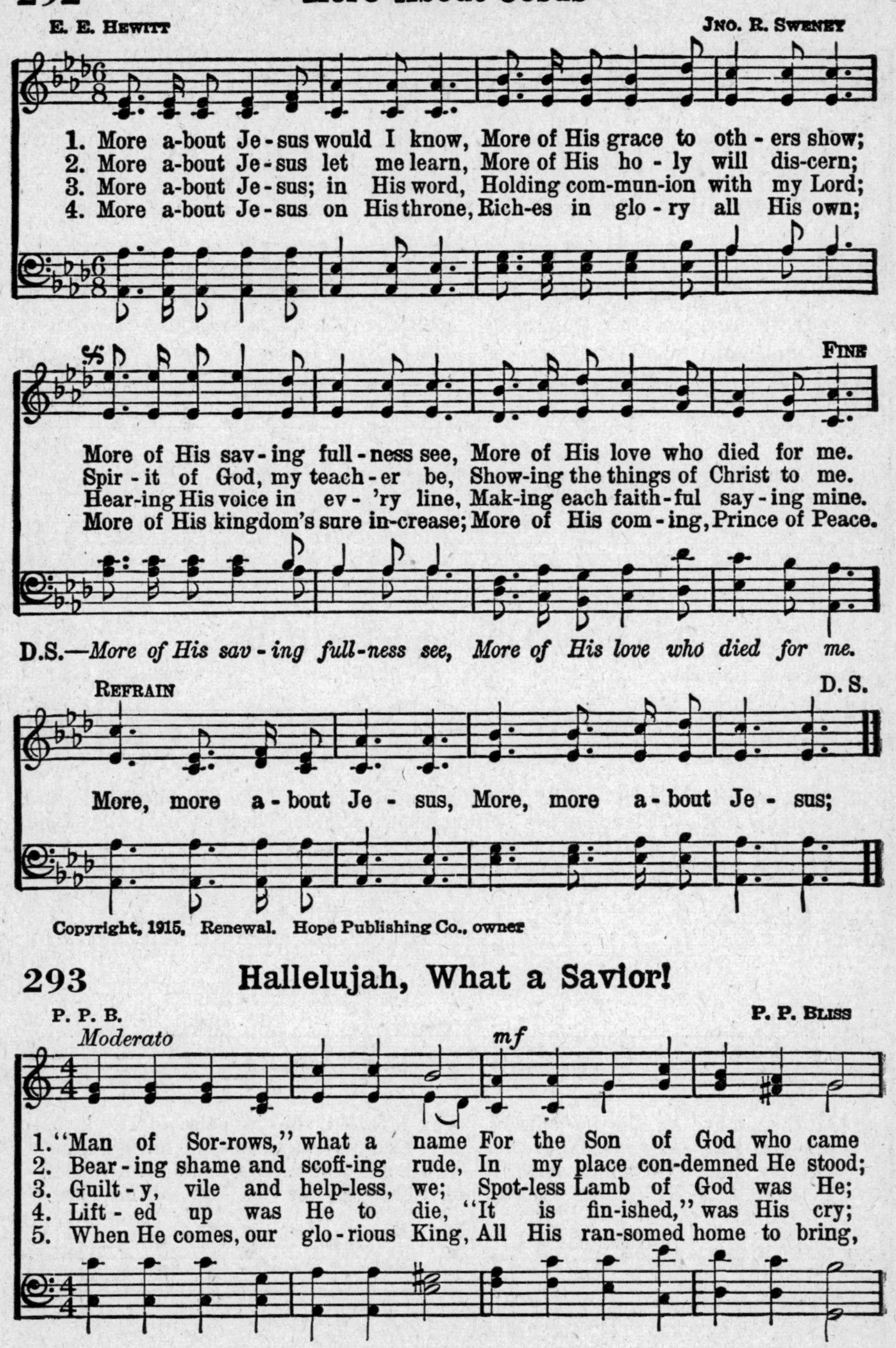
292
More About Jesus
E. E. Hewitt
Jno. R. Sweney
1. More a-bout Je-sus would I know, More of His grace to oth-ers show;
2. More a-bout Je-sus let me learn, More of His ho-ly will dis-cern;
3. More a-bout Je-sus; in His word, Holding com-mun-ion with my Lord;
4. More a-bout Je-sus on His throne, Rich-es in glo-ry all His own;
Fine
More of His sav-ing full-ness see, More of His love who died for me.
Spir-it of God, my teach-er be, Show-ing the things of Christ to me.
Hear-ing His voice in ev-'ry line, Mak-ing each faith-ful say-ing mine.
More of His kingdom's sure in-crease; More of His com-ing, Prince of Peace.
D.S.—More of His sav-ing full-ness see, More of His love who died for me.
Refrain
D. S.
More, more a-bout Je-sus, More, more a-bout Je-sus;
Copyright, 1915, Renewal. Hope Publishing Co., owner
293
Hallelujah, What a Savior!
P. P. B.
P. P. Bliss
Moderato
mf
1. "Man of Sor-rows," what a name For the Son of God who came
2. Bear-ing shame and scoff-ing rude, In my place con-demned He stood;
3. Guilt-y, vile and help-less, we; Spot-less Lamb of God was He;
4. Lift-ed up was He to die, "It is fin-ished," was His cry;
5. When He comes, our glo-rious King, All His ran-somed home to bring,

Hallelujah, What a Savior!

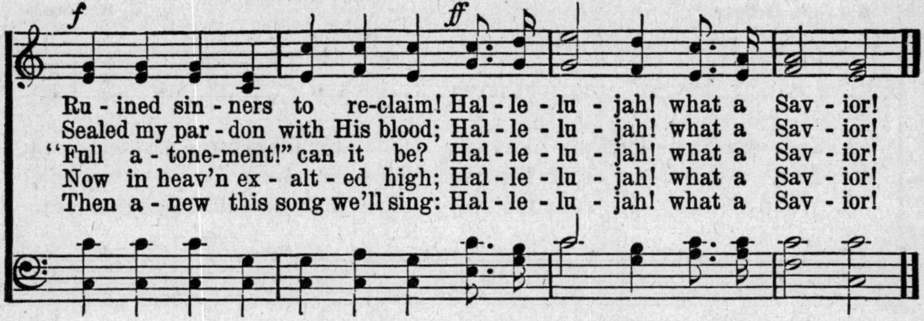

Ru - ined sin - ners to re-claim! Hal - le - lu - jah! what a Sav - ior!
Sealed my par - don with His blood; Hal - le - lu - jah! what a Sav - ior!
"Full a - tone-ment!" can it be? Hal - le - lu - jah! what a Sav - ior!
Now in heav'n ex - alt - ed high; Hal - le - lu - jah! what a Sav - ior!
Then a - new this song we'll sing: Hal - le - lu - jah! what a Sav - ior!

O Love That Wilt Not Let Me Go 294

GEORGE MATHESON A. L. PEACE

1. O Love that wilt not let me go, I rest my wea - ry soul on Thee; I give Thee back the life I owe, That in Thine o - cean depths its flow May rich - er, full - er be.
2. O Light that fol - low'st all my way, I yield my flick-'ring torch to Thee; My heart re - stores its bor - rowed ray, That in Thy sun-shine's glow its day May bright-er, fair - er be.
3. O Joy that seek - est me thro' pain, I can - not close my heart to Thee; I trace the rain - bow thro' the rain, And feel the prom - ise is not vain That morn shall tear - less be.
4. O Cross that lift - est up my head, I dare not ask to hide from Thee; I lay in dust life's glo - ry dead, And from the ground there blossoms red Life that shall end - less be.

295
Jesus, Savior, Pilot Me
Edward Hopper
J. E. Gould
1. Je - sus, Sav - ior, pi - lot me O - ver life's tem - pes-tuous sea;
2. As a moth - er stills her child, Thou canst hush the o - cean wild;
3. When at last I near the shore, And the fear - ful break-ers roar
Un-known waves be - fore me roll, Hid - ing rock and treacherous shoal;
Boisterous waves o - bey Thy will When Thou say'st to them "Be still!"
'Twixt me and the peace-ful rest, Then, while lean - ing on Thy breast,
Chart and com - pass came from Thee: Je - sus, Sav - ior, pi - lot me.
Won-drous Sov-'reign of the sea, Je - sus, Sav - ior, pi - lot me.
May I hear Thee say to me, "Fear not, I will pi - lot thee."
296
Sun of My Soul
John Keble
Peter Ritter
1. Sun of my soul! Thou Sav - ior dear, It is not night if Thou be near;
2. When the soft dews of kind - ly sleep My wea - ry eye - lids gen - tly steep,
3. A - bide with me from morn till eve, For with-out Thee I can - not live;
4. Be near to bless us when we wake, Ere thro' the world our way we take;

Sun of My Soul

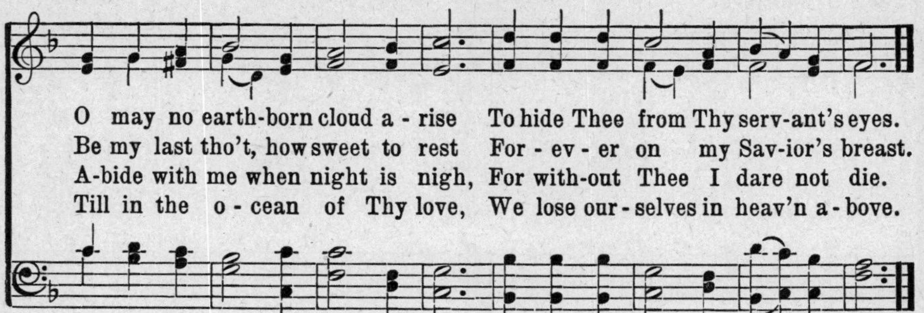

O may no earth-born cloud a - rise To hide Thee from Thy serv-ant's eyes.
Be my last tho't, how sweet to rest For - ev - er on my Sav-ior's breast.
A-bide with me when night is nigh, For with-out Thee I dare not die.
Till in the o - cean of Thy love, We lose our - selves in heav'n a - bove.

His Matchless Worth 297

SAMUEL MEDLEY — LOWELL MASON

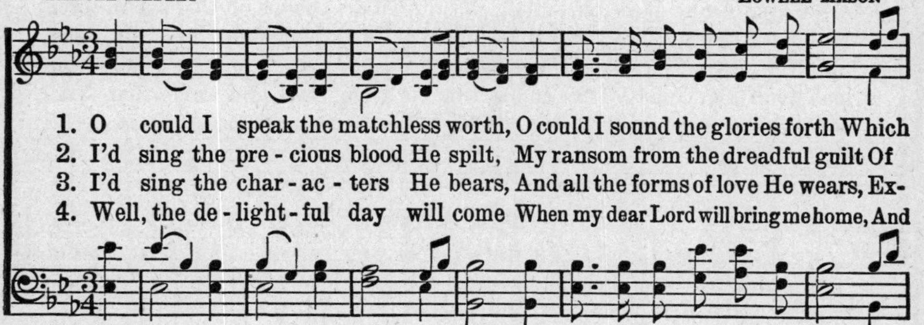

1. O could I speak the matchless worth, O could I sound the glories forth Which
2. I'd sing the pre - cious blood He spilt, My ransom from the dreadful guilt Of
3. I'd sing the char - ac - ters He bears, And all the forms of love He wears, Ex-
4. Well, the de - light - ful day will come When my dear Lord will bring me home, And

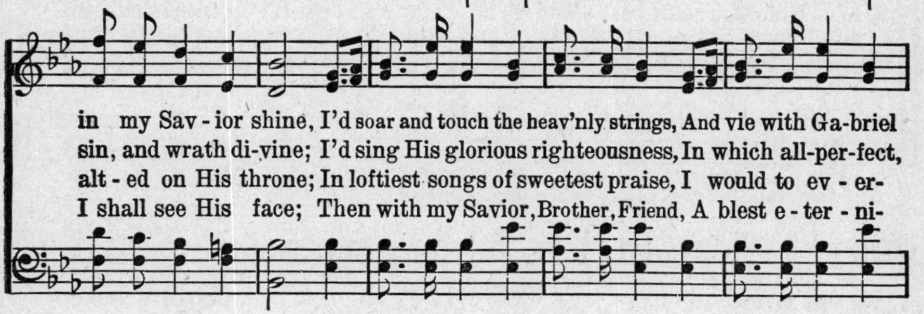

in my Sav - ior shine, I'd soar and touch the heav'nly strings, And vie with Ga-briel
sin, and wrath di-vine; I'd sing His glorious righteousness, In which all-per-fect,
alt - ed on His throne; In loftiest songs of sweetest praise, I would to ev - er-
I shall see His face; Then with my Savior, Brother, Friend, A blest e - ter - ni-

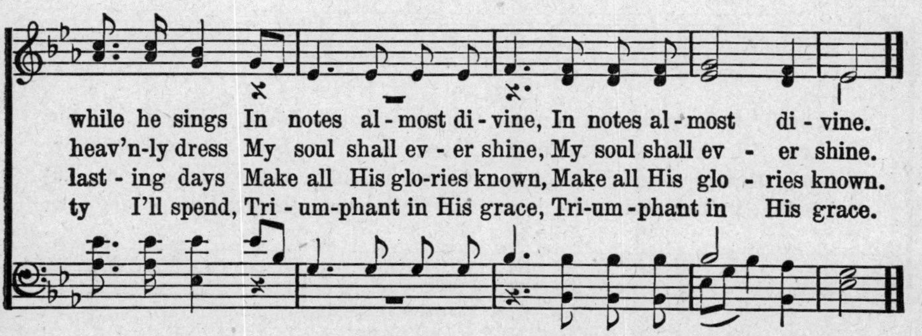

while he sings In notes al - most di - vine, In notes al - most di - vine.
heav'n-ly dress My soul shall ev - er shine, My soul shall ev - er shine.
last - ing days Make all His glo-ries known, Make all His glo - ries known.
ty I'll spend, Tri - um-phant in His grace, Tri-um-phant in His grace.

298 Take Time to Be Holy

W. D. LONGSTAFF — GEO. C. STEBBINS

1. Take time to be ho - ly, Speak oft with thy Lord; A - bide in Him
2. Take time to be ho - ly, The world rush-es on;.. Spend much time in
3. Take time to be ho - ly, Let Him be thy Guide, And run not be-
4. Take time to be ho - ly, Be calm in thy soul;. Each tho't and each

al - ways, And feed on His Word. Make friends of God's chil-dren;
se - cret With Je - sus a - lone; By look - ing to Je - sus,
fore Him, What - ev - er be - tide;.. In joy or in sor - row,
mo - tive Be - neath His con - trol;.. Thus led by His Spir - it

Help those who are weak; For - get-ting in noth-ing His bless-ing to seek.
Like Him thou shalt be;.. Thy friends in thy con-duct His likeness shall see..
Still fol - low thy Lord, And, look-ing to Je - sus, Still trust in His Word.
To foun-tains of love, Thou soon shalt be fit - ted For serv- ice a - bove.

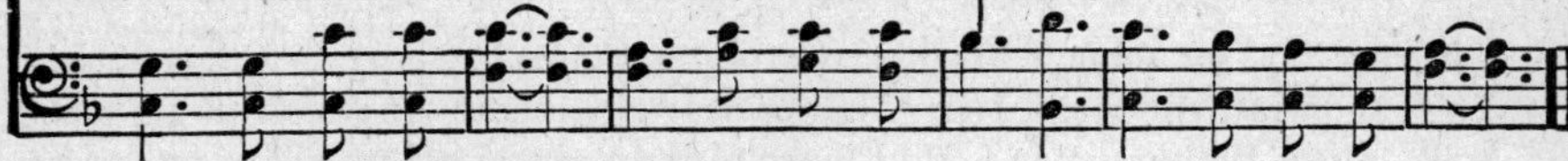

Copyright, 1918, Renewal. Hope Publishing Co., owner

299 Lord, I Have Shut the Door

SANCTUARY

WILLIAM M. RUNYAN — WILLIAM M. RUNYAN

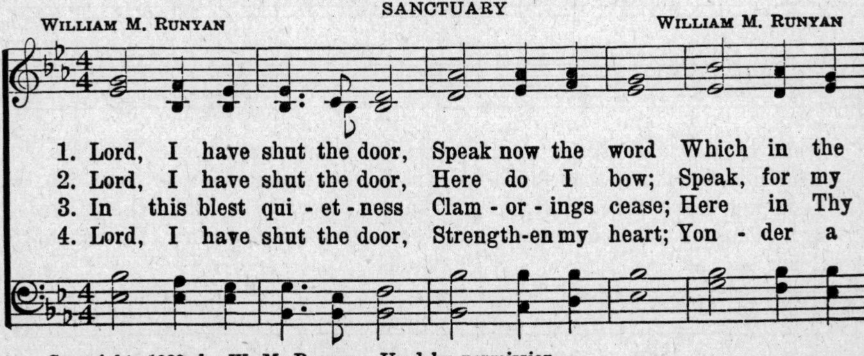
1. Lord, I have shut the door, Speak now the word Which in the
2. Lord, I have shut the door, Here do I bow; Speak, for my
3. In this blest qui - et - ness Clam - or - ings cease; Here in Thy
4. Lord, I have shut the door, Strength-en my heart; Yon - der a

Copyright, 1923, by W. M. Runyan. Used by permission.

Lord, I Have Shut the Door

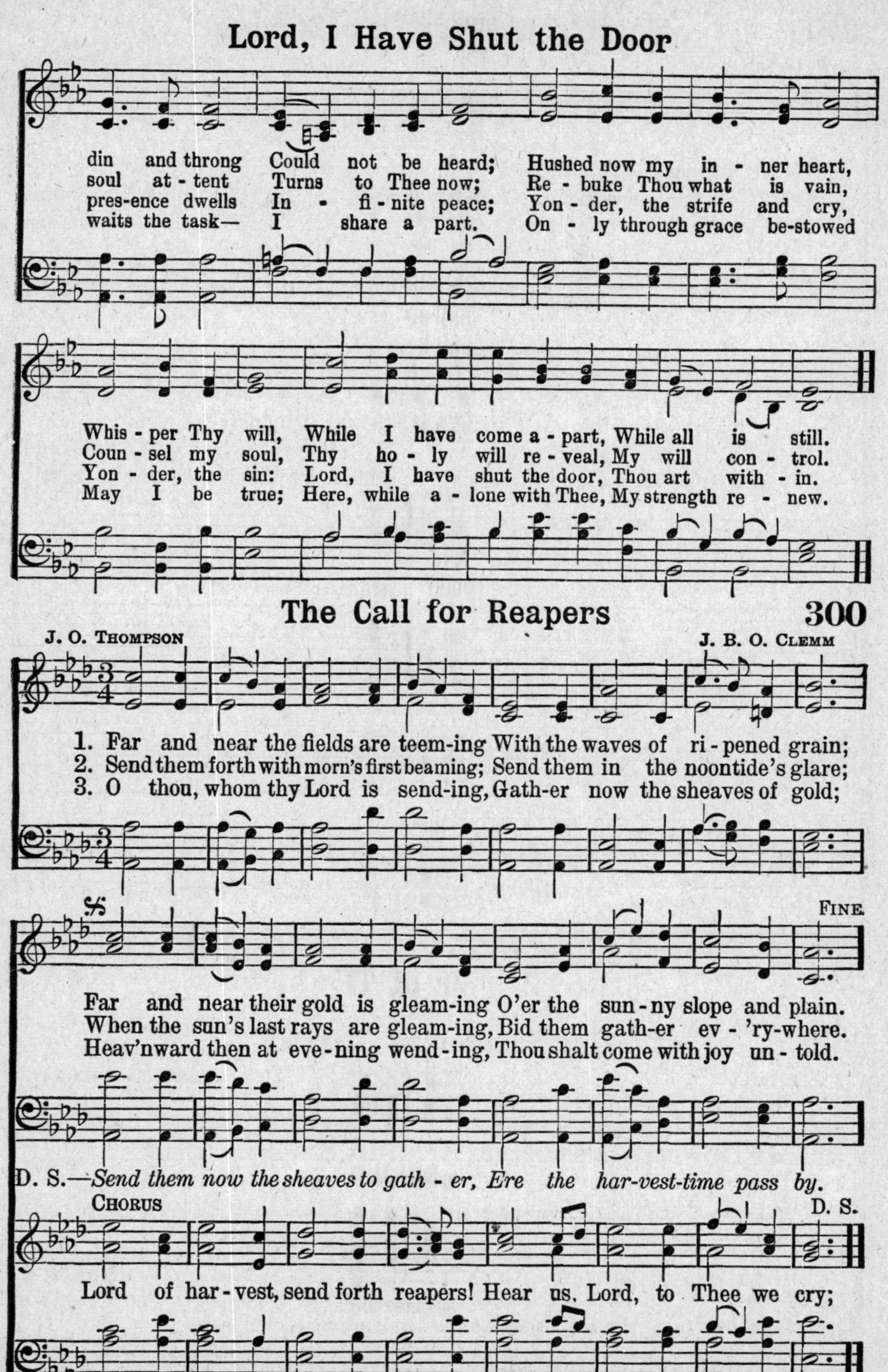
din and throng Could not be heard; Hushed now my in - ner heart,
soul at - tent Turns to Thee now; Re - buke Thou what is vain,
pres-ence dwells In - fi - nite peace; Yon - der, the strife and cry,
waits the task— I share a part. On - ly through grace be-stowed
Whis - per Thy will, While I have come a - part, While all is still.
Coun - sel my soul, Thy ho - ly will re - veal, My will con - trol.
Yon - der, the sin: Lord, I have shut the door, Thou art with - in.
May I be true; Here, while a - lone with Thee, My strength re - new.
The Call for Reapers
300
J. O. Thompson
J. B. O. Clemm
1. Far and near the fields are teem-ing With the waves of ri - pened grain;
2. Send them forth with morn's first beaming; Send them in the noontide's glare;
3. O thou, whom thy Lord is send-ing, Gath-er now the sheaves of gold;
Fine
Far and near their gold is gleam-ing O'er the sun - ny slope and plain.
When the sun's last rays are gleam-ing, Bid them gath-er ev - 'ry-where.
Heav'nward then at eve - ning wend - ing, Thou shalt come with joy un - told.
D. S.—Send them now the sheaves to gath - er, Ere the har-vest-time pass by.
Chorus
D. S.
Lord of har - vest, send forth reapers! Hear us, Lord, to Thee we cry;

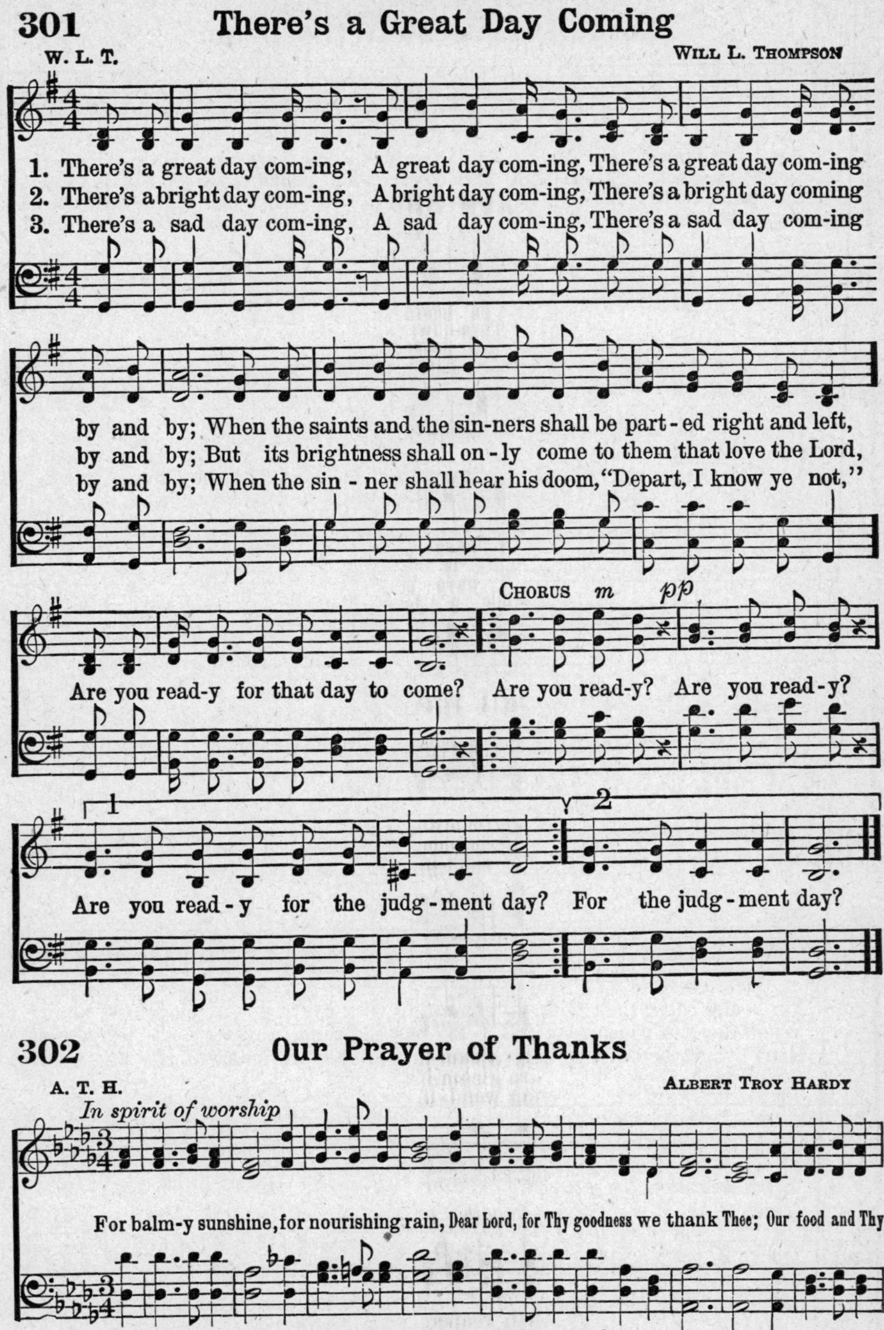
301 There's a Great Day Coming
W. L. T.
Will L. Thompson
1. There's a great day com-ing, A great day com-ing, There's a great day com-ing
2. There's a bright day com-ing, A bright day com-ing, There's a bright day coming
3. There's a sad day com-ing, A sad day com-ing, There's a sad day com-ing
by and by; When the saints and the sin-ners shall be part - ed right and left,
by and by; But its brightness shall on - ly come to them that love the Lord,
by and by; When the sin - ner shall hear his doom, "Depart, I know ye not,"
Chorus
m
pp
Are you read-y for that day to come? Are you read-y? Are you read - y?
1
2
Are you read - y for the judg - ment day? For the judg - ment day?
302 Our Prayer of Thanks
A. T. H.
Albert Troy Hardy
In spirit of worship
For balm-y sunshine, for nourishing rain, Dear Lord, for Thy goodness we thank Thee; Our food and Thy

Copyright, 1941, by A. T. Hardy. International Copyright secured

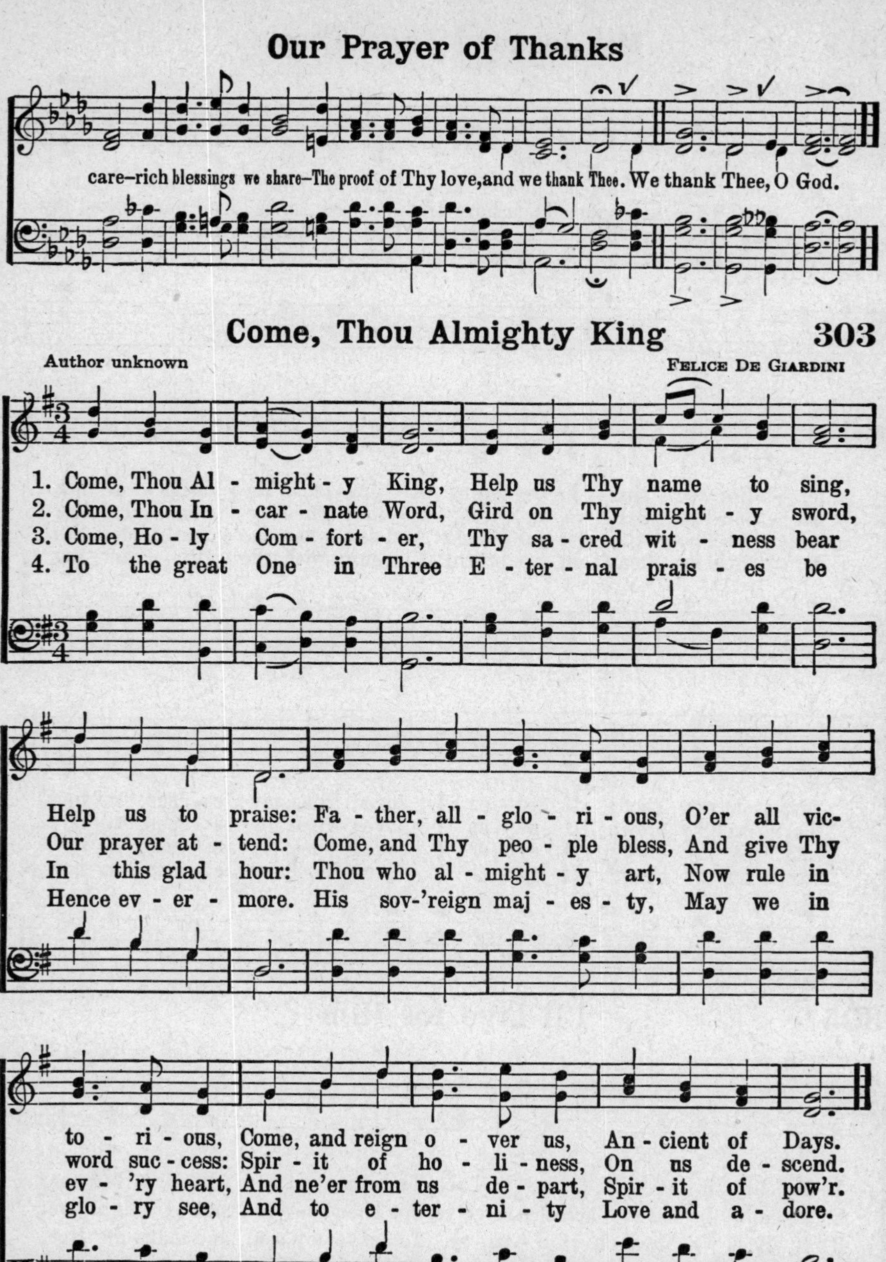
Our Prayer of Thanks
care–rich blessings we share–The proof of Thy love, and we thank Thee. We thank Thee, O God.
Come, Thou Almighty King
303
Author unknown
Felice De Giardini
1. Come, Thou Al - might - y King, Help us Thy name to sing,
2. Come, Thou In - car - nate Word, Gird on Thy might - y sword,
3. Come, Ho - ly Com - fort - er, Thy sa - cred wit - ness bear
4. To the great One in Three E - ter - nal prais - es be
Help us to praise: Fa - ther, all - glo - ri - ous, O'er all vic-
Our prayer at - tend: Come, and Thy peo - ple bless, And give Thy
In this glad hour: Thou who al - might - y art, Now rule in
Hence ev - er - more. His sov-'reign maj - es - ty, May we in
to - ri - ous, Come, and reign o - ver us, An - cient of Days.
word suc - cess: Spir - it of ho - li - ness, On us de - scend.
ev - 'ry heart, And ne'er from us de - part, Spir - it of pow'r.
glo - ry see, And to e - ter - ni - ty Love and a - dore.

304 My Jesus, I Love Thee

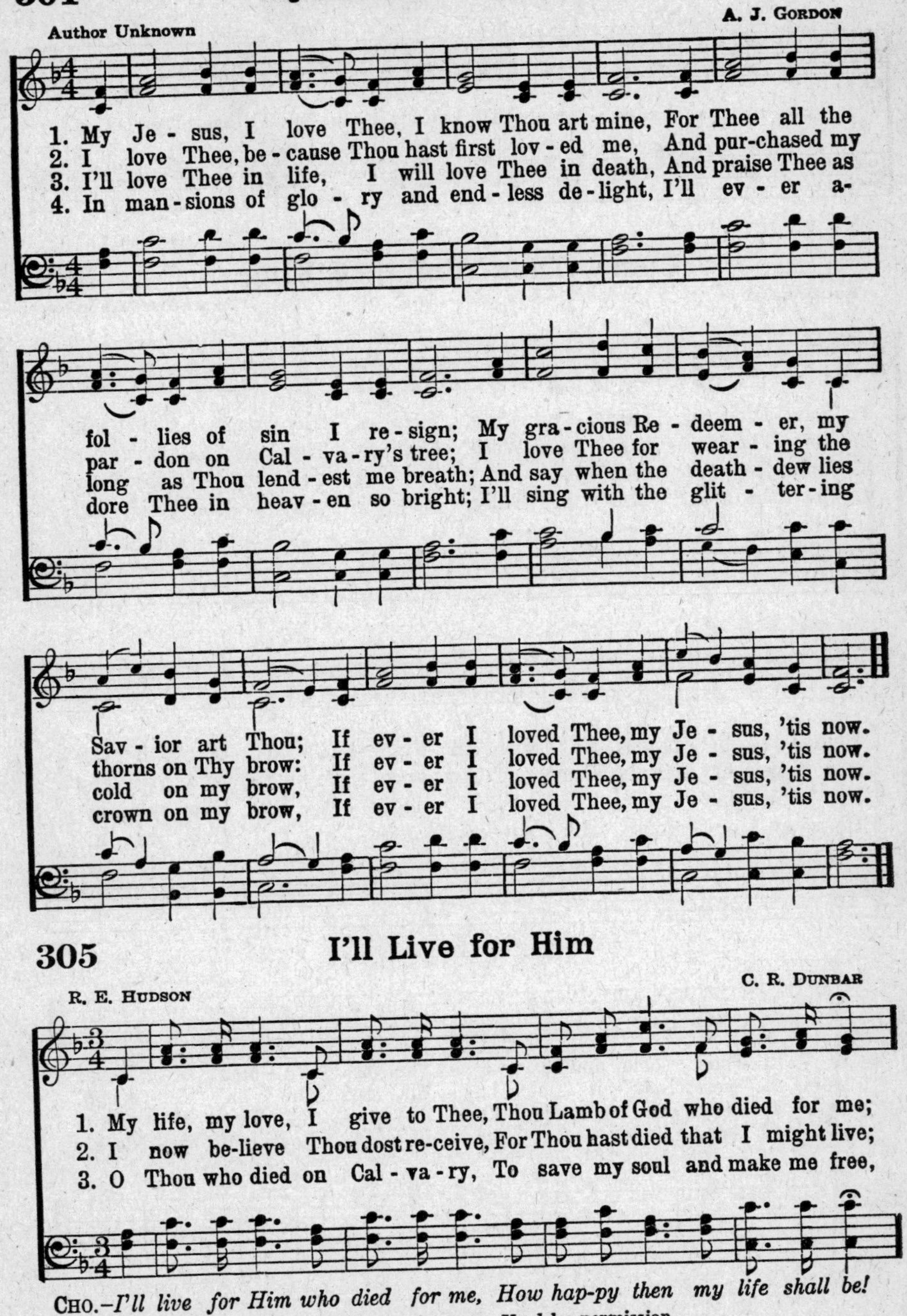
A. J. Gordon
Author Unknown
1. My Jesus, I love Thee, I know Thou art mine, For Thee all the follies of sin I resign; My gracious Redeemer, my Savior art Thou; If ever I loved Thee, my Jesus, 'tis now.
2. I love Thee, because Thou hast first loved me, And purchased my pardon on Calvary's tree; I love Thee for wearing the thorns on Thy brow: If ever I loved Thee, my Jesus, 'tis now.
3. I'll love Thee in life, I will love Thee in death, And praise Thee as long as Thou lendest me breath; And say when the deathdew lies cold on my brow, If ever I loved Thee, my Jesus, 'tis now.
4. In mansions of glory and endless delight, I'll ever adore Thee in heaven so bright; I'll sing with the glittering crown on my brow, If ever I loved Thee, my Jesus, 'tis now.
305
I'll Live for Him
C. R. Dunbar
R. E. Hudson
1. My life, my love, I give to Thee, Thou Lamb of God who died for me;
2. I now believe Thou dost receive, For Thou hast died that I might live;
3. O Thou who died on Calvary, To save my soul and make me free,
Cho.–I'll live for Him who died for me, How happy then my life shall be!

Copyright, 1918. Renewal. M. Hudson, owner. Used by permission.

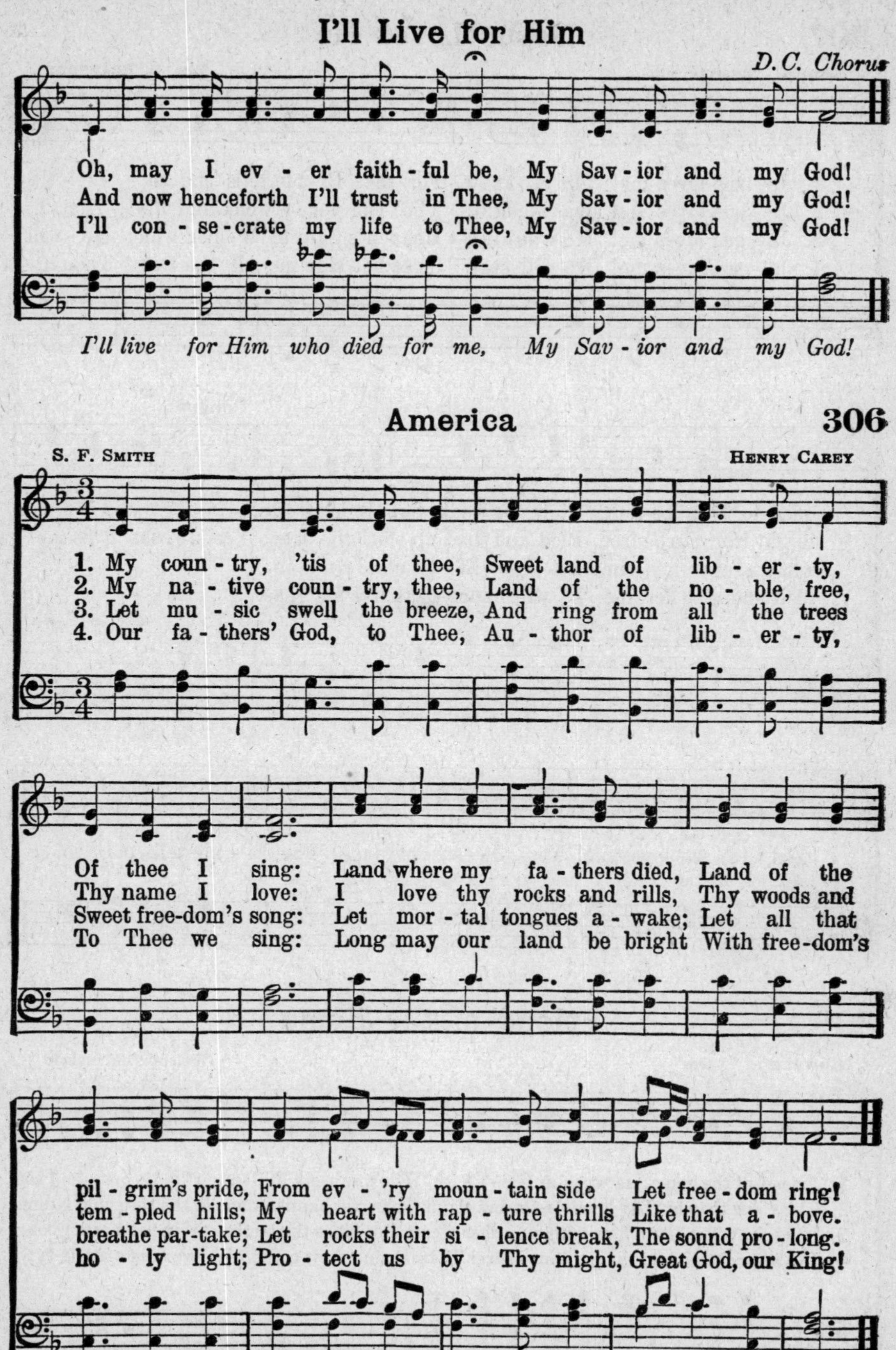
I'll Live for Him
D.C. Chorus
Oh, may I ev - er faith - ful be, My Sav - ior and my God!
And now henceforth I'll trust in Thee, My Sav - ior and my God!
I'll con - se - crate my life to Thee, My Sav - ior and my God!
I'll live for Him who died for me, My Sav - ior and my God!
America
306
S. F. Smith
Henry Carey
1. My coun - try, 'tis of thee, Sweet land of lib - er - ty,
2. My na - tive coun - try, thee, Land of the no - ble, free,
3. Let mu - sic swell the breeze, And ring from all the trees
4. Our fa - thers' God, to Thee, Au - thor of lib - er - ty,
Of thee I sing: Land where my fa - thers died, Land of the
Thy name I love: I love thy rocks and rills, Thy woods and
Sweet free-dom's song: Let mor - tal tongues a - wake; Let all that
To Thee we sing: Long may our land be bright With free-dom's
pil - grim's pride, From ev - 'ry moun - tain side Let free - dom ring!
tem - pled hills; My heart with rap - ture thrills Like that a - bove.
breathe par-take; Let rocks their si - lence break, The sound pro - long.
ho - ly light; Pro - tect us by Thy might, Great God, our King!

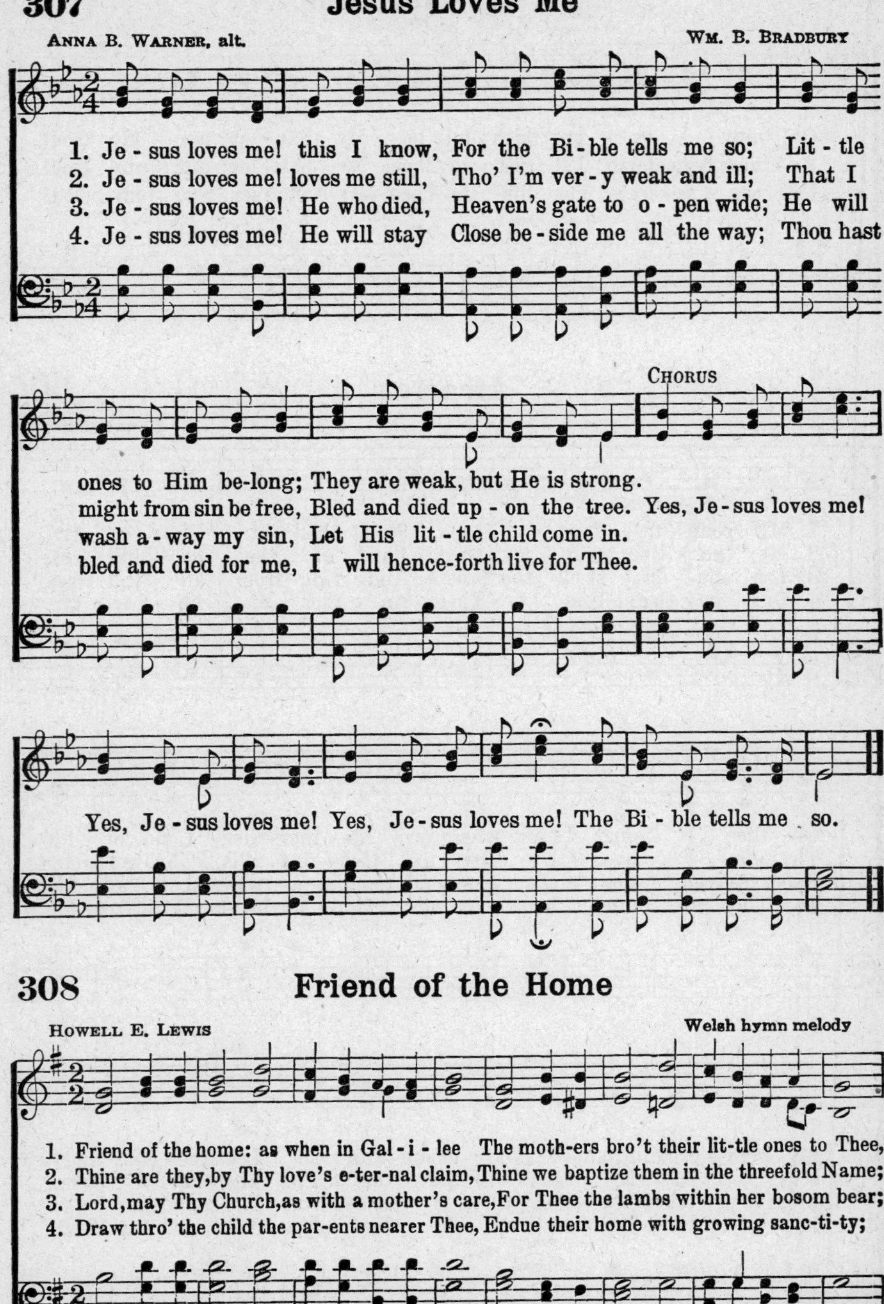
307 Jesus Loves Me
Anna B. Warner, alt.
Wm. B. Bradbury
1. Je - sus loves me! this I know, For the Bi - ble tells me so; Lit - tle ones to Him be-long; They are weak, but He is strong.
2. Je - sus loves me! loves me still, Tho' I'm ver - y weak and ill; That I might from sin be free, Bled and died up - on the tree.
3. Je - sus loves me! He who died, Heaven's gate to o - pen wide; He will wash a - way my sin, Let His lit - tle child come in.
4. Je - sus loves me! He will stay Close be - side me all the way; Thou hast bled and died for me, I will hence-forth live for Thee.
Chorus
Yes, Je - sus loves me! Yes, Je - sus loves me! Yes, Je - sus loves me! The Bi - ble tells me so.
308 Friend of the Home
Howell E. Lewis
Welsh hymn melody
1. Friend of the home: as when in Gal-i-lee The moth-ers bro't their lit-tle ones to Thee,
2. Thine are they, by Thy love's e-ter-nal claim, Thine we baptize them in the threefold Name;
3. Lord, may Thy Church, as with a mother's care, For Thee the lambs within her bosom bear;
4. Draw thro' the child the par-ents nearer Thee, Endue their home with growing sanc-ti-ty;

Words used by permission of Howell E. Lewis

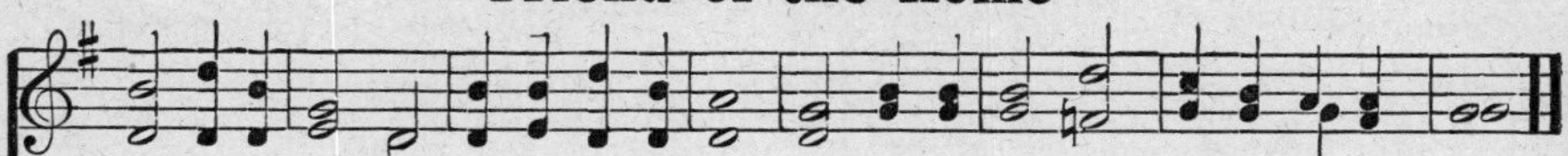

So we, dear Lord, would now the children bring, And seek for them the shelter of Thy wing.
Yet not the sign we trust, Lord, but the grace That in Thy fold prepared the lambs a place.
And grant, as morning grows to noon, that they Still in her love and ho-ly serv - ice stay.
And gath-er all, by earth-ly homes made one, In heav'n, O Christ, when earthly days are done.

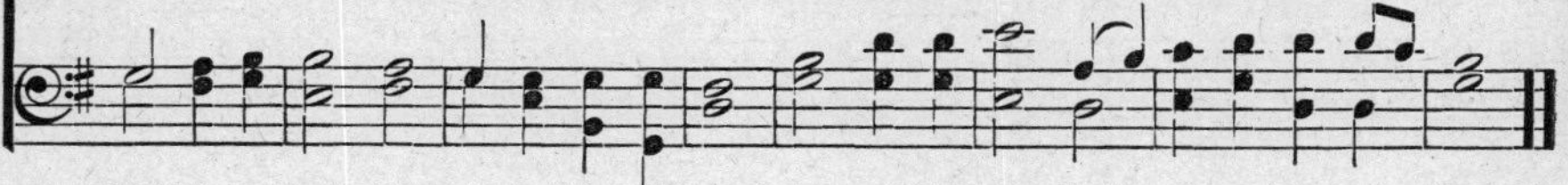

Jesus Said That "Whosoever Will" 309

ARTHUR J. PANKRATZ ARTHUR J. PANKRATZ

Je - sus said that who-so - ev-er will, who-so - ev - er will, who-so - ev - er will;

Je - sus said that who-so-ev - er will, who-so-ev - er will may come. I'm so glad that

He in-clud - ed me, He in-clud-ed me, He in-clud-ed me; I'm so glad that

He in - clud-ed me When Je - sus said that who - so - ev - er will may come!

Words and Music Copyright, 1940, by Arthur J. Pankratz. Used by permission

310
Cleanse Me
Edwin Orr
Maori Melody by John McNeill
1. Search me, O God,........ and know my heart to - day;......
2. I praise Thee, Lord,........ for cleans - ing me from sin:......
3. Lord, take my life,......... and make it whol - ly Thine:....
4. O Ho - ly Ghost,....... re - viv - al comes from Thee:.....
Try me, O Sav - ior, know my thoughts, I pray:....
Ful - fill Thy Word, and make me pure with - in;......
Fill my poor heart with Thy great love di - vine;....
Send a re - viv - al— start the work in me:.....
See if there be........ some wick - ed way in me:.....
Fill me with fire,...... where once I burned with shame:...
Take all my will,...... my pas - sion, self and pride;....
Thy Word de - clares...... Thou wilt sup - ply our need:....
Cleanse me from ev - 'ry sin, and set me free.......
Grant my de - sire to mag - ni - fy Thy name......
I now sur - ren - der: Lord, in me a - bide.......
For bless - ing now, O Lord, I hum - bly plead......
311
I'll Be So Glad
Anon.
I'll be so glad when day is done, I'll be so glad when vic - t'ry's won;

I'll Be So Glad

There'll be no sor - row in God's to-mor-row, I'll be so glad when Je-sus comes.

Jesus, Always the Same 312

GEORGE HEADLEY GEORGE HEADLEY

Je - sus, He al-ways is the same; Je - sus, O glo - ry to His name! He shed His

blood up - on the cross of Cal - va - ry, Suf - f'ring death to set me free.....

Some day He's com-ing back for me, When all His glo - ry I shall see; And I shall

dwell with Him thro' all e - ter - ni - ty, And sing His praise for - ev - er - more.

Copyright, 1940, by Rev. George Headley. Used by permission

Dedicated to the Converts' Bible Class of Sunday Breakfast Association

313 Lead Me to Some Soul To-day

WILL H. HOUGHTON — WENDELL P. LOVELESS

Lead me to some soul to-day, O teach me, Lord, just what to say; Friends of mine are lost in sin, And cannot find their way. Few there are who seem to care, And few there are who pray; who pray; Melt my heart and fill my life, Give me one soul to - day.

Copyright, 1936, by Wendell P. Loveless. Used by permission of Moody Bible Institute of Chicago

314 On the Cross For Me

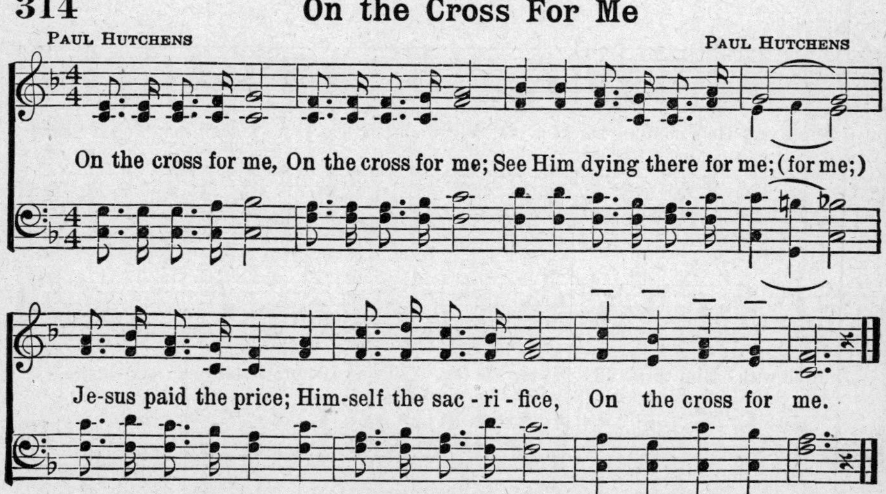
PAUL HUTCHENS
PAUL HUTCHENS
On the cross for me, On the cross for me; See Him dying there for me; (for me;)
Je-sus paid the price; Him-self the sac - ri - fice, On the cross for me.

Copyright, 1927. Mary G. Clarke, Publications, owner. Used by permission.

Safe Am I

Mildred Leightner Dillon   Mildred Leightner Dillon

Safe am I, (Safe am I,) safe am I, (safe am I,) In the
hol - low of His hand. Shel - tered o'er, (Sheltered o'er,) shel-tered
o'er (sheltered o'er) With His love for - ev - er - more No ill can
harm me, No foe a-larm me; For He keeps both day and night. Safe am
I, (Safe am I,) safe am I, (safe am I,) In the hol - low of His hand.

Copyright, 1938, by Wm. Dillon in "The Voice of Melody." International Copyright
Used by permission

316
To Whom Shall We Go?
D. D. McCurdy
D. D. McCurdy
Arr. W. G. Winans
When I need a friend and guide, When my sins I must con-fide, That my heart and
softly
life be right, To whom shall I go? To Je-sus! oh, to Je-sus! Full of wondrous
love is He, And He'll flood it, oh, He'll flood it, Yes, He'll flood it all on me!
317
Prayer Chorus
Ps. 19: 14
Albert Allen Ketchum
Let the words of my mouth and the med-i-ta-tion of my
heart . . . Be ac-cept-a-ble in Thy sight, Be ac-cept-a-ble
in Thy sight, O Lord, my Strength and my Re-deem-er!

Copyright, 1925, by Harry W. Vom Bruch, owner. Used by permission

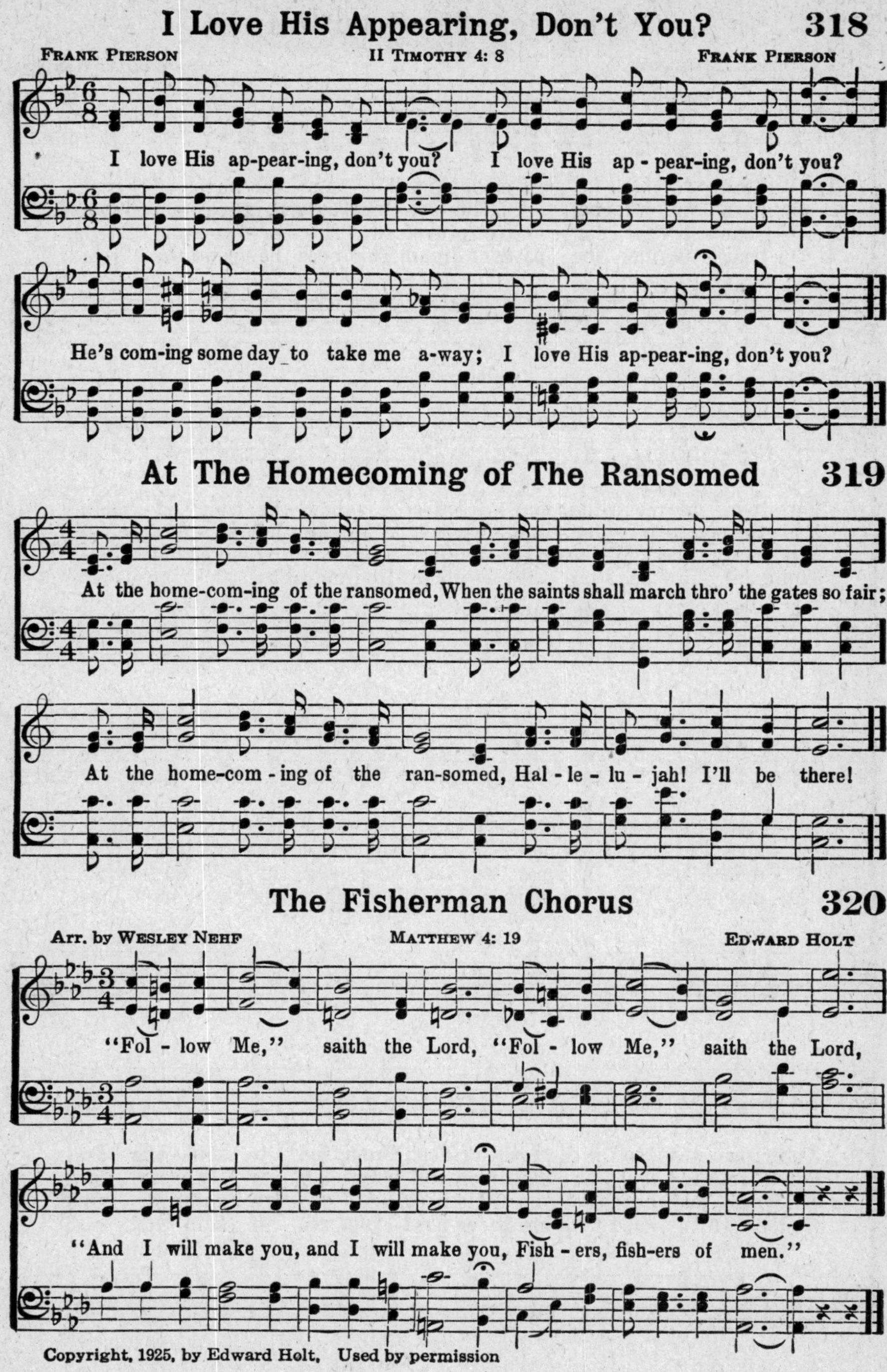
I Love His Appearing, Don't You? 318
Frank Pierson
II Timothy 4: 8
Frank Pierson
I love His ap-pear-ing, don't you? I love His ap - pear-ing, don't you?
He's com-ing some day to take me a-way; I love His ap-pear-ing, don't you?
At The Homecoming of The Ransomed 319
At the home-com-ing of the ransomed, When the saints shall march thro' the gates so fair;
At the home-com - ing of the ran-somed, Hal - le - lu - jah! I'll be there!
The Fisherman Chorus 320
Arr. by Wesley Nehf
Matthew 4: 19
Edward Holt
"Fol - low Me," saith the Lord, "Fol - low Me," saith the Lord,
"And I will make you, and I will make you, Fish - ers, fish-ers of men."
Copyright, 1925, by Edward Holt, Used by permission

321 America the Beautiful

KATHERINE LEE BATES SAMUEL A. WARD

1. O beau - ti - ful for spa-cious skies, For am - ber waves of grain,
2. O beau - ti - ful for pil - grim feet, Whose stern, im-pas-sioned stress
3. O beau - ti - ful for he-roes proved In lib - er - at - ing strife,
4. O beau - ti - ful for pa-triot dream That sees be - yond the years
For pur - ple moun-tain maj - es - ties A - bove the fruit - ed plain!
A thor-ough-fare for free - dom beat A - cross the wil - der - ness!
Who more than self their coun-try loved, And mer - cy more than life!
Thine al - a - bas - ter cit - ies gleam, Undimmed by hu - man tears!
A - mer - i - ca! A - mer - i - ca! God shed His grace on thee,
A - mer - i - ca! A - mer - i - ca! God mend thine ev - 'ry flaw,
A - mer - i - ca! A - mer - i - ca! May God thy gold re - fine
A - mer - i - ca! A - mer - i - ca! God shed His grace on thee,
And crown thy good with broth - er-hood From sea to shin - ing sea!
Con - firm thy soul in self - con-trol, Thy lib - er - ty in law!
Till all suc - cess be no - ble-ness And ev - 'ry gain di - vine!
And crown thy good with broth - er-hood From sea to shin - ing sea!

It Came Upon the Midnight Clear

Edmund H. Sears

Richard S. Willis

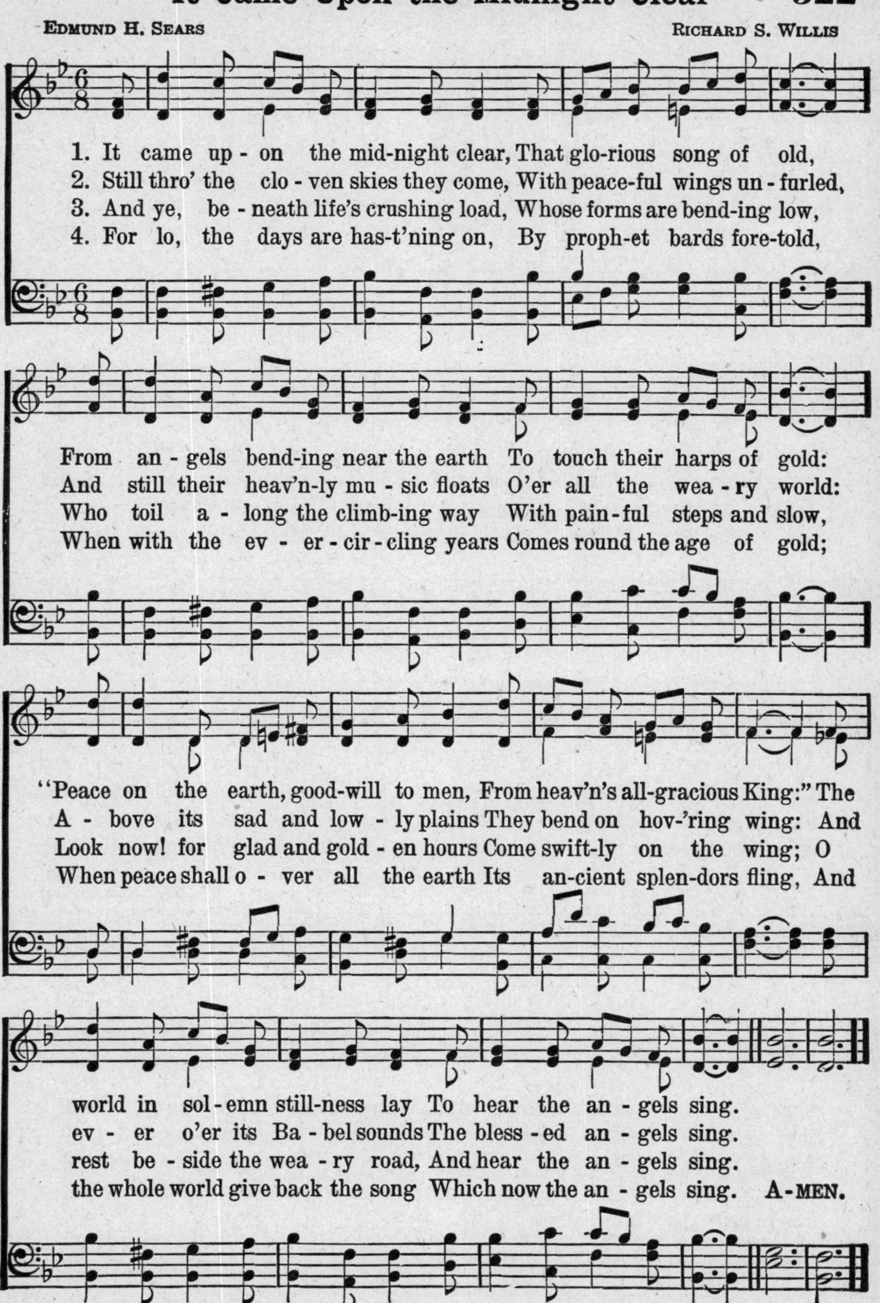
1. It came up - on the mid-night clear, That glo-rious song of old,
2. Still thro' the clo - ven skies they come, With peace-ful wings un - furled,
3. And ye, be - neath life's crushing load, Whose forms are bend-ing low,
4. For lo, the days are has-t'ning on, By proph-et bards fore-told,
From an - gels bend-ing near the earth To touch their harps of gold:
And still their heav'n-ly mu - sic floats O'er all the wea - ry world:
Who toil a - long the climb-ing way With pain-ful steps and slow,
When with the ev - er - cir - cling years Comes round the age of gold;
"Peace on the earth, good-will to men, From heav'n's all-gracious King:" The
A - bove its sad and low - ly plains They bend on hov-'ring wing: And
Look now! for glad and gold - en hours Come swift-ly on the wing; O
When peace shall o - ver all the earth Its an-cient splen-dors fling, And
world in sol - emn still-ness lay To hear the an - gels sing.
ev - er o'er its Ba - bel sounds The bless - ed an - gels sing.
rest be - side the wea - ry road, And hear the an - gels sing.
the whole world give back the song Which now the an - gels sing. A-MEN.

323 Joy to the World!

Isaac Watts
Arr. from George F. Handel
1. Joy to the world! the Lord is come; Let earth re-
2. Joy to the world! the Sav - ior reigns; Let men their
3. No more let sins and sor - rows grow, Nor thorns in-
4. He rules the world with truth and grace, And makes the
ceive her King; Let ev - 'ry heart pre - pare Him room,
songs em - ploy; While fields and floods, rocks, hills and plains
fest the ground; He comes to make His bless - ings flow
na - tions prove The glo - ries of His right - eous - ness,
And heav'n and na - ture sing, And heav'n and na - ture
Re - peat the sound - ing joy, Re - peat the sound - ing
Far as the curse is found, Far as the curse is
And won - ders of His love, And won - ders of His
1. And heav'n and na - ture sing,.......... And
sing, And heav'n, and heav'n and na - ture sing.
joy, Re - peat, re - peat the sound - ing joy.
found, Far as, far as the curse is found.
love, And won - ders, and won - ders of His love.
heav'n and na - ture sing,

O Come, All Ye Faithful

Tr. by FREDERICK OAKELEY

WADE'S Cantus Diversi

1. O come, all ye faith - ful, joy - ful and tri - um - phant,
2. Sing, choirs of an - gels, sing in ex - ul - ta - tion,
3. Yea, Lord, we greet Thee, born this hap - py morn - ing,
O come ye, O come ye to Beth - le - hem;
O sing, all ye bright hosts of heav'n a - bove;
Je - sus, to Thee be all glo - - ry giv'n;
Come and be - hold Him born the King of an - gels;
Glo - ry to God, all glo - ry in the high - est;
Word of the Fa - ther, now in flesh ap - pear - ing;
REFRAIN
O come, let us a - dore Him, O come, let us a - dore Him,
O come, let us a - dore Him, Christ, the Lord. A - MEN.

325 Hark! the Herald Angels Sing

CHARLES WESLEY MENDELSSOHN

1. Hark! the her-ald an-gels sing, "Glo-ry to the new-born King;
2. Christ, by high-est Heav'n a-dored, Christ, the ev-er-last-ing Lord:
3. Hail the Heav'n-born Prince of Peace! Hail the Sun of right-eous-ness!
4. Come, De-sire of na-tions, come! Fix in us Thy hum-ble home:
Peace on earth, and mer-cy mild; God and sin-ners rec-on-ciled."
Late in time be-hold Him come, Off-spring of a vir-gin's womb.
Light and life to all He brings, Ris'n with heal-ing in His wings:
Rise, the wom-an's con-qu'ring seed, Bruise in us the ser-pent's head;
Joy-ful, all ye na-tions, rise, Join the tri-umph of the skies;
Veiled in flesh the God-head see, Hail th' in-car-nate De-i-ty!
Mild He lays His glo-ry by, Born that man no more may die;
Ad-am's like-ness now ef-face, Stamp Thine im-age in its place:
With an-gel-ic hosts pro-claim, "Christ is born in Beth-le-hem."
Pleased as man with men to ap-pear, Je-sus our Im-man-uel here.
Born to raise the sons of earth; Born to give them sec-ond birth.
Sec-ond Ad-am from a-bove, Re-in-state us in Thy love.

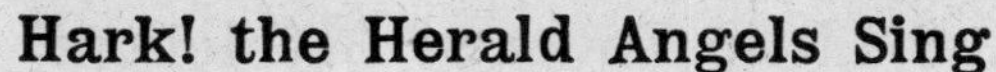
Hark! the Herald Angels Sing

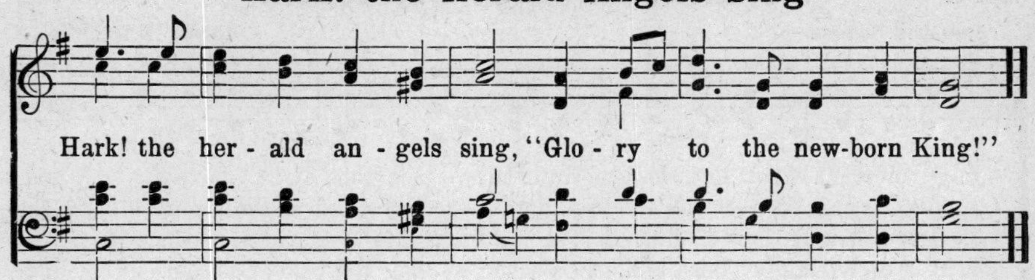
Hark! the her - ald an - gels sing, "Glo - ry to the new-born King!"

Silent Night! Holy Night! 326

JOSEPH MOHR — FRANZ GRUBER

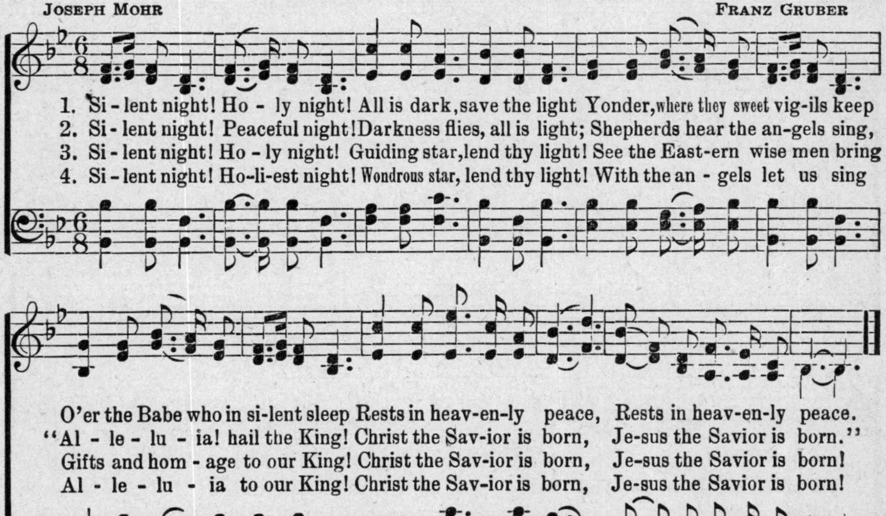
1. Si - lent night! Ho - ly night! All is dark, save the light Yonder, where they sweet vig-ils keep
2. Si - lent night! Peaceful night! Darkness flies, all is light; Shepherds hear the an-gels sing,
3. Si - lent night! Ho - ly night! Guiding star, lend thy light! See the East-ern wise men bring
4. Si - lent night! Ho-li-est night! Wondrous star, lend thy light! With the an - gels let us sing
O'er the Babe who in si-lent sleep Rests in heav-en-ly peace, Rests in heav-en-ly peace.
"Al - le - lu - ia! hail the King! Christ the Sav-ior is born, Je-sus the Savior is born."
Gifts and hom - age to our King! Christ the Sav-ior is born, Je-sus the Savior is born!
Al - le - lu - ia to our King! Christ the Sav-ior is born, Je-sus the Savior is born!

Silent Night! Holy Night! 327

TUNE—ABOVE

1 Silent night! Holy night!
All is calm, all is bright
'Round yon virgin mother and Child!
Holy Infant, so tender and mild,
Sleep in heavenly peace,
Sleep in heavenly peace.

2 Silent night! Holy night!
Shepherds quake at the sight!
Glories stream from heaven afar,
Heav'nly hosts sing Alleluia;
Christ, the Savior, is born,
Christ, the Savior, is born.

3 Silent night! Holy night!
Son of God, love's pure light
Radiant beams from Thy holy face,
With the dawn of redeeming grace,
Jesus, Lord, at Thy birth,
Jesus, Lord, at Thy birth.

328 O Little Town of Bethlehem

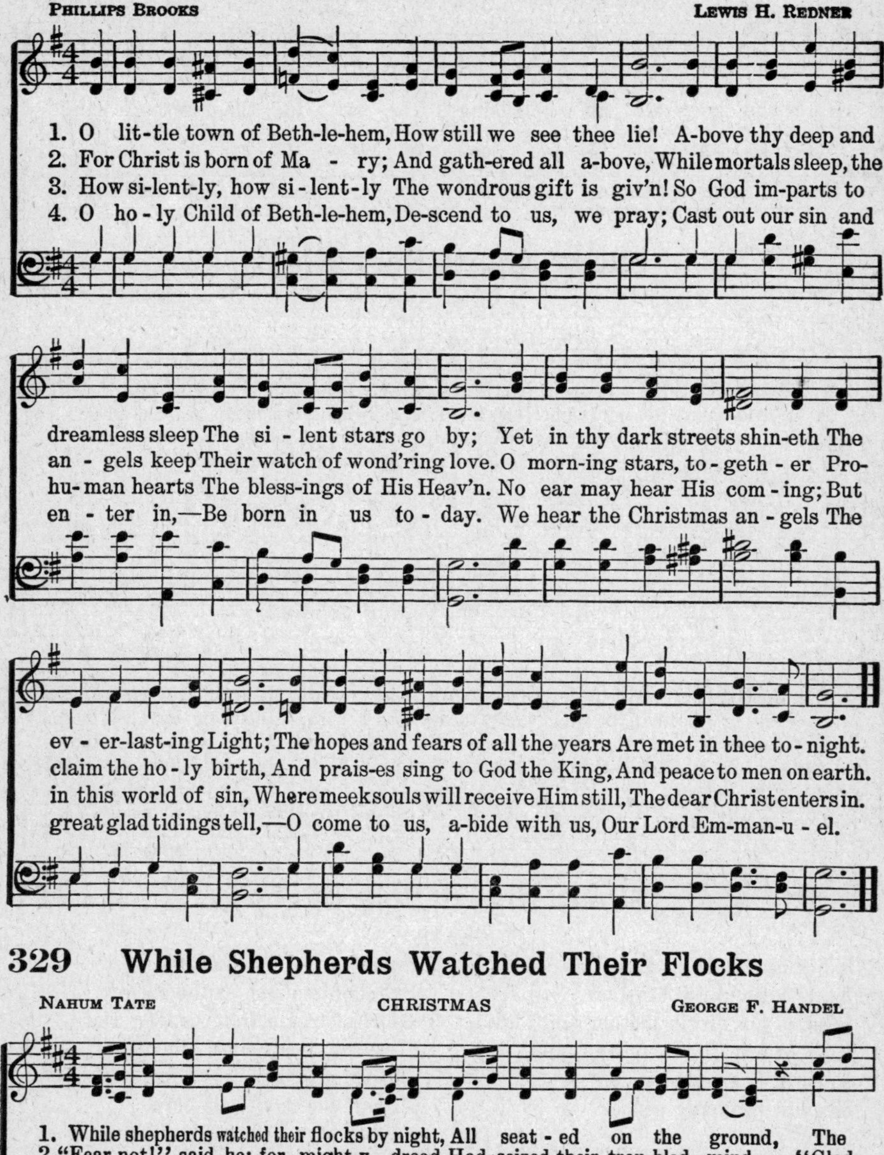
PHILLIPS BROOKS
LEWIS H. REDNER
1. O lit-tle town of Beth-le-hem, How still we see thee lie! A-bove thy deep and
2. For Christ is born of Ma - ry; And gath-ered all a-bove, While mortals sleep, the
3. How si-lent-ly, how si-lent-ly The wondrous gift is giv'n! So God im-parts to
4. O ho-ly Child of Beth-le-hem, De-scend to us, we pray; Cast out our sin and
dreamless sleep The si - lent stars go by; Yet in thy dark streets shin-eth The
an - gels keep Their watch of wond'ring love. O morn-ing stars, to-geth - er Pro-
hu-man hearts The bless-ings of His Heav'n. No ear may hear His com - ing; But
en - ter in,—Be born in us to - day. We hear the Christmas an - gels The
ev - er-last-ing Light; The hopes and fears of all the years Are met in thee to - night.
claim the ho - ly birth, And prais-es sing to God the King, And peace to men on earth.
in this world of sin, Where meek souls will receive Him still, The dear Christ enters in.
great glad tidings tell,—O come to us, a-bide with us, Our Lord Em-man-u - el.

329 While Shepherds Watched Their Flocks

NAHUM TATE CHRISTMAS GEORGE F. HANDEL

1. While shepherds watched their flocks by night, All seat - ed on the ground, The
2. "Fear not!" said he; for might-y dread Had seized their trou-bled mind, "Glad
3. "To you, in Dav-id's town this day, Is born of Dav-id's line, The
4. "The heav'n-ly Babe you there shall find To hu - man view dis - played, All
5. "All glo - ry be to God on high, And to the earth be peace: Good

While Shepherds Watched Their Flocks
an - gel of the Lord came down, And glo-ry shone a - round, And glo-ry shone a-round
ti - dings of great joy I bring, To you and all man-kind, To you and all man-kind.
Sav - ior who is Christ the Lord; And this shall be the sign: And this shall be the sign:
meanly wrapped in swathing-bands, And in a man-ger laid, And in a man-ger laid.
will henceforth from heav'n to men, Begin and nev-er cease, Be - gin and nev-er cease."
The First Noel
330
Traditional
Traditional
1. The first No - el the angel did say Was to certain poor shepherds in fields as they lay;
2. And by the light of that same Star, Three wise men came from country far;
3. This Star drew nigh to the northwest, O'er Beth - le-hem it took its rest,
4. Then enter-ed in, those wise men three, Full rev-'rent-ly up-on their knee,
In fields where they lay keeping their sheep, On a cold winter's night that was so deep.
To seek for a King was their in - tent, And to follow the Star wherever it went.
And there it did both stop and stay, Right o-ver the place where Jesus lay.
And of - fered there in His pres-ence, Their gold, and myrrh, and frank-incense.
Refrain.
No - el, No - el, No - el, No - el, Born is the King of Is - ra - el.

331 Jesus Arose!

LUETTA SNYDER
HOWARD SNYDER, JR.
Slowly
1. Forth from God's throne, in-to this world of woe, Came God's own Son, sal - va - tion
2. Three days He lay with - in that dark do-main, Then with new life, forth from the
3. Tho' He's on high, He's com-ing back some day, Then from this earth, He'll car-ry
to be - stow; Nailed to the cross in pain and ag - o - ny, Laid in the tomb
tomb He came; Christ has the key, oh, death, where is thy sting? Our Lord doth live!
us a - way; E'en tho' we die, we know we'll rise a - gain, For Christ a - rose,
CHORUS Faster
to save both you and me.
oh, let your prais-es ring! Je - sus a - rose! Praise His ho - ly name! Je - sus a-
our pre-cious souls to win!
rose! Death He o-ver-came! An an-gel rolled a - way the stone, My Lord a - rose to
save His own, And now He reigns up-on His throne! Hal-le - lu-jah! Hal - le - lu - jah!

Copyright, 1941. Hope Publishing Company, owner

Christ the Lord is Risen To-day

Charles Wesley
Lyra Davidica
1. Christ the Lord is ris'n to - day, Al - - le - lu - ia!
2. Love's re - deem - ing work is done, Al - - le - lu - ia!
3. Lives a - gain our glo - rious King; Al - - le - lu - ia!
4. Soar we now, where Christ has led, Al - - le - lu - ia!
Sons of men and an - gels say: Al - - - le - lu - ia!
Fought the fight, the bat - tle won; Al - - - le - lu - ia!
Where, O death, is now thy sting? Al - - - le - lu - ia!
Fol - l'wing our ex - alt - ed Head; Al - - - le - lu - ia!
Raise your joys and tri - umphs high, Al - - - le - lu - ia!
Death in vain for - bids Him rise; Al - - - le - lu - ia!
Dy - ing once, He all doth save: Al - - - le - lu - ia!
Made like Him, like Him we rise; Al - - - le - lu - ia!
Sing, ye heav'ns, and earth re - ply. Al - - - le - lu - ia!
Christ has o - pened Par - a - dise. Al - - - le - lu - ia!
Where thy vic - to - ry, O grave? Al - - - le - lu - ia!
Ours the cross, the grave, the skies. Al - - - le - lu - ia!

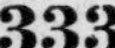

333 Look, Ye Saints, the Sight is Glorious

THOMAS KELLY — JOHN HUGHES, Welsh hymn melody

1. Look, ye saints! The sight is glo - rious: See the Man of
2. Crown the Sav - ior! An - gels, crown Him! Rich the tro - phies
3. Sin - ners in de - ri - sion crowned Him, Mock-ing thus the
4. Hark! those bursts of ac - cla - ma - tion! Hark, those loud tri-

Sor - rows now; From the fight re-turned vic - to - rious, Ev - 'ry knee to
Je - sus brings; In the seat of pow'r en-throne Him, While the vault of
Sav-ior's claim; Saints and an - gels crowd a - round Him, Own His ti - tle,
umphant chords! Je - sus takes the high - est sta - tion; O what joy the

Him shall bow: Crown Him! Crown Him! Crown Him! Crown Him!
heav - en rings: Crown Him! Crown Him! Crown Him! Crown Him!
praise His name: Crown Him! Crown Him! Crown Him! Crown Him!
sight af - fords! Crown Him! Crown Him! Crown Him! Crown Him!

Crowns be-come the Vic-tor's brow, Crowns be-come the Vic - tor's brow.
Crown the Sav - ior King of kings, Crown the Sav - ior King of kings.
Spread a - broad the Vic-tor's fame, Spread a - broad the Vic - tor's fame.
King of kings, and Lord of lords! King of kings, and Lord of lords!

Music used by permission of Mrs. John Hughes, owner of copyright

Hallelujah! He is Risen!

Mabel Glen Haldeman — Mrs. Walter G. Taylor

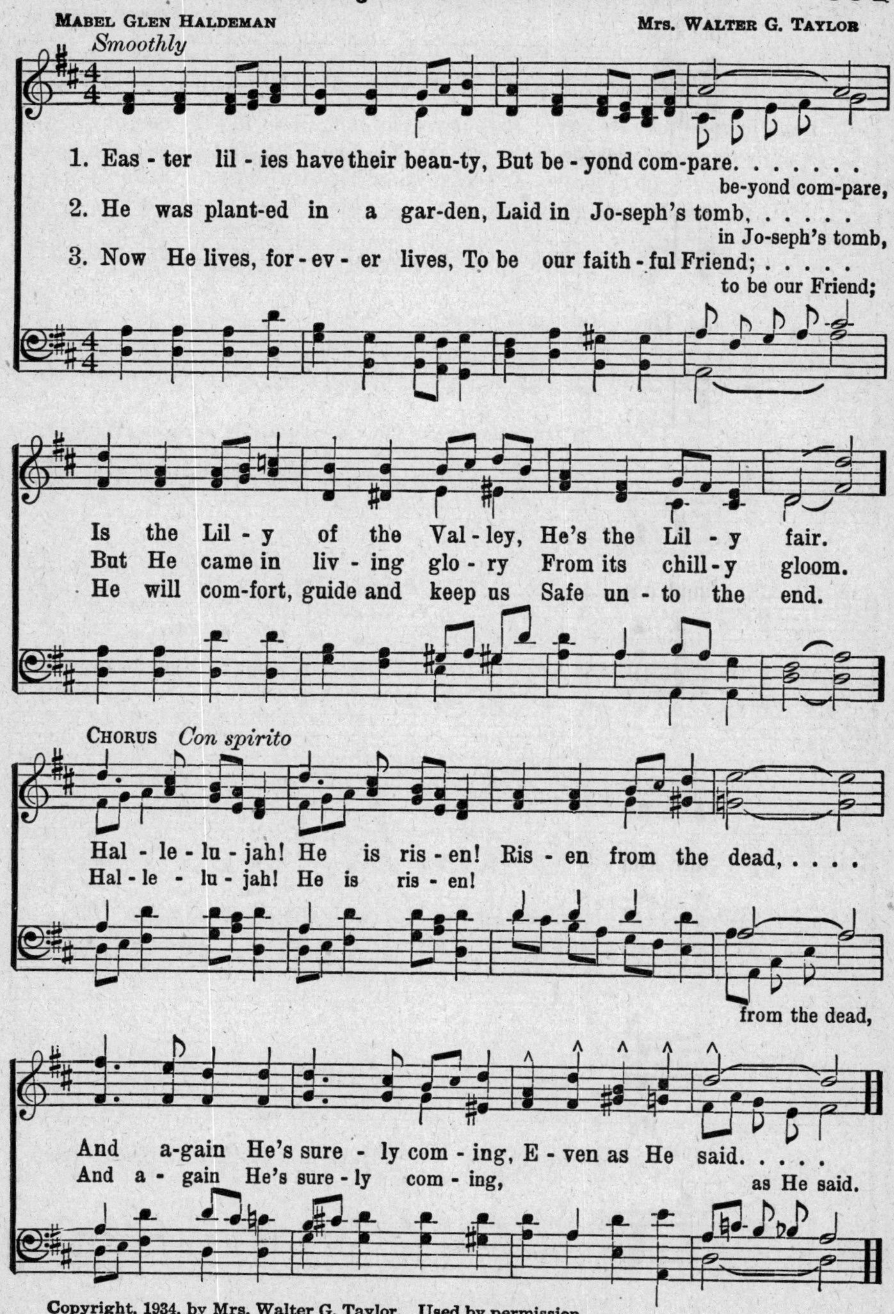
Smoothly
1. Eas - ter lil - ies have their beau-ty, But be - yond com-pare. . . . . . .
be-yond com-pare,
2. He was plant-ed in a gar-den, Laid in Jo-seph's tomb, ...
in Jo-seph's tomb,
3. Now He lives, for - ev - er lives, To be our faith - ful Friend; . . . . .
to be our Friend;
Is the Lil - y of the Val - ley, He's the Lil - y fair.
But He came in liv - ing glo - ry From its chill - y gloom.
He will com-fort, guide and keep us Safe un - to the end.
Chorus Con spirito
Hal - le - lu - jah! He is ris - en! Ris - en from the dead, ...
Hal - le - lu - jah! He is ris - en!
from the dead,
And a-gain He's sure - ly com - ing, E - ven as He said. . . . .
And a - gain He's sure - ly com - ing,
as He said.

Copyright, 1934, by Mrs. Walter G. Taylor. Used by permission

335 Christ Arose

ROBERT LOWRY ROBERT LOWRY

1. Low in the grave He lay— Je-sus my Sav-ior! Wait-ing the com-ing day—
2. Vain-ly they watch His bed—Je-sus my Sav-ior! Vain-ly they seal the dead—
3. Death cannot keep his prey—Je-sus my Sav-ior! He tore the bars a-way—

Je-sus my Lord!

REFRAIN *Faster*

Up from the grave He a-rose, (He a-rose,) With a might-y tri-umph o'er His foes; (He a-rose!) He a-rose a Vic-tor from the dark do-main, And He lives for-ev-er with His saints to reign. He a-rose! He a-rose! He a-rose! He a-rose! Hal-le-lu-jah! Christ a-rose!

Faith of Our Mothers 336

ST. CATHERINE

A. B. PATTEN — H. F. HEMY, Arr. by JAMES G. WALTON

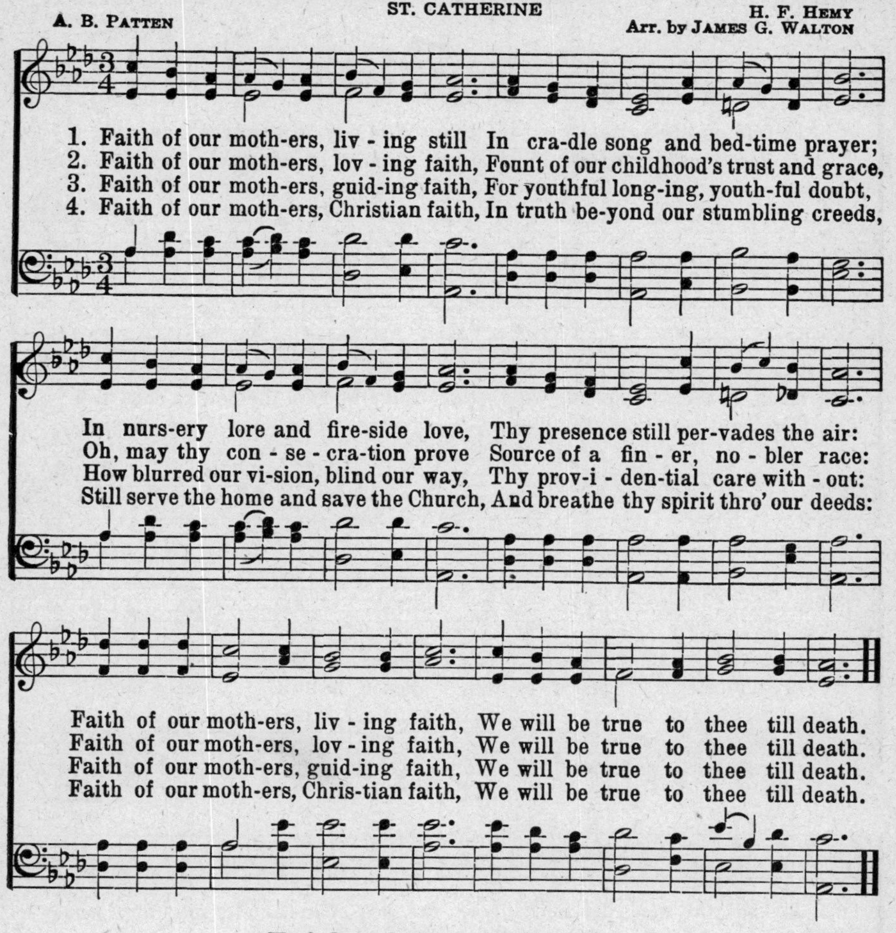
1. Faith of our moth-ers, liv - ing still In cra-dle song and bed-time prayer;
2. Faith of our moth-ers, lov - ing faith, Fount of our childhood's trust and grace,
3. Faith of our moth-ers, guid-ing faith, For youthful long-ing, youth-ful doubt,
4. Faith of our moth-ers, Christian faith, In truth be-yond our stumbling creeds,
In nurs-ery lore and fire-side love, Thy presence still per-vades the air:
Oh, may thy con - se - cra-tion prove Source of a fin - er, no - bler race:
How blurred our vi-sion, blind our way, Thy prov-i - den-tial care with - out:
Still serve the home and save the Church, And breathe thy spirit thro' our deeds:
Faith of our moth-ers, liv - ing faith, We will be true to thee till death.
Faith of our moth-ers, lov - ing faith, We will be true to thee till death.
Faith of our moth-ers, guid-ing faith, We will be true to thee till death.
Faith of our moth-ers, Chris-tian faith, We will be true to thee till death.

Faith of Our Fathers 337

TUNE—ABOVE

1 Faith of our fathers! living still
In spite of dungeon, fire and sword:
O how our hearts beat high with joy
Whene'er we hear that glorious word!
Faith of our fathers! holy faith!
We will be true to thee till death!

2 Our fathers, chained in prisons dark,
Were still in heart and conscience free:
How sweet would be their children's fate,
If they, like them, could die for thee!
Faith of our fathers! holy faith!
We will be true to thee till death!

3 Faith of our fathers, we still strive
To win all nations unto thee!
And thro' the truth that comes from God
Mankind shall then indeed be free:
Faith of our fathers! holy faith!
We will be true to thee till death:

4 Faith of our fathers! we will love
Both friend and foe in all our strife,
And preach thee, too, as love knows how,
By kindly words and virtuous life:
Faith of our fathers! holy faith!
We will be true to thee till death!

—*Words by Frederick W. Faber*

338 When Jesus Whispers, "Peace"

HALDOR LILLENAS | HALDOR LILLENAS

1. Out on life's storm - y o - cean Wild - ly the waves may roll;
2. Far from the peace-ful har - bor, Doomed by the waves to die,
Loud is their fierce com - mo - tion, But One can the pow'rs con - trol.
Cour-age! be - hold thy Sav - ior To res - cue—now draw-eth nigh.
*LADIES' QUARTETTE pp
Je - sus whis - pers, "Peace, be still!". . . .
Peace be still, peace be still, Peace be still, peace be still!
rit.
pp
Je - sus, the won - der-ful King of the sea, Can calm its roll - ing waves.
MALE VOICES Allegro ff
Loud the an - gry bil - lows Beat a - bout my soul,
Rag - ing waves o - bey Him, Tem - pest gales have gone,

*The quartettes should be seated in the body of the chorus, and not apart from it.

Copyright, 1922. Hope Publishing Co., owner

When Jesus Whispers, "Peace"
rit.
But they on - ly drive me Near - er to my goal. . . . .
All is calm be - fore Him, Christ, the might - y One. . . . .
Full Chorus Legato mf
What tho' the night be fall - ing O - ver the rest - less sea, ...
Safe from the storms of sor - row, En-tered the ha - ven, blest; . . . .
One nev - er will for - sake me, He safe - ly will pi - lot me.
Peace for the trou-bled spir - it, And realms of e - ter - nal rest.
*Ladies' Quartette mf
*Male Quartette
pp
Tem-pest and storm must cease, When Je-sus whis-pers, "Peace;"
Full Chorus ff
rit.
pp
Tem-pest and storm must cease,. . . When Je-sus whis - pers, "Peace."

339 Peace! Be Still!

Mary A. Baker

H. R. Palmer
Arr. by Fred Jacky

6/8
1. Mas-ter, the tem-pest is rag-ing! The bil-lows are toss-ing high!
2. Mas-ter, with an-guish of spir-it I bow in my grief to-day;
3. Mas-ter, the ter-ror is o-ver, The el-e-ments sweet-ly rest;
The sky is o'ershadowed with blackness, No shel-ter or help is nigh;
The depths of my sad heart are trou-bled; O wak-en and save, I pray!
Earth's sun in the calm lake is mir-rored, And heav-en's with-in my breast.
Solo
Parts
(Hum)
"Car-est Thou not that we per-ish?" How canst Thou lie a-sleep,
Tor-rents of sin and of an-guish Sweep o'er my sink-ing soul!
Lin-ger, O bless-ed Re-deem-er, Leave me a-lone no more;
(Hum)
When each moment so mad-ly is threat'ning A grave in the an-gry deep?
And I per-ish! I per-ish, dear Mas-ter; O has-ten, and take con-trol!
And with joy I shall make the blest har-bor, And rest on the bliss-ful shore.

Arr. Copyright, 1941. Hope Publishing Company, owner

Peace! Be Still!

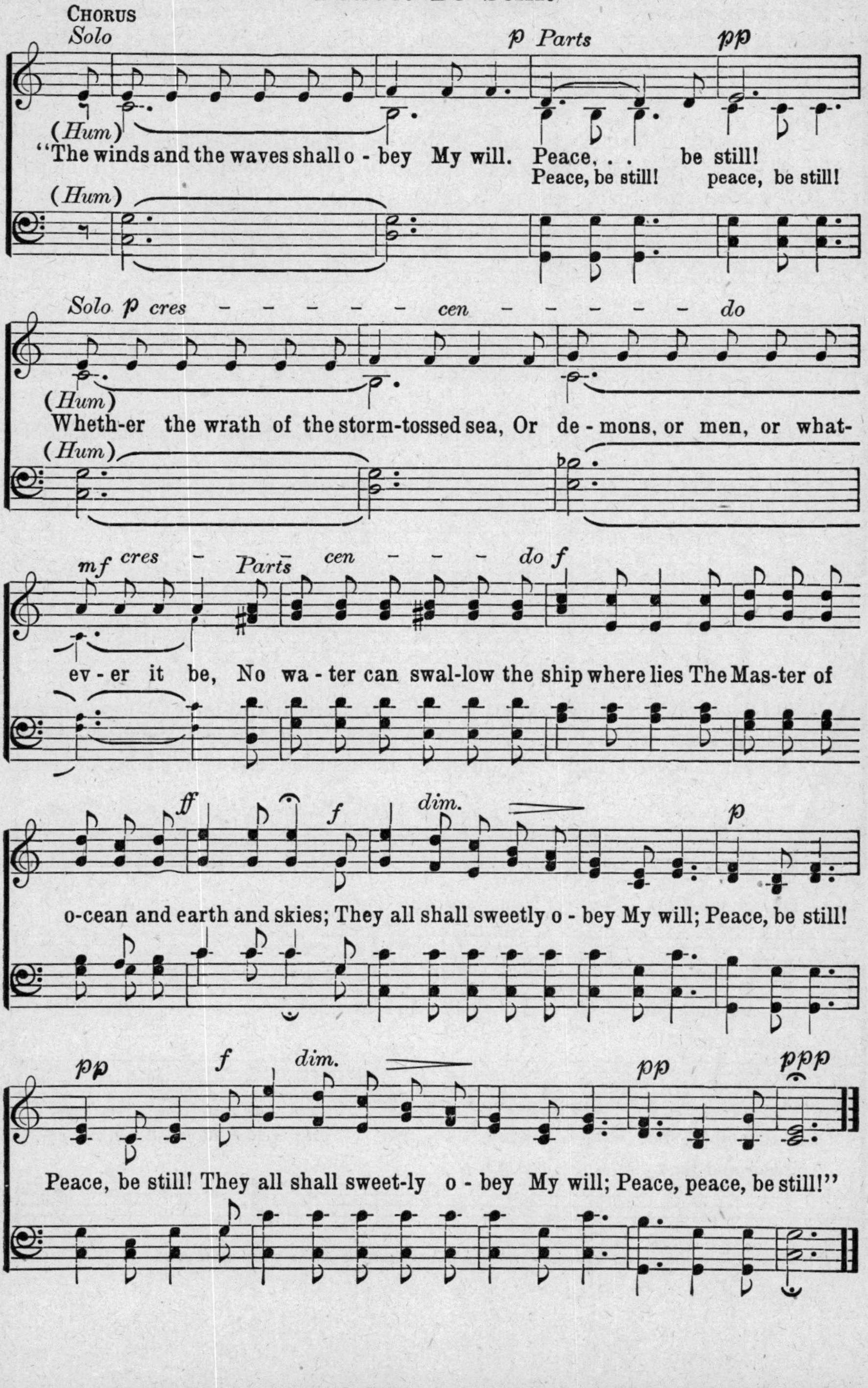

CHORUS

Solo — *p* *Parts* — *pp*

(Hum)

"The winds and the waves shall o - bey My will. Peace, . . be still!

Peace, be still! peace, be still!

(Hum)

Solo *p* *cres - - - - - - - - cen - - - - - - - do*

(Hum)

Wheth-er the wrath of the storm-tossed sea, Or de - mons, or men, or what-

(Hum)

mf *cres - Parts cen - - - - do* *f*

ev - er it be, No wa - ter can swal-low the ship where lies The Mas-ter of

ff *f* *dim.* *p*

o-cean and earth and skies; They all shall sweetly o - bey My will; Peace, be still!

pp *f* *dim.* *pp* *ppp*

Peace, be still! They all shall sweet-ly o - bey My will; Peace, peace, be still!"

340 Hallelujah For the Cross!

HORATIUS BONAR, arr. JAMES McGRANAHAN

1. The cross it stand-eth fast, Hal-le - lu - jah, hal-le - lu - jah! De - fy - ing
2. It is the old cross still, Hal-le - lu - jah, hal-le - lu - jah! Its tri-umph
3. 'Twas here the debt was paid, Hal-le - lu - jah, hal-le - lu - jah! Our sins on
ev - 'ry blast, Hal-le - lu - jah, hal-le - lu - jah! The winds of hell have blown, The
let us tell, Hal-le - lu - jah, hal-le - lu - jah! The grace of God here shone Thro'
Je - sus laid, Hal-le - lu - jah, hal-le - lu - jah! So round the cross we sing Of
cres
world its hate hath shown, Yet it is not o-ver-thrown, Hal-le-lu-jah for the cross!
Christ the bless-ed Son, Who did for sin a - tone, Hal-le-lu-jah for the cross!
Christ our of - fer - ing, Of Christ our liv-ing King, Hal-le-lu-jah for the cross!
ff
OBBLIGATO DUET Sop. (or Ten.) and Alto
Hal - le - lu - jah, hal - le - lu - jah, hal - le-
Soprano and Alto*
CHORUS mp. Hal - le - lu - jah hal - le - lu - jah, hal - le-
Tenor and Bass

*If desired, the Soprano and Alto may sing the upper staff, omitting the middle staff.

Hallelujah For the Cross!

lu - - jah for the cross! Hal - le - lu - jah,
lu - jah for the cross, hal-le-lu - jah for the cross! Hal - le - lu - jah,
hal - le - lu - jah, It shall nev - er suf - fer loss!
hal - le - lu - jah, It shall nev - er suf - fer, nev - er suf - fer loss!
Full Chorus
f
*Hal - le - lu - jah, hal - le - lu - jah, hal - le - lu - jah for the cross!
cres.
ff
Hal - le - lu - jah, hal - le - lu - jah, It shall nev - er suf - fer loss!

*For a final ending, all the voices may sing the melody in unison through the last eight measures—the instrument playing the harmony.

341 Wonderful Grace of Jesus

H. L. HALDOR LILLENAS

1. Won - der - ful grace of Je - sus, Great - er than all my sin; . .
2. Won - der - ful grace of Je - sus, Reach-ing to all the lost, . .
3. Won - der - ful grace of Je - sus, Reach-ing the most de - filed, . .
How shall my tongue de - scribe it, Where shall its praise be - gin? . . .
By it I have been pardoned, Saved to the ut - ter - most, . . .
By its trans-form-ing pow - er, Mak - ing him God's dear child, . .
Tak - ing a - way my bur - den, Set - ting my spir - it free; . .
Chains have been torn a - sun - der, Giv - ing me lib - er - ty; . . .
Pur - chas-ing peace and heav - en, For all e - ter - ni - ty; . . .
For the won - der - ful grace of Je - sus reach - es me.
For the won - der - ful grace of Je - sus reach - es me.
And the won - der - ful grace of Je - sus reach - es me.
CHORUS
the matchless grace of Je-sus,
Won-der-ful the matchless grace of Je - - - sus, Deep-er than the

Copyright, 1918, by Charles M. Alexander. Hope Publishing Co., owner

Wonderful Grace of Jesus

the roll-ing sea; Won - - - der - ful
might - y roll - ing sea; Higher than the mountain,
grace, all - suf - fi - - - cient for
spar-kling like a foun - tain, All - suf - fi - cient grace for e - ven
me, for e - ven me, Broad - er than the scope of my trans-
me,
gres - sions, Great - er far than all my sin and shame,
gres-sions, sing it! my sin and shame,
O mag - ni - fy the pre-cious name of Je - sus, Praise His name!

342 All Hail the Power

Oliver Holden
1. All hail the pow'r of Je - sus' name! Let an - gels pros - trate fall;
2. Ye cho - sen seed of Is - rael's race, Ye ran-somed from the fall,
3. Let ev - 'ry kin - dred, ev - 'ry tribe On this ter - res - trial ball,
4. O that with yon - der sa - cred throng We at His feet may fall!
Bring forth the roy - al di - a - dem, And crown Him Lord of all,
Hail Him who saves you by His grace, And crown Him Lord of all,
To Him all maj - es - ty as - cribe, And crown Him Lord of all,
We'll join the ev - er - last - ing song, And crown Him Lord of all,
Bring forth the roy - al di - a - dem, And crown Him Lord of all!
Hail Him who saves you by His grace, And crown Him Lord of all!
To Him all maj - es - ty as - cribe, And crown Him Lord of all!
We'll join the ev - er - last - ing song, And crown Him Lord of all!
[Second Tune]
Miles' Lane
William Shrubsole
1. All hail the pow'r of Je - sus' name! Let an-gels pros-trate fall; Bring forth the roy- al
di - a - dem, And crown Him, crown Him, crown Him, Crown Him Lord of all!

Athalia

Processional

F. MENDELSSOHN-BARTHOLDY

344 March

mf
f
mf
f
mf
mf
f
345
Allegretto
Prelude
Arr. from T. J. HAYDN
p
mf

p
f
p
pp
rit

346
Melody
Andante
BEETHOVEN
p
mf
p
rit.
347
Andante Religioso
Postlude
Andante
FRANCIS THOME
p e sostenuto

p rall.
dolce e sostenuto
p
cresc. simile
rall.
a tempo
p
cres - cen - do
f

Andante

Postlude

SCHUBERT

p

mf

decresc.

p

p

cresc.

p

pp

rit.

dim.

349 The Holy Scriptures

Study to shew thyself approved unto God, a workman that needeth not to be ashamed, rightly dividing the word of truth.

But continue thou in the things which thou hast learned and hast been assured of, knowing of whom thou hast learned them;

And that from a child thou hast known the holy scriptures, which are able to make thee wise unto salvation through faith which is in Christ Jesus.

All scripture is given by inspiration of God, and is profitable for doctrine, for reproof, for correction, for instruction in righteousness:

That the man of God may be perfect, thoroughly furnished unto all good works.

Preach the word; be instant in season, out of season; reprove, rebuke, exhort with all longsuffering and doctrine.

—II Timothy 2:15; 3:14-17; 4:2.

Thy word have I hid in mine heart, that I might not sin against thee.

For ever, O Lord, thy word is settled in heaven.

Thy word is a lamp unto my feet, and a light unto my path.

Thy testimonies are wonderful: therefore doth my soul keep them. The entrance of thy words giveth light; it giveth understanding unto the simple.

Order my steps in thy word: and let not any iniquity have dominion over me.

—Psalm 119:11, 89, 105, 129, 130, 133.

But these are written, that ye might believe that Jesus is the Christ, the Son of God; and that believing ye might have life through his name. —John 20:31.

350 The Creator, Our Savior

In the beginning was the Word, and the Word was with God, and the Word was God.

The same was in the beginning with God.

All things were made by him; and without him was not any thing made that was made.

In him was life; and the life was the light of men. And the light shineth in darkness: and the darkness comprehended it not.

That was the true Light, which lighteth every man that cometh into the world.

He was in the world, and the world was made by him, and the world knew him not.

—John 1:1-5, 9, 10.

For by him were all things created, that are in heaven, and that are in earth, visible and invisible, whether they be thrones, or dominions, or principalities, or powers: all things were created by him, and for him:

And he is before all things, and by him all things consist.

—Colossians 1:16, 17.

But we see Jesus, who was made a little lower than the angels for the suffering of death, crowned with glory and honour; that he by the grace of God should taste death for every man. —Hebrews 2:9.

And being made perfect, he became the author of eternal salvation unto all them that obey him.

—Hebrews 5:9.

For ye know the grace of our Lord Jesus Christ, that, though he was rich, yet for your sakes he became poor, that ye through his poverty might be rich.

—II Corinthians 8:9.

This is a faithful saying, and worthy of all acceptation, that Christ Jesus came into the world to save sinners. —I Timothy 1:15.

(over)

Moreover, brethren, I declare unto you the gospel which I preached unto you, which also ye have received, and wherein ye stand;

By which also ye are saved, if ye keep in memory what I preached unto you, unless ye have believed in vain.

For I delivered unto you first of all that which I also received, how that Christ died for our sins according to the scriptures;

And that he was buried, and that he rose again the third day according to the scriptures:

—I Corinthians 15:1-4.

Herein is love, not that we loved God, but that he loved us, and sent his Son to be the propitiation for our sins. —I John 4:10.

For the wages of sin is death; but the gift of God is eternal life through Jesus Christ our Lord.

—Romans 6:23.

351 The Glory of God

The heavens declare the glory of God; and the firmament sheweth his handywork.

Day unto day uttereth speech, and night unto night sheweth knowledge.

There is no speech nor language, where their voice is not heard.

Their line is gone out through all the earth, and their words to the end of the world. In them hath he set a tabernacle for the sun,

Which is as a bridegroom coming out of his chamber, and rejoiceth as a strong man to run a race.

His going forth is from the end of the heaven, and his circuit unto the ends of it: and there is nothing hid from the heat thereof.

The law of the Lord is perfect, converting the soul: the testimony of the Lord is sure, making wise the simple.

The statutes of the Lord are right, rejoicing the heart: the commandment of the Lord is pure, enlightening the eyes.

The fear of the Lord is clean, enduring for ever: the judgments of the Lord are true and righteous altogether.

More to be desired are they than gold, yea, than much fine gold: sweeter also than honey and the honeycomb.

Moreover by them is thy servant warned: and in keeping of them there is great reward.

Who can understand his errors? cleanse thou me from secret faults.

Keep back thy servant also from presumptuous sins; let them not have dominion over me: then shall I be upright, and I shall be innocent from the great transgression.

Let the words of my mouth, and the meditation of my heart, be acceptable in thy sight, O Lord, my strength, and my redeemer. —Psalm 19.

352 God's Revelation Spiritually Discerned

But we speak the wisdom of God in a mystery, even the hidden wisdom which God ordained before the world unto our glory: Which none of the princes of this world knew: for had they known it, they would not have crucified the Lord of glory.

But as it is written, Eye hath not seen, nor ear heard, neither have entered into the heart of man, the things which God hath prepared for them that love him.

But God hath revealed them unto us by his Spirit; for the Spirit searcheth all things, yea, the deep things of God.

For what man knoweth the things of a man, save the spirit of

man which is in him? even so the things of God knoweth no man, but the Spirit of God.

Now we have received, not the spirit of the world, but the spirit which is of God; that we might know the things that are freely given to us of God.

Which things also we speak, not in the words which man's wisdom teacheth, but which the Holy Ghost teacheth; comparing spiritual things with spiritual.

But the natural man receiveth not the things of the Spirit of God: for they are foolishness unto him: neither can he know them, because they are spiritually discerned.

But he that is spiritual judgeth all things.

—I Corinthians 2:7-15

353 God's Omnipresence

O Lord, thou hast searched me, and known me.

Thou knowest my downsitting and mine uprising, thou understandest my thought afar off.

Thou compassest my path and my lying down, and art acquainted with all my ways.

For there is not a word in my tongue, but, lo, O Lord, thou knowest it altogether.

Thou hast beset me behind and before, and laid thine hand upon me.

Such knowledge is too wonderful for me: it is high, I cannot attain unto it.

Whither shall I go from thy Spirit? or whither shall I flee from thy presence?

If I ascend up into heaven, thou art there: if I make my bed in hell, behold, thou art there.

If I take the wings of the morning, and dwell in the uttermost parts of the sea;

Even there shall thy hand lead me, and thy right hand shall hold me.

If I say, Surely the darkness shall cover me; even the night shall be light about me.

Yea, the darkness hideth not from thee; but the night shineth as the day: the darkness and the light are both alike to thee.

How precious also are thy thoughts unto me, O God! how great is the sum of them!

If I should count them, they are more in number than the sand: when I awake, I am still with thee.

Search me, O God, and know my heart: try me, and know my thoughts:

And see if there be any wicked way in me, and lead me in the way everlasting.

—Psalm 139:1-12, 17, 18, 23, 24.

354 Our Refuge

God is our refuge and strength, a very present help in trouble.

—Psalm 46:1.

The eyes of the Lord run to and fro throughout the whole earth, to show himself strong in the behalf of them whose heart is perfect toward him. —II Chronicles 16:9.

The Lord also will be a refuge for the oppressed, a refuge in times of trouble.

And they that know thy name will put their trust in thee, for thou, Lord, hast not forsaken them that seek thee. —Psalm 9:9, 10.

In him we live, and move, and have our being. —Acts 17:28.

The eyes of the Lord are over the righteous, and his ears are open unto their prayers. —I Peter 3:12.

The Lord knoweth how to deliver the godly out of temptation.

—II Peter 2:9.

God is faithful, who will not suffer you to be tempted above that ye are able; but will with the temptation also make a way to escape, that ye may be able to bear it.

—I Corinthians 10:13.

(over)

The Lord is faithful, who shall stablish you, and keep you from evil. —II Thessalonians 3:3.

The eternal God is thy refuge, and underneath are the everlasting arms. —Dueteronomy 33:27.

But thou, O Lord, art a shield for me; my glory, and the lifter up of mine head. —Psalm 3:3.

I will say of the Lord, He is my refuge and my fortress; my God; in him will I trust. —Psalm 91:2.

355 Christ's Humiliation and Exaltation

Who hath believed our report? and to whom is the arm of the Lord revealed?

For he shall grow up before him as a tender plant, and as a root out of a dry ground: he hath no form nor comeliness; and when we shall see him, there is no beauty that we should desire him.

He is despised and rejected of men; a man of sorrows, and acquainted with grief: and we hid as it were our faces from him; he was despised, and we esteemed him not.

Surely he hath borne our griefs, and carried our sorrows: yet we did esteem him stricken, smitten of God, and afflicted.

But he was wounded for our transgressions, he was bruised for our iniquities: the chastisement of our peace was upon him; and with his stripes we are healed.

All we like sheep have gone astray; we have turned every one to his own way; and the Lord hath laid on him the iniquity of us all.

He was oppressed, and he was afflicted, yet he opened not his mouth: he is brought as a lamb to the slaughter, and as a sheep before her shearers is dumb, so he openeth not his mouth.

He was taken from prison and from judgment: and who shall declare his generation? for he was cut off out of the land of the living: for the transgression of my people was he stricken.

And he made his grave with the wicked, and with the rich in his death; because he had done no violence, neither was any deceit in his mouth. —Isaiah 53:1-9.

Let this mind be in you, which was also in Christ Jesus:

Who, being in the form of God, thought it not robbery to be equal with God: But made himself of no reputation, and took upon him the form of a servant, and was made in the likeness of men:

And being found in fashion as a man, he humbled himself, and became obedient unto death, even the death of the cross.

Wherefore God also hath highly exalted him, and given him a name which is above every name:

That at the name of Jesus every knee should bow, of things in heaven, and things in earth, and things under the earth;

And that every tongue should confess that Jesus Christ is Lord, to the glory of God the Father. —Philippians 2:5-11.

Worthy is the Lamb that was slain to receive power, and riches, and wisdom, and strength, and honour, and glory, and blessing. —Revelation 5:12.

356 God's Plan of Salvation

All have sinned, and come short of the glory of God: Romans 3:23.

Whosoever shall call upon the name of the Lord shall be saved. —Romans 10:13.

The grace of God that bringeth salvation hath appeared to all men. —Titus 2:11

For God so loved the world, that he gave his only begotten Son, that whosoever believeth in him should not perish, but have everlasting life.

For God sent not his Son into the world to condemn the world; but that the world through him might be saved.

He that believeth on him is not condemned: but he that believeth not is condemned already, because he hath not believed in the name of the only begotten Son of God.

And this is the condemnation, that light is come into the world, and men loved darkness rather than light, because their deeds were evil.

For every one that doeth evil hateth the light, neither cometh to the light, lest his deeds should be reproved.

He that believeth on the Son hath everlasting life: and he that believeth not the Son shall not see life; but the wrath of God abideth on him. —John 3:16-20, 36.

Neither is there salvation in any other: for there is none other name under heaven given among men, whereby we must be saved.
—Acts 4:12.

Verily, verily, I say unto you, He that heareth my word, and believeth on him that sent me, hath everlasting life, and shall not come into condemnation; but is passed from death unto life.
—John 5:24.

All that the Father giveth me shall come to me; and him that cometh to me I will in no wise cast out.

And this is the Father's will which hath sent me, that of all which he hath given me I should lose nothing, but should raise it up again at the last day.

And this is the will of him that sent me, that every one which seeth the Son, and believeth on him, may have everlasting life: and I will raise him up at the last day.
—John 6:37, 39, 40.

357 The Two Ways

Blessed is the man that walketh not in the counsel of the ungodly, nor standeth in the way of sinners, nor sitteth in the seat of the scornful:

But his delight is in the law of the Lord; and in his law doth he meditate day and night.

And he shall be like a tree planted by the rivers of water, that bringeth forth his fruit in his season;

His leaf also shall not wither; and whatsoever he doeth shall prosper.

The ungodly are not so: but are like the chaff which the wind driveth away. Therefore the ungodly shall not stand in the judgment, nor sinners in the congregation of the righteous.

For the Lord knoweth the way of the righteous: but the way of the ungodly shall perish. —Psalm 1.

All we, like sheep, have gone astray; we have turned every one to his own way; and the Lord hath laid on him the iniquity of us all. —Isaiah 53:6.

But there were false prophets also among the people, even as there shall be false teachers among you, who privily shall bring in destructive heresies, even denying the Lord, that bought them, and bring upon themselves swift destruction.

And many shall follow their pernicious ways; by reason of whom the way of truth shall be evil spoken of.

For it had been better for them not to have known the way of righteousness, than, after they have known it, to turn from the holy commandment delivered unto them.
—II Peter 2:1, 2, 21.

(over)

Let him know, that he which converteth the sinner from the error of his way shall save a soul from death, and shall hide a multitude of sins. —James 5:20.

And whither I go ye know, and the way ye know.

Thomas saith unto him, Lord, we know not whither thou goest; and how can we know the way?

Jesus saith unto him, I am the way, the truth, and the life: no man cometh unto the Father, but by me. —John 14:4-6.

358 Justification By Faith

Not by works of righteousness which we have done, but according to his mercy he saved us, by the washing of regeneration, and renewing of the Holy Ghost;

Which he shed on us abundantly through Jesus Christ our Savior;

That being justified by his grace, we should be made heirs according to the hope of eternal life. —Titus 3:5-7.

Therefore we conclude that a man is justified by faith without the deeds of the law.

But to him that worketh not, but believeth on him that justifieth the ungodly, his faith is counted for righteousness.

Blessed is the man to whom the Lord will not impute sin. —Romans 3:28; 4:5, 8.

For by grace are ye saved through faith; and that not of yourselves: it is the gift of God:

Not of works, lest any man should boast. —Ephesians 2:8, 9.

Therefore being justified by faith, we have peace with God through our Lord Jesus Christ:

By whom also we have access by faith into this grace wherein we stand, and rejoice in hope of the glory of God.

And not only so, but we glory in tribulations also; knowing that tribulation worketh patience;

And patience, experience; and experience, hope:

And hope maketh not ashamed; because the love of God is shed abroad in our hearts by the Holy Ghost which is given unto us.

For when we were yet without strength, in due time Christ died for the ungodly.

For scarcely for a righteous man will one die: yet peradventure for a good man some would even dare to die.

But God commendeth his love toward us, in that, while we were yet sinners, Christ died for us.

Much more then, being now justified by his blood, we shall be saved from wrath through him.

For if, when we were enemies, we were reconciled to God by the death of his Son,

Much more, being reconciled, we shall be saved by his life.

And not only so, but we also joy in God through our Lord Jesus Christ, by whom we have now received the atonement. —Romans 5:1-11.

359 Victory Over Sin

What shall we say then? Shall we continue in sin, that grace may abound?

God forbid. How shall we, that are dead to sin, live any longer therein?

Know ye not, that so many of us as were baptized into Jesus Christ were baptized into his death?

Therefore we are buried with him by baptism into death: that like as Christ was raised up from the dead by the glory of the Father, even so we also should walk in newness of life.

For if we have been planted together in the likeness of his death, we shall be also in the likeness of his resurrection:

Knowing this, that our old man is crucified with him, that the body of sin might be destroyed, that henceforth we should not serve sin.

For he that is dead is freed from sin.

Now if we be dead with Christ, we believe that we shall also live with him:

Knowing that Christ being raised from the dead dieth no more; death hath no more dominion over him.

For in that he died, he died unto sin once: but in that he liveth, he liveth unto God.

Likewise reckon ye also yourselves to be dead indeed unto sin, but alive unto God through Jesus Christ our Lord.

Let not sin therefore reign in your mortal body, that ye should obey it in the lusts thereof.

Neither yield ye your members as instruments of unrighteousness unto sin: but yield yourselves unto God, as those that are alive from the dead, and your members as instruments of righteousness unto God.

For sin shall not have dominion over you: for ye are not under the law, but under grace.

—Romans 6:1-14.

360 Reasonable Service

I beseech you therefore, brethren, by the mercies of God, that ye present your bodies a living sacrifice, holy, acceptable unto God, which is your reasonable service.

And be not conformed to this world: but be ye transformed by the renewing of your mind, that ye may prove what is that good, and acceptable, and perfect will of God.

—Romans 12:1, 2.

Forasmuch then as Christ hath suffered for us in the flesh, arm yourselves likewise with the same mind; for he that hath suffered in the flesh hath ceased from sin;

That he no longer should live the rest of his time in the flesh to the lusts of men, but to the will of God.

Beloved, think it not strange concerning the fiery trial which is to try you, as though some strange thing happened unto you;

But rejoice, inasmuch as ye are partakers of Christ's sufferings; that, when his glory shall be revealed, ye may be glad also with exceeding joy.

If ye be reproached for the name of Christ, happy are ye; for the Spirit of glory and of God resteth upon you: on their part he is evil spoken of, but on your part he is glorified.

—I Peter 4:1, 2, 12-14.

For God hath not given us the spirit of fear; but of power, and of love, and of a sound mind.

Be not thou therefore ashamed of the testimony of our Lord, nor of me his prisoner: but be thou partaker of the afflictions of the gospel according to the power of God.

Who hath saved us, and called us with an holy calling, not according to our works, but according to his own purpose and grace, which was given us in Christ Jesus before the world began;

But is now made manifest by the appearing of our Savior Jesus Christ, who hath abolished death, and hath brought life and immortality to light through the gospel:

Whereunto I am appointed a preacher, and an apostle, and a teacher of the Gentiles.

For the which cause I also suffer these things: nevertheless I am not ashamed;

For I know whom I have believed, and am persuaded that he is able to keep that which I have committed unto him against that day.

—II Timothy 1:7-12.

(over)

By him therefore let us offer the sacrifice of praise to God continually, that is, the fruit of our lips giving thanks to his name.

But to do good and to communicate forget not: for with such sacrifices God is well pleased.

—Hebrews 13:15, 16.

361 God's Care For His Own

The Lord is my shepherd; I shall not want.

He maketh me to lie down in green pastures: he leadeth me beside the still waters.

He restoreth my soul: he leadeth me in the paths of righteousness for his name's sake.

Yea, though I walk through the valley of the shadow of death, I will fear no evil: for thou art with me; thy rod and thy staff they comfort me.

Thou preparest a table before me in the presence of mine enemies: thou anointest my head with oil; my cup runneth over.

Surely goodness and mercy shall follow me all the days of my life: and I will dwell in the house of the Lord for ever. —Psalm 23.

I am the good shepherd; the good shepherd giveth his life for the sheep.

I am the good shepherd, and know my sheep, and am known of mine.

As the Father knoweth me, even so know I the Father: and I lay down my life for the sheep.

And other sheep I have, which are not of this fold: them also I must bring, and they shall hear my voice; and there shall be one fold, and one shepherd.

Therefore doth my Father love me, because I lay down my life, that I might take it again.

No man taketh it from me, but I lay it down of myself. I have power to lay it down, and I have power to take it again. This commandment have I received of my Father.

My sheep hear my voice, and I know them, and they follow me;

And I give unto them eternal life and they shall never perish, neither shall any man pluck them out of my hand.

My Father, which gave them me, is greater than all; and no man is able to pluck them out of my Father's hand.

I and my Father are one.

—John 10:11, 14-18, 27-30.

362 Comfort

Let not your heart be troubled: ye believe in God, believe also in me.

In my Father's house are many mansions: if it were not so, I would have told you. I go to prepare a place for you.

And if I go and prepare a place for you, I will come again, and receive you unto myself; that where I am, there ye may be also.

And whither I go ye know, and the way ye know.

And I will pray the Father, and he shall give you another Comforter, that he may abide with you for ever;

Even the Spirit of truth; whom the world cannot receive, because it seeth him not, neither knoweth him: but ye know him; for he dwelleth with you, and shall be in you.

I will not leave you comfortless; I will come to you. These things have I spoken unto you, being yet present with you.

But the Comforter, which is the Holy Ghost, whom the Father will send in my name, he shall teach you all things, and bring all things to your remembrance, whatsoever I have said unto you.

Peace I leave with you, my peace I give unto you: not as the world giveth, give I unto you. Let not your heart be troubled, neither let it be afraid.

—John 14:1-4, 16-18, 25-27.

Blessed be God, even the Father of our Lord Jesus Christ, the Father of mercies, and the God of all comfort;

Who comforteth us in all our tribulation, that we may be able to comfort them which are in any trouble, by the comfort wherewith we ourselves are comforted of God.

For as the sufferings of Christ abound in us, so our consolation also aboundeth by Christ.

And whether we be afflicted, it is for your consolation and salvation, which is effectual in the enduring of the same sufferings which we also suffer: or whether we be comforted, it is for your consolation and salvation.

And our hope of you is stedfast, knowing, that as ye are partakers of the sufferings, so shall ye be also of the consolation.

—II Corinthians 1:3-7.

363 Love

A new commandment I give unto you, That ye love one another; as I have loved you, that ye also love one another.

—John 13:34.

Though I speak with the tongues of men and of angels, and have not love, I am become as sounding brass, or a tinkling cymbal.

And though I have the gift of prophecy, and understand all mysteries, and all knowledge; and though I have all faith, so that I could remove mountains, and have not love, I am nothing.

And though I bestow all my goods to feed the poor, and though I give my body to be burned, and have not love, it profiteth me nothing.

Love suffereth long, and is kind; love envieth not; love vaunteth not itself, is not puffed up,

Doth not behave itself unseemly, seeketh not her own, is not easily provoked, thinketh no evil;

Rejoiceth not in iniquity, but rejoiceth in the truth;

Beareth all things, believeth all things, hopeth all things, endureth all things.

Love never faileth; but whether there be prophecies, they shall fail; whether there be tongues, they shall cease; whether there be knowledge, it shall vanish away.

For we know in part, and we prophesy in part. But when that which is perfect is come, then that which is in part shall be done away.

When I was a child, I spake as a child, I understood as a child, I thought as a child; but when I became a man, I put away childish things.

For now we see through a glass, darkly; but then face to face:

Now I know in part; but then shall I know even as also I am known.

And now abideth faith, hope, love, these three; but the greatest of these is love.

—I Corinthians 13. R.V.

(In I Corinthian passage, "Love" is rendered "charity" in the King James Version.)

364 Joy

Rejoice in the Lord alway: and again I say, Rejoice.

Let your moderation be known unto all men. The Lord is at hand.

Be careful for nothing; but in every thing by prayer and supplication with thanksgiving let your requests be made known unto God.

And the peace of God, which passeth all understanding, shall keep your hearts and minds through Christ Jesus.

(over)

Finally, brethren, whatsoever things are true, whatsoever things are honest, whatsoever things are just, whatsoever things are pure, whatsoever things are lovely, whatsoever things are of good report; if there be any virtue, and if there be any praise, think on these things.

Those things, which ye have both learned, and received, and heard, and seen in me, do: and the God of peace shall be with you.

But I rejoiced in the Lord greatly, that now at the last your care of me hath flourished again: wherein ye were also careful, but ye lacked opportunity.

Not that I speak in respect of want: for I have learned, in whatsoever state I am, therewith to be content.

I know both how to be abased, and I know how to abound: everywhere and in all things I am instructed both to be full and to be hungry, both to abound and to suffer need.

I can do all things through Christ which strengtheneth me.

—Philippians 4:4-13.

365 Patience

Blessed be the God and Father of our Lord Jesus Christ, which according to his abundant mercy hath begotten us again unto a lively hope by the resurrection of Jesus Christ from the dead.

To an inheritance incorruptible, and undefiled, and that fadeth not away, reserved in heaven for you,

Who are kept by the power of God through faith unto salvation ready to be revealed in the last time.

Wherein ye greatly rejoice, though now for a season, if need be, ye are in heaviness through manifold temptations:

That the trial of your faith, being much more precious than of gold that perisheth, though it be tried with fire, might be found unto praise and honour and glory at the appearing of Jesus Christ:

Whom having not seen, ye love; in whom, though now ye see him not, yet believing, ye rejoice with joy unspeakable and full of glory:

Receiving the end of your faith, even the salvation of your souls.

—I Peter 1:3-9.

For what glory is it, if, when ye be buffeted for your faults, ye shall take it patiently?

But if, when ye do well, and suffer for it, ye take it patiently, this is acceptable with God.

For even hereunto were ye called: because Christ also suffered for us, leaving us an example, that ye should follow his steps:

Who did no sin, neither was guile found in his mouth:

Who, when he was reviled, reviled not again; when he suffered, he threatened not; but committed himself to him that judgeth righteously:

Who his own self bare our sins in his own body on the tree, that we, being dead to sins, should live unto righteousness: by whose stripes ye were healed.

For ye were as sheep going astray; but are now returned unto the Shepherd and Bishop of your souls.

—I Peter 2:20-25.

366 Christian Conduct

If ye then be risen with Christ, seek those things which are above, where Christ sitteth on the right hand of God.

Set your affection on things above, not on things on the earth.

For ye are dead, and your life is hid with Christ in God.

When Christ, who is our life, shall appear, then shall ye also appear with him in glory.

Mortify therefore your members which are upon the earth; fornication, uncleanness, inordinate affection, evil concupiscence, and covetousness, which is idolatry:

For which things' sake the wrath of God cometh on the children of disobedience:

In the which ye also walked some time, when ye lived in them.

But now ye also put off all these; anger, wrath, malice, blasphemy, filthy communication out of your mouth.

Lie not one to another, seeing that ye have put off the old man with his deeds;

And have put on the new man, which is renewed in knowledge after the image of him that created him:

Where there is neither Greek nor Jew, circumcision nor uncircumcision, Barbarian, Scythian, bond nor free: but Christ is all, and in all.

Put on therefore, as the elect of God, holy and beloved, bowels of mercies, kindness, humbleness of mind, meekness, longsuffering;

Forbearing one another, and forgiving one another, if any man have a quarrel against any: even as Christ forgave you, so also do ye.

And above all these things put on love, which is the bond of perfectness.

And let the peace of God rule in your hearts, to the which also ye are called in one body; and be ye thankful.

Let the word of Christ dwell in you richly in all wisdom;

Teaching and admonishing one another in psalms and hymns and spiritual songs, singing with grace in your hearts to the Lord.

And whatsoever ye do in word or deed, do all in the name of the Lord Jesus, giving thanks to God and the Father by him.

—Colossians 3:1-17.

367 Christian Triumph

For I reckon that the sufferings of this present time are not worthy to be compared with the glory which shall be revealed in us.

And we know that all things work together for good to them that love God, to them who are the called according to his purpose.

For whom he did foreknow, he also did predestinate to be conformed to the image of his Son, that he might be the firstborn among many brethren.

Moreover whom he did predestinate, them he also called: and whom he called, them he also justified: and whom he justified, them he also glorified.

What shall we then say to these things? If God be for us, who can be against us?

He that spared not his own Son, but delivered him up for us all, how shall he not with him also freely give us all things?

Who shall lay any thing to the charge of God's elect? It is God that justifieth.

Who is he that condemneth? It is Christ that died, yea rather, that is risen again, who is even at the right hand of God, who also maketh intercession for us.

Who shall separate us from the love of Christ? shall tribulation, or distress, or persecution, or famine, or nakedness, or peril, or sword?

As it is written, For thy sake we are killed all the day long; we are accounted as sheep for the slaughter.

Nay, in all these things we are more than conquerors through him that loved us.

(over)

For I am persuaded, that neither death, nor life, nor angels, nor principalities, nor powers, nor things present, nor things to come. Nor height, nor depth, nor any other creature, shall be able to separate us from the love of God, which is in Christ Jesus our Lord.

—Romans 8:18, 28-39.

368 Chastening, Its Purpose

My son, despise not thou the chastening of the Lord, nor faint when thou art rebuked of him:

For whom the Lord loveth he chasteneth, and scourgeth every son whom he receiveth.

If ye endure chastening, God dealeth with you as with sons; for what son is he whom the father chasteneth not?

But if ye be without chastisement, whereof all are partakers, then are ye bastards, and not sons.

Furthermore we have had fathers of our flesh which corrected us, and we gave them reverence: shall we not much rather be in subjection unto the Father of spirits, and live?

For they verily for a few days chastened us after their own pleasure; but he for our profit, that we might be partakers of his holiness.

Now no chastening for the present seemeth to be joyous, but grievous:

Nevertheless afterward it yieldeth the peaceable fruit of righteousness unto them which are exercised thereby.

—Hebrews 12:5-11.

Before I was afflicted I went astray: but now have I kept thy word.

Thou art good and doest good; teach me thy statutes.

It is good for me that I have been afflicted; that I might learn thy statutes; thy hands have made me and fashioned me; give me understanding that I might learn thy commandments.

I know, O Lord, that thy judgments are right, and that thou in faithfulness hast afflicted me.

—Psalm 119:67, 68, 71, 73, 76.

For his anger endureth but a moment; in his favor is life: weeping may endure for a night, but joy cometh in the morning.

—Psalm 30:5.

Call upon me in the day of trouble: I will deliver thee and thou shalt glorify me.

—Psalm 50:15.

369 Prayer for Growth in Christ

Wherefore I also, after I heard of your faith in the Lord Jesus, and love unto all the saints,

Cease not to give thanks for you, making mention of you in my prayers;

That the God of our Lord Jesus Christ, the Father of glory, may give unto you the spirit of wisdom and revelation in the knowledge of him:

The eyes of your understanding being enlightened; that ye may know what is the hope of his calling, and what the riches of the glory of his inheritance in the saints,

And what is the exceeding greatness of his power to us-ward who believe, according to the working of his mighty power,

Which he wrought in Christ, when he raised him from the dead, and set him at his own right hand in the heavenly places,

Far above all principality, and power, and might, and dominion, and every name that is named, not only in this world, but also in that which is to come:

And hath put all things under his feet, and gave him to be the head over all things to the church, which is his body, the fulness of him that filleth all in all.

—Ephesians 1:15-23.

For this cause I bow my knees unto the Father of our Lord Jesus Christ,

Of whom the whole family in heaven and earth is named,

That he would grant you, according to the riches of his glory, to be strengthened with might by his Spirit in the inner man;

That Christ may dwell in your hearts by faith; that ye, being rooted and grounded in love,

May be able to comprehend with all saints what is the breadth, and length, and depth, and height;

And to know the love of Christ, which passeth knowledge, that ye might be filled with all the fulness of God.

Now unto him that is able to do exceeding abundantly above all that we ask or think, according to the power that worketh in us.

Unto him be glory in the church by Christ Jesus throughout all ages, world without end. Amen.

—Ephesians 3:14-21.

370 Heaven

And I saw a new heaven and a new earth: for the first heaven and the first earth were passed away; and there was no more sea.

And I John saw the holy city, new Jerusalem, coming down from God out of heaven, prepared as a bride adorned for her husband.

And I heard a great voice out of heaven saying, Behold, the tabernacle of God is with men, and he will dwell with them, and they shall be his people, and God himself shall be with them, and be their God.

And God shall wipe away all tears from their eyes; and there shall be no more death, neither sorrow, nor crying, neither shall there be any more pain: for the former things are passed away.

And he carried me away in the spirit to a great and high mountain, and shewed me that great city, the holy Jerusalem, descending out of heaven from God,

Having the glory of God: and her light was like unto a stone most precious, even like a jasper stone, clear as crystal:

And had a wall great and high, and had twelve gates, and at the gates twelve angels, and names written thereon, which are the names of the twelve tribes of the children of Israel:

And the wall of the city had twelve foundations, and in them the names of the twelve apostles of the Lamb.

And I saw no temple therein; for the Lord God Almighty and the Lamb are the temple of it.

And the city had no need of the sun, neither of the moon, to shine in it: for the glory of God did lighten it, and the Lamb is the light thereof.

And the nations of them which are saved shall walk in the light of it: and the kings of the earth do bring their glory and honour into it.

And the gates of it shall not be shut at all by day: for there shall be no night there.

And they shall bring the glory and honour of the nations into it.

And there shall in no wise enter into it any thing that defileth, neither whatsoever worketh abomination, or maketh a lie: but they which are written in the Lamb's book of life.

—Revelation 21:1-4, 10-12, 14, 22-27.

And he shewed me a pure river of water of life, clear as crystal, proceeding out of the throne of God and of the Lamb.

(over)

In the midst of the street of it, and on either side of the river, was there the tree of life, which bare twelve manner of fruits, and yielded her fruit every month: and the leaves of the tree were for the healing of the nations.

And there shall be no more curse: but the throne of God and of the Lamb shall be in it; and his servants shall serve him:

And they shall see his face; and his name shall be in their foreheads.

And there shall be no night there;

And they need no candle, neither light of the sun; for the Lord God giveth them light: and they shall reign for ever and ever.

—Revelation 22:1-5.

371 Second Coming of Christ

The former treatise have I made, O Theophilus, of all that Jesus began both to do and teach,

Until the day in which he was taken up, after that he through the Holy Ghost had given commandments unto the apostles whom he had chosen:

To whom also he shewed himself alive after his passion by many infallible proofs, being seen of them forty days, and speaking of the things pertaining to the kingdom of God:

And, being assembled together with them, commanded them that they should not depart from Jerusalem, but wait for the promise of the Father, which, saith he, ye have heard of me.

For John truly baptized with water; but ye shall be baptized with the Holy Ghost not many days hence.

When they therefore were come together, they asked of him, saying, Lord, wilt thou at this time restore again the kingdom to Israel?

And he said unto them, It is not for you to know the times or the seasons, which the Father hath put in his own power.

But ye shall receive power, after that the Holy Ghost is come upon you: and ye shall be witnesses unto me both in Jerusalem, and in all Judea, and in Samaria, and unto the uttermost part of the earth.

And when he had spoken these things, while they beheld, he was taken up; and a cloud received him out of their sight.

And while they looked steadfastly toward heaven as he went up, behold, two men stood by them in white apparel;

Which also said, Ye men of Galilee, why stand ye gazing up into heaven? this same Jesus, which is taken up from you into heaven, shall so come in like manner as ye have seen him go into heaven. —Acts 1:1-11.

But I would not have you to be ignorant, brethren, concerning them which are asleep, that ye sorrow not, even as others which have no hope.

For if we believe that Jesus died and rose again, even so them also which sleep in Jesus will God bring with him.

For this we say unto you by the word of the Lord, that we which are alive and remain unto the coming of the Lord shall not prevent them which are asleep.

For the Lord himself shall descend from heaven with a shout, with the voice of the archangel, and with the trump of God; and the dead in Christ shall rise first:

Then we which are alive and remain shall be caught up together with them in the clouds, to meet the Lord in the air: and so shall we ever be with the Lord. Wherefore comfort one another with these words.

—I Thessalonians 4:13-18.

372 Praise

Bless the Lord, O my soul: and all that is within me, bless his holy name.

Bless the Lord, O my soul, and forget not all his benefits.

Who forgiveth all thine iniquities; who healeth all thy diseases;

Who redeemeth thy life from destruction; who crowneth thee with lovingkindness and tender mercies;

Who satisfieth thy mouth with good things; so that thy youth is renewed like the eagle's.

The Lord executeth righteousness and judgment for all that are oppressed.

He made known his ways unto Moses, his acts unto the children of Israel.

The Lord is merciful and gracious, slow to anger, and plenteous in mercy.

He will not always chide: neither will he keep his anger for ever.

He hath not dealt with us after our sins; nor rewarded us according to our iniquities.

For as the heaven is high above the earth, so great is his mercy toward them that fear him.

As far as the east is from the west, so far hath he removed our transgressions from us.

Like as a father pitieth his children, so the Lord pitieth them that fear him.

For he knoweth our frame; he remembereth that we are dust.

As for man, his days are as grass: as a flower of the field, so he flourisheth.

For the wind passeth over it, and it is gone; and the place thereof shall know it no more.

But the mercy of the Lord is from everlasting to everlasting upon them that fear him, and his righteousness unto children's children;

To such as keep his covenant, and to those that remember his commandments to do them.

The Lord hath prepared his throne in the heavens; and his kingdom ruleth over all.

Bless the Lord, ye his angels, that excel in strength, that do his commandments hearkening unto the voice of his word.

Bless ye the Lord, all ye his hosts; ye ministers of his, that do his pleasure.

Bless the Lord, all his works in all places of his dominion: bless the Lord, O my soul.

—Psalm 103.

373 Benedictions

A — The Lord bless thee and keep thee: the Lord make his face shine upon thee, and be gracious unto thee: the Lord lift up his countenance upon thee, and give thee peace. Amen. Numbers 6:24, 26.

B — Be perfect, be of good comfort, be of one mind, live in peace; and the God of love and peace shall be with you. The grace of the Lord Jesus Christ, and the love of God, and the communion of the Holy Spirit be with you. Amen.

II Corinthians 13:11, 14.

C — Now our Lord Jesus Christ himself, and God, even our Father, which hath loved us, and hath given us everlasting consolation and good hope through grace, Comfort your hearts, and stablish you in every good word and work. Amen. II Thessalonians 2:16, 17.

D — Now the God of peace, that brought again from the dead our Lord Jesus, that great Shepherd of the sheep, through the blood of the everlasting covenant, make you perfect in every good work to do his will, working in you that which is wellpleasing in his sight, through Jesus Christ; to whom be glory for ever and ever. Amen.

Hebrews 13:20, 21.

(over)

E — And the very God of peace sanctify you wholly; and I pray God your whole spirit and soul and body be preserved blameless unto the coming of our Lord Jesus Christ. Amen. I Thessalonians 5:23.

F — Now unto him that is able to keep you from falling, and to present you faultless before the presence of his glory with exceeding joy, to the only wise God our Savior, be glory and majesty, dominion and power, both now and ever. Amen. Jude 24, 25.

G — The grace of our Lord Jesus Christ be with your spirit. Amen. Philemon 25.

SUGGESTED SCRIPTURE READINGS FOR SPECIAL OCCASIONS

Children's Day
Luke 2:40-52
Matt. 18:1-6, 10
Matt. 19:13-15

Christmas
Luke 2:8-20
Isa. 9:2-7
Matt. 2:1-12

Day of Prayer
John 17
I Kings 8:22, 23, 27, 28, 54-61

Easter
Luke 24:13-35
John 20:1-18
I Cor. 15:12-26

Good Friday
Luke 23:33-46
Isa. 53

Missions
Romans 10:8-18
Psalm 96
Acts 17:22-31
Luke 10:2; 14:23
II Tim. 2:1, 2; 4:1-5

Mother's Day
Prov. 22:6
Deut. 6:4-9, 25
Prov. 31:10-31

Palm Sunday
Mark 11:1-11

Patriotism
Ps. 33, 144
I Pet. 2:11-17
I Tim. 2:1-4
Titus 3:1

Temperance
Gal. 5:13-25
Eph. 5:8-21
Jer. 35:1-19

Thanksgiving Day
Deut. 8:6-20
Ps. 147
Ps. 107:1-22

The New Year
Joshua 1:1-9
Phil. 3:12-14

INDEX OF RESPONSIVE AND UNISON READINGS

1. SUBJECT TITLES

2. SCRIPTURE REFERENCES

Bold face figures in parenthesis indicate numbers of readings.

3. SUGGESTED ADDITIONAL USES FOR READINGS

TOPICAL INDEX

TOPICAL INDEX

TOPICAL INDEX

TOPICAL INDEX

GENERAL INDEX

Titles are in Small Caps; first lines in lower case type.

GENERAL INDEX

GENERAL INDEX

GENERAL INDEX